THE SCIENCE OF
DENTAL MATERIALS

By

EUGENE W. SKINNER, Ph.D.

Associate Professor of Physics,
Northwestern University Dental School

ILLUSTRATED

PHILADELPHIA AND LONDON

W. B. SAUNDERS COMPANY

1938

To my former teacher,
GEORGE WALTER STEWART
Professor of Physics,
University of Iowa.

PREFACE

A COURSE dealing exclusively with dental materials and their manipulation has been introduced into the dental curriculum only within the last four or five years, and only within the last two years, since the appearance of *A Course of Study in Dentistry* (Report of the Curriculum Survey Committee, American Association of Dental Schools, 1935), has such a course been generally adopted as a basic subject worthy of a place alongside of histology, chemistry, anatomy, and the other preclinical sciences.

One of the obstacles to be overcome in adapting such a course to the dental curriculum is the proper organization of the necessary knowledge. The fundamental background material for this course is scattered throughout the literature of engineering and chemistry, as well as of dentistry. If this book is of help in overcoming this particular obstacle, the author will feel amply repaid for his efforts.

However, the primary motive of the present volume is to provide a textbook for such a course. The objectives kept constantly in mind by the author are those formulated in the report mentioned above, quoted as follows:

"The general objective of the instruction suggested for this course is to familiarize the student with the materials used in the construction of dental restorations and orthodontic appliances. The instruction should aid the student: (1) To understand the sources, composition, and properties of all the materials used. (2) To understand the scientific basis of the use of the materials. (3) To manipulate the materials intelligently. (4) To evaluate new materials and processes on a rational and scientific basis. (5) To develop an interest in research for the further improvement of materials and their application in dental health service.

"Although the course is not at all designed for training in research, yet the emphasis on scientific method necessarily involved in the instruction and study will indirectly contribute to the student's appreciation of, and interest in, methods of research. Frontiers of effort may be pointed out to him as a challenge to his imagination."

All of the topics presented for class discussion in the portion of the report dealing with *Materials Used in Dentistry and Their Manipulation* have been included, with the exception of the four optional topics dealing with the metallurgy of a few metals. It is felt that such material offers little of a practical value to the student of dentistry, and that its inclusion is not in the spirit of the general ideal sought for.

The sequence of topics presented in the report has been altered in the present volume. In selecting a sequence of subjects, the author has been torn between a logical presentation and one that is teachable. As a result, the book appears at first glance to be divided into two parts; the first half deals largely with nonmetallic materials and the second half is mainly metallographical. However, such a logical sequence is considerably disturbed in the second half of the book by the introduction of inlay waxes and investments in Chapters XXVIII and XXIX. The reason for this sequence is that the casting procedure is discussed at this point, and, whether or not the introduction of waxes and investments is logical, it is certainly educationally sound to include these materials with the dental processes with which they are identified as accessory materials.

However, it is doubtful whether any two teachers of the subject can agree as to what constitutes a good sequence of subjects. Moreover, as shown by a recent survey, the curricular time allotted to this course varies considerably from one institution to another. Consequently, the author has attempted to make the book sufficiently flexible so that the teacher may adapt it to his individual needs. Chapters II, III, IV, XX, XXI, XXIII, and XXIV are fundamentally essential, but otherwise, interdependent references have been kept to a minimum in order to simplify the rearrangement of the subject matter according to the desires of the teacher. Furthermore, the length of the chapters has been limited so far as is possible to three or four thousand words, in the hope that a single chapter may constitute one assignment. When two or more chapters are devoted to a single material, the first chapter or chapters are devoted to theoretical considerations of chemical and physical applications; the discussion in each case is closed with the practical applications and manipulation of the material, thus allowing the teacher further latitude in his selection of chapters for the shorter courses. As to how successful such an arrangement is, only time will tell.

As an educational prerequisite for the study of this book, it is assumed that the student has the equivalent in training of a junior in a college of liberal arts, i. e., he is a freshman dental student, with two years of training in liberal arts. Such a student is presumably a rational and reasoning person, and he is prepared to master a formal style of writing in advance of that which often appears in an elementary college chemistry or physics textbook. It is for this type of student that the book has been written. As to individual predental subjects, the only course assumed is general chemistry of college or university grade.

The list of acknowledgements is so long that each reviewer cannot be given the individual thanks which he deserves. In the first place, I am indebted to Dean Arthur D. Black for his encouragement and cooperation, without which the book would not have been written, and for his consent to the use of certain material from the seventh edition of Black's Operative Dentistry (Medico-Dental Publishing Company), which appears verbatim in the following pages. Second, words cannot express my gratitude and thanks to P. B. Taylor of Western Reserve University, who not only read and reread the manuscript many times, but also contributed Chapters XXXVI–XXXVIII inclusive, and furnished data and photographs from his original researches. I am also indebted to Stanley D. Tylman, R. L. Coleman and L. H. DeWald for furnishing certain illustrations.

Others who have read the entire manuscript and have offered very valuable criticism are: C. E. Friesell, S. D. Tylman, C. W. Gieler, R. E. Myers, L. E. Blauch, and G. B. Denton.

The following men have read those portions of the manuscript dealing with their particular specialties and have been of inestimable aid in correcting the factual material: R. O. Schlosser, L. H. DeWald, H. L. Hansen, L. S. Fosdick, A. W. Gray, J. E. Wertheimer, B. S. Radcliffe, M. C. Dailey, R. E. Blackwell, and J. T. Blake.

I also am indebted to Hazel D. Skinner for her patience and painstaking care in reading proof sheets. I further wish to thank the many authors and publishers who have consented to my use of their publications and illustrations. Lastly I wish to express my gratitude to the publishers of this book for their patience and cooperation throughout our work together.

E. W. SKINNER.

CHICAGO, ILLINOIS.

CONTENTS

13

CHAPTER XIII

CHAPTER XIV

CHAPTER XV

CHAPTER XVI

CHAPTER XVII

CHAPTER XVIII

CHAPTER XIX

CHAPTER XX

CHAPTER XXI

CHAPTER XXII

CHAPTER XXIII

CHAPTER XXIV

CHAPTER XXV

CHAPTER XXVI

CHAPTER XXVII

CHAPTER XXVIII

CHAPTER XXIX

CHAPTER XXX

CHAPTER XXXI

CHAPTER XXXII

CHAPTER XXXIII

CHAPTER XXXIV

CHAPTER XXXV

CHAPTER XXXVI

CHAPTER XXXVII

CHAPTER XXXVIII

CHAPTER XXXIX

CHAPTER XL

THE SCIENCE OF DENTAL MATERIALS

CHAPTER I

INTRODUCTION

Historical.—Strange as it may seem, there is comparatively little historical background for the science of dental materials and their manipulation, in spite of the fact that the practice of dentistry itself antedates the Christian era. For example, gold bands and wires were used by the Phoenicians and Etruscans for the construction of partial dentures. Gold foil has been employed for dental restorative purposes for so long a period that its origin is not known.

Modern dentistry is said to have had its start during the year 1726, when Fauchard published a treatise describing many types of dental restorations, including a method for the construction of artificial dentures from ivory. Somewhat later, in 1756, Pfaff first described the method for obtaining impressions of the mouth in wax, from which he constructed a model with plaster of Paris. The year 1792 is important as the date when de Chamant patented a process for the construction of porcelain teeth; this was followed by the introduction of the porcelain inlay early in the next century.

It is evident, then, that many of the restorative and accessory materials of today have been in use for some time, yet little scientific information about them has been available until recently. Their use was entirely an art, and the only testing laboratory was the mouth of the long-suffering patient.

The first important awakening of interest was during the middle of the nineteenth century, when research studies on amalgam began. At about the same time there are also some reports in the literature of studies on porcelain and gold foil. The extremely interesting history of dental amalgams will be given later on. These rather sporadic advances in knowledge finally culminated in the brilliant investigations of Dr. G. V. Black which began in 1895. There is hardly a phase of dentistry which was not touched upon and advanced by this tireless worker.

The next great advance in the knowledge of dental materials and their manipulation began in 1919. During this year, the United States Government requested the National Bureau of Standards to set up specifications for the selection and grading of dental amalgams for use in federal service. This research was done under the leadership of Dr. Wilmer Souder, and a very excellent report was published in

1920.[1] The information contained in the report was enthusiastically received by the profession, and information along the same line was demanded for other dental materials.

Unfortunately at the time the United States Government could not allocate sufficient funds to continue the work, so an associateship was created and supported by the Weinstein Research Laboratories. Under such an arrangement, the private party provides the salary for a research associate and a certain amount of equipment and supplies. The associate then works at the National Bureau of Standards under the direction of their staff members, being to all intents and purposes a member of their staff, supported by private interests. All findings are published and become common property under such an arrangement.

R. L. Coleman, W. L. Swanger, and W. A. Poppe were the Research Associates first appointed under this arrangement. Working under Dr. Souder, they investigated the properties of dental wrought and casting golds and accessory casting materials. The results were published in the well known "Research Paper No. 32." [2] Much of the information published in this book is fundamental, and forms the basis for much of the discussion in the present volume.

In April, 1928, the Research Associateship was taken over by the American Dental Association Research Commission and great advances have been made and are being made at the present time. Dental materials of all varieties are being studied, and specifications are being set up as standards by which a product may be certified by the manufacturer. If the conscientious manufacturer guarantees that his product meets a certain American Dental Association Specification, the dentist may rest assured that the product is satisfactory. Hence, only materials which bear this guarantee should be used by the dentist, provided, of course, that a specification exists for such a product.

There are eight specifications in existence at the present time:* dental amalgams, casting investments, inlay waxes, impression materials, dental casting golds, dental wrought golds, mercury, and zinc phosphate cements; others for silicate cements and denture base materials will follow in the near future.

The present Research Associates at the Bureau are George C. Paffenbarger, W. T. Sweeney, and John R. Beall.

The beneficial results from this work cannot be overestimated. In order to meet the specifications and to produce products which will merit attention on the basis of the new standards, the manufacturers have established private research laboratories, headed by highly trained men whose sole duties are to insure uniform manufacture of old products, and to search for new and superior products. For the first time in history the dentist has criteria available by which he may form a critical judgment of the materials which he uses without

* See Appendix pp. 381–396 for these specifications.

being influenced unduly by advertising propaganda. The interest of the dental schools has been stirred to the extent that courses have been introduced in order to give the prospective dentist a proper background for the appreciation and application of such work.

Although the principal aim of the work at the National Bureau of Standards has been to set up specifications, much of interest in regard to the properties and manipulation of dental materials has been evolved. Other sources of information have come from the experimental research laboratories of the dentists and dental schools, and from certain manufacturers who have been farsighted enough to see that secretiveness is not always the best policy.

Scope of the Course.—It is by no means proposed to study all of the materials used in dentistry. For example, anesthetics and medicaments are not within the scope of this book; only those materials and accessories used directly for restorative dentistry and orthodontics are to be included. These materials include: gold and its alloys, dental amalgams, zinc phosphate, copper, and silicate cements, gypsum products, vulcanite and other denture base materials, waxes, gutta-percha, impression plastics, dental porcelain, and abrasives. To the beginner, many of these materials will seem strange and unfamiliar, but it is one of the aims of the book to introduce them and to study their physical and chemical properties, their manipulations, and, to a limited extent, their actual application in dental work.

A study of these materials involves a knowledge of at least two basic sciences, viz., physics and chemistry. It is assumed that the reader has a working knowledge of general chemistry. For the most part, the physical principles involved are developed in the following pages. The following applied sciences are freely drawn upon:

Metallography, or *physical metallurgy,* is the science of metals. This term is not to be confused with "metallurgy," which connotes the extraction and refining of metals from their ores, and has little or nothing of practical value to offer the modern dentist. *Ceramics* is the science of pottery and porcelain. Various specialized branches of chemistry will be drawn upon, such as rubber chemistry, chemistry of plastics, etc. Certain terms from the various branches of mechanical engineering will be found later on. Lastly, it must not be forgotten that the study of dental materials is a science in itself, with its own terminology and scientific principles, the new science being built as a part of the entire structure of dental science.

Need for the Course.—What kind of a bridge would an engineer build over a wide river, if he knew nothing concerning the physical and chemical properties of the materials which he is to use? Assuming that the bridge could be completed, it would be unsightly and unsafe. It very likely would have its bulk improperly distributed—greatest at a position where it was little needed, and insufficient at the portions of greatest stress.

The principles which apply in structural engineering may be used as well in restorative dentistry. A dental restoration must have strength and elasticity; it must be hard enough to withstand the abrasion of mastication; it must not corrode; and it must not be unsightly. Noting only these few simple mechanical requirements, it is evident that the engineer and dentist have much in common; but the dentist has to consider also the physiological requirements of the dental material, which often complicates matters even beyond the engineer's problem.

Another reason for a course in dental materials is to give the dentist a background, so that he may form criteria for judgment in the selection of his materials. The engineer will carefully evaluate the claims of the manufacturers who wish to sell him the materials for the bridge; he applies the knowledge gained in his professional training, and, if necessary, he will submit specimens of the material to a testing laboratory before accepting it. Unfortunately there are too many unscrupulous dental manufacturers who make impossible claims for inferior products, thus deceiving the dentist. There have been actual cases of highly advertised dental materials which have been made extremely popular among dentists simply by clever advertising methods, whereas careful laboratory tests have shown the products to be distinctly inferior. The well-informed dentist will be able to discriminate between fact and propaganda, and will refuse to be duped in this manner.

LITERATURE

1. Souder, W. H. and Peters, C. G., *An Investigation of the Physical Properties of Dental Materials.* Bur. St. Tech. Paper. No. 157 (1920); Dent. Cos. 62: 305 (March) 1920.

2. Coleman, R. L., *Physical Properties of Dental Materials (Gold Alloys and Accessory Materials).* Research Paper No. 32. U. S. Government Printing Office.

CHAPTER II

FORCES AND STRESSES. PHYSICAL PROPERTIES OF DENTAL MATERIALS

Definitions.—In modern dentistry there are many terms employed which are descriptive of certain properties and qualities of the materials used. Many of these terms are loosely employed, and for this reason they will be defined according to their usage in subsequent pages.

Force.—A force is any push or pull upon matter, either external or internal. Force carries the concept of both *magnitude* and *direction*.

Moment of Force.—Moment of force, or torque, is the effectiveness of a force in tending to rotate a body about an axis, as in a lever. It is measured by the product of the force and its perpendicular distance from the axis of rotation or fulcrum.

Stress.—Any *internal force* which resists the application of an external force, usually designated as the *load*, is called a *stress*. A *unit stress* is a stress measured as force per unit area, such as pounds per square inch, kilograms per square centimeter, etc.

Strain.—A strain is any change in shape of a body while the latter is under stress. Note that a strain is essentially a *deformation*. A *unit strain* is a strain measured in terms of deformation per unit dimension, such as inch per inch, cubic centimeter per cubic centimeter, etc.

Types of Deformation.—After a structure has been deformed, it may or may not return to its original shape, depending upon the magnitude of the applied load. If it does return to its original size, the deformation is said to be *elastic*, but if it tends to retain the deformation to any degree whatsoever, the deformation is called *inelastic* or *permanent*. Any stresses or strains induced during elastic deformation are said to be *elastic*, but if the deformation is permanent, they are said to be *inelastic* or *permanent*.

Elastic Deformation.—In elastic deformation, the stresses and strains exist only during the deformation, and disappear completely when the load is removed.

Inelastic Deformation.—In inelastic deformation the strains do not disappear completely when the load is removed. This type of deformation is not so simple as that of elastic deformation; furthermore, there is no simple mathematical connection describing it. In fact, considerable space will be devoted in succeeding chapters to various aspects of this type of deformation. If this type of deformation is carried too far, *rupture* or breaking results.

21

Types of Stresses.—As noted above, a force is defined physically by stating its direction and magnitude. Since stresses are special types of forces, they also must be described by their direction and magnitude. By means of their direction they may be classified as being of three types: tensile, compressive, and shear.

Tensile Stress.—A tensile stress is any induced force which resists a deformation caused by a load which tends to stretch or elongate a body. A tensile stress is always accompanied by a *tensile strain*.

Compressive Stress.—If a body is placed under a load which tends to compress or shorten it, the internal forces which resist such a load are called *compressive stresses*. A compressive stress is always accompanied by a *compressive strain*.

Shear.—A stress which tends to resist a twisting motion, or a sliding of one portion of a body over another, is a *shear* or *shearing stress*. For example, if this book is closed and placed horizontally upon a table, then deformed by pressing the hand on the upper cover, at the same time exerting a force parallel in direction to the cover, the pages will slip over one another and the shape of the book viewed from an end will be that of a parallelogram, with two acute angles. A shear or shearing stress is thus induced in the book, which is accompanied by a *shearing strain*.

Complex Stresses.—It is extremely difficult to induce a pure stress type into a body. For example, when a wire is stretched, the very conception of stretching connotes an internal sliding of molecules over one another. Hence, although the tensile stresses are predominant, the shearing stresses are also present. Furthermore, during the deformation, the wire decreases slightly in cross section area, which indicates the presence of compressive stresses.

Dental Applications.—The forces of mastication are supplied by the muscles of mastication. The effectiveness of these forces is governed by their moments, or torques, with the temporomandibular articulation acting as the fulcrum.

The masticating stresses are the forces induced in the food bolus, the mouth structures, the dental restorations, and in fact all structures which resist the action of the masticating forces. The food undergoes a permanent deformation and rupture, but obviously the mouth structures and restorations should be only elastically deformed while chewing. Consideration of such stresses and their action upon the mouth structures are important to all divisions of dentistry; hence, a few illustrations will be given.

The field of orthodontics is filled with principles of force application and design. In the movement of teeth, the anchor bands, arch wire, and finger springs must be so constructed that a delicate balance of torques and forces results. The arch wire must be anchored to certain teeth and the torques balanced so that the anchor teeth will not move, and yet the appliance must move certain other teeth slowly and accurately. Such design involves the consideration of very complex forces and torques.

A partial denture with a lingual bar must be fitted so as to balance without undue pressure on either the soft or hard tissues. The lingual bar and clasps act as compensating fulcra, or points of force application, so as to completely balance other disturbing stresses and torques. All deformations must be elastic, otherwise the structure will assume a shape which will react in an injurious manner to both the hard and soft tissues.

Although design is important, the materials of which the structure is made are the criteria which determine the allowable elastic stresses. In the selection of materials for use in dentistry, it is not sufficient merely to know the stresses to which a structure is to be subjected. The materials must be tested quantitatively outside the mouth and the results indicated in some universal manner in order to be of use in the determination of the probable elasticity, strength, etc., which the dentist may employ as a basis for the selection and use of dental materials. Such data are indicated by the obtaining of certain measurements which directly, or by inference, give the physical properties of the material.

Elastic Limit.—If a sufficiently small load of a certain value is applied to a wire under tension, the strain measured, and then the load released, the wire will return to its original dimension. Now if the load is increased progressively by small amounts, and released after each addition of stress as before, a stress value will be reached when the wire does not return to its original dimension, *i. e.*, a permanent deformation occurs, or in other words, the wire has been stressed beyond its *elastic limit*.

The elastic limit may be defined, then, as the greatest unit stress to which a material or structure may be subjected, such that it will return to its original dimensions when the forces are released. Tensile stress was used above as an illustration, yet it should be noted that the definition includes all types of stresses. The elastic limit is expressed as a unit stress, in order to rate the material regardless of what its cross section area may be when tested. For example, assume that a round wire 0.01 square inch in cross section area is found to withstand a tensile stress of 250 pounds at its elastic limit. Then:

$$\text{Unit stress} = \frac{250}{0.01} = 25{,}000 \text{ pounds per square inch.}$$

This means that, if the wire were 1 square inch in cross section area, it would have an elastic limit of 25,000 pounds. Thus, if the quantity is expressed as a unit stress, the actual load on any size of wire of similar material may be calculated, and its maximum elastic stress established. This is very convenient, and allows for comparison of materials of different composition and treatment, and of the same material in different bulk.

Proportional Limit.—If the wire discussed in the previous section had been loaded in tension progressively by small increments,* until the wire ruptured, without a removal of the load each time, and if each unit stress had been plotted on a vertical coordinate, or *ordinate*, and the corresponding unit strain plotted on the horizontal coordinate, or *abscissa*, a curve similar to that in Fig. 2 would have been obtained. It may be noted that the curve starts as a straight line but gradually curves after a certain stress value is exceeded. If a ruler is laid on the straight line portion of the curve, and the straight line is ex-

Fig. 1.—A tensile and compression testing machine. (Courtesy of the Tinius Olsen Testing Machine Co.)

tended in a dotted line as shown (ob), the point P at which the dotted line begins, is known as the *proportional limit*.

It is a fundamental law (Hooke's law) that the stress is directly proportional to the strain in elastic deformation. Direct proportionality between two quantities is always graphically a straight line; hence the straight line portion of the graph in Fig. 2, which was plotted from actual data, is confirmation of this law. Since the proportional limit (point P) is the greatest stress possible, such that this law is obeyed, it may be defined as *the greatest unit stress which*

* Such tests are usually carried out on a testing machine similar to the one shown in Fig. 1.

may be produced in a structure such that the unit stress is directly proportional to the unit strain.

Practically, the proportional limit is identical in most cases with the elastic limit, but they are theoretically different. Any experi-

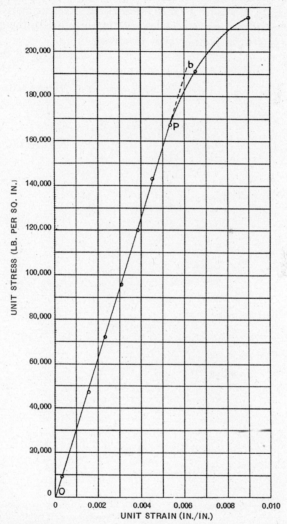

Fig. 2.—Stress-strain curve of a stainless steel orthodontia arch wire. Proportional limit, 167,000 pounds per square inch; modulus of elasticity, 33,300,000 pounds per square inch; modulus of resilience 419 inch-pounds per cubic inch; tensile strength, 234,000 pounds per square inch.

mental difference between the two seems to indicate that the elastic limit is slightly higher in stress value than is the proportional limit. However, as the accuracy in the measurement of strain values increases, the measured value of the elastic limit decreases;[1] hence, any observed differences in the two quantities may be due to errors in measurement.

As in the case of elastic limit, the proportional limit is expressed in units of force per unit area (pounds per square inch, kilograms per square centimeter, etc.). Unless otherwise stated, proportional limit will be given in terms of tensile stress in this text, although it also may be applied to any other type of stress.

LITERATURE

1. Jeffries, Zay and Archer, R. S., *The Science of Metals,* p. 15. McGraw-Hill Book Company.

CHAPTER III

PHYSICAL PROPERTIES OF DENTAL MATERIALS

(Continued)

THE physical properties described in the preceding chapter may be called primary or fundamental properties, since they are measured directly from the material. There are certain secondary, or derived properties which are also of interest. These properties are computed mathematically from the fundamental or primary properties.

Modulus of Elasticity.—Consider the stress-strain curve shown in Fig. 2, page 25. If any elastic stress value on the curve is divided by its corresponding unit strain, within the limits of experimental error, a constant quantity will result. This constant is known as the *modulus of elasticity, or Young's modulus,* and is expressed in units of force per unit area (pounds per square inch, kilograms per square centimeter, etc.).

This property may be expressed mathematically:
Let F = the applied load within the elastic limit.
E = modulus of elasticity.
A = cross section area of the wire.
e = the corresponding increase in length, or strain.
l = original length of the wire.
Then, by definition, the unit stress = F/A and the unit strain = e/l.

Also, by definition: $E = \dfrac{\text{unit stress}}{\text{unit strain}}$ (1)

Hence $E = \dfrac{F/A}{e/l}$

or $E = \dfrac{Fl}{Ae}$ (2)

Flexibility.—The significance of the modulus of elasticity is very great. For example, it may be noted from formula (1) that the less the value of the unit strain, the greater will be the modulus of elasticity. This means that for a given elastic stress a structure will deform less with a high modulus of elasticity than with a low one, if it is assumed that the structure is of the same dimensions in both cases. This property of elastic deformation under load is known as *flexibility*.

Assume that a wire is to be selected for a clasp. The dimensions are quite small, and the flexibility must be quite great, but at the same time the material must withstand considerable elastic stress. Naturally, a criterion of selection will be determined, to a great extent, by the magnitude of flexibility possible without the occurrence of permanent deformation. This maximum flexibility is the maximum elastic unit strain; or, in other words, it is the unit strain which occurs at the proportional limit of the material. Since the physical properties of these materials, which are usually supplied by the manufacturer, are proportional limit and modulus of elasticity, the maximum flexibility may be computed from these quantities by dividing the value for the proportional limit by the modulus of elasticity, the quotient being the maximum flexibility.

This may be proved mathematically:
Let E = Modulus of elasticity.
  P = Proportional limit.
  e = Maximum unit elastic strain, or maximum flexibility.

Then, by definition, $E = \dfrac{P}{e}$

or $e = \dfrac{P}{E}$ (3)

Resilience.—Popularly, the term "resilience" is usually associated with "springiness," but technically it connotes something more than this. *Resilience is the amount of energy absorbed by a structure when it is deformed.* According to this definition, the body does not necessarily have to be springy or elastic to be resilient. For example, sand is placed beneath a vaulting standard, in order to "break" the fall of the athlete. It successfully absorbs his energy generated in falling, yet if he were to fall the same distance into a trapeze net, for example, he would rebound several times before finally coming to rest. Both the sand and the net are resilient, but in the former case, a permanent deformation takes place, while in the latter an elastic deformation is present.

It is a principle of physics that energy can be neither created nor destroyed. In the permanent deformation of the sand, some of the absorbed energy was changed into heat and the rest was used up in the scattering of the sand, which had to be smoothed over before the next vaulter used the pit.

In the case of the net, although some of the energy was transformed into heat, the greater amount of it was used up in elastically deforming the cord. Now the net, when stretched by the falling body, contained energy of deformation which in turn had to be equilibrated; hence, it sprang back to its normal position, and the athlete was thrown into the air.

Another method of stating the foregoing ideas is that when work is done upon a body, energy is imparted to it. By definition, work is the product of the acting force and the distance through which the force moves. Hence, when a dental restoration is deformed, work must be done upon it by the external force. Since it is to be tacitly assumed that the acting force is not greater than the proportional limit—in order that the structure may not be permanently deformed, only the resilience due to elastic deformation need be discussed. When a dental restoration is deformed, the acting force is obviously the masticating force as it acts upon the structure, and the distance through which it moves will be the strain induced in the restoration. From the physical definition of work, it may be noted that either the strain may be made large, and the stress relatively small in magnitude or the stress may be made large, and the strain small. In either case, the resilience may be the same, provided that the values are correctly chosen; but in most dental restorations, large strains are precluded because of the dangers of tooth displacement. For example, a proximal inlay might cause excessive movement of the adjacent tooth, if large strains were allowed. Hence, the restorative material should exhibit a type of resilience which allows stresses of considerable magnitude with but little elastic strain; in other words, the material should possess a high modulus of elasticity.

The *modulus of resilience* is the amount of energy stored up in a body, when one unit volume of a material is stressed to its proportional limit. The modulus of resilience is determined mathematically by dividing the square of the proportional limit by twice the modulus of elasticity.

Mathematical Proof:
Let R = Modulus of resilience.
    P = Proportional limit.
    e = Unit strain occurring at the proportional limit.
    E = Modulus of elasticity.
Since P acts as an increasing force from zero to P, the average force will be

$$\frac{0 + P}{2} = \frac{P}{2}$$

Since R equals the work done on unit volume of material when stressed to the proportional limit:

$$R = \frac{P}{2} \times e$$

But from formula (3) above: $e = \dfrac{P}{E}$

$$\text{Hence } R = \frac{P}{2} \times \frac{P}{E} = \frac{P^2}{2E} \qquad (4)$$

Impact Force.—All of the forces discussed thus far have been static forces, *i. e.*, forces at rest. Most of the masticating forces, that is, those forces which would be most likely to injure the dental restoration, are *impact forces*. Simply the laying of a hammer on a nail head will not drive the nail into the board, but if a motion is added to the weight of the hammer, the resulting force is effective. If either the weight of the hammer or its velocity is too great, the nail may be bent or even shattered under the impact. Hence the mouth structures and restorations must be able to withstand such impact forces or blows, and not become permanently deformed.

It is not possible to calculate the force of impact itself, but its energy may be calculated with considerable accuracy. Although such a calculation is not within the scope of this book, it may be stated that the energy at impact is proportional to the product of the static force acting and the square of its velocity at the instant of impact. This energy must be dissipated by the restorations and mouth structures, thus leaving them in the same condition as before impact. Hence, the deformation must be elastic, and the resilience of the materials and structures involved is a measure of their ability to absorb such energy.

Since the modulus of resilience is, by definition, the maximum amount of energy which may be dissipated in this manner, the following law may be given:

The ability of a unit volume of a material to resist an impact force elastically is directly proportional to the modulus of resilience of the material.

Thus, the modulus of resilience becomes a very important physical property. In fact, it appears to be the most accurate measure of the expectant life value of a material in use in the mouth.

Other applications of this valuable physical property will be made later on.

CHAPTER IV

PHYSICAL PROPERTIES OF DENTAL MATERIALS (Continued): PERMANENT DEFORMATION

IN Fig. 2, page 25, after the proportional limit is reached, the curve is no longer a straight line. As has already been noted, no simple laws can be given which describe this form of deformation. Nevertheless, it should be studied inasmuch as plasticity of materials is very important from a dental standpoint; without it, dental restorations and appliances could not be bent, contoured, swaged, or burnished.

Yield Point.—As may be noted from the stress-strain curve (Fig. 2, page 25), after the stresses exceed the proportional limit, slight increases in stress values result in rather large strains. The *yield point* is the lowest unit stress at which an easily perceptible increase in length occurs for a slight increase in load. The exact amount of such a strain is generally specified for the material being tested. The yield point is sometimes erroneously called the elastic limit.

Ductility and Malleability.—*Ductility* is the ability of a material to withstand permanent deformation under a tensile load without rupture. A metal which may be drawn readily into a wire is said to be ductile. It is dependent upon plasticity and tensile strength.

Malleability is the ability of a material to withstand permanent deformation without rupture under pressure, as when the material is hammered or rolled into sheets. It is also dependent on plasticity, but is not as dependent upon tensile strength as is ductility.

In general, ductility decreases with increase in temperature, whereas malleability increases with increase in temperature. Table I shows the order of malleability and ductility of various common metals.

Ductility is commonly associated with the degree of plasticity allowable when a material is bent or contoured at room temperature, and hence, it is quite important from a dental standpoint.

TABLE I
ORDER OF MALLEABILITY AND DUCTILITY OF VARIOUS METALS

Malleability	Ductility
1. Gold	Gold
2. Silver	Silver
3. Copper	Platinum
4. Aluminum	Iron
5. Tin	Nickel
6. Platinum	Copper
7. Lead	Aluminum
8. Zinc	Zinc
9. Iron	Tin
10. Nickel	Lead

Ultimate Strength.—The *ultimate strength* is the greatest unit stress which may be induced in a body before or during rupture. Under a tensile load, it is called *ultimate tensile strength,* or *tensile strength,* or, simply, strength. In compression, it is called *ultimate compressive strength,* or *crushing strength.*

It should be noted that the structure must be ruptured in order to obtain this value.

Elongation.—After rupture in tension, the specimen is usually longer than it was originally. If the difference between the length of the specimen after rupture and its original length is divided by the original length, and the quotient expressed in per cent, the result will be the *elongation,* or *percentage elongation.*

This computation may be expressed as follows:

$$\frac{\text{Increase in length after rupture}}{\text{Original length}} \times 100 = \text{Elongation (\%)} \qquad (1)$$

This term must not be confused with *unit elongation* which is sometimes used synonymously with unit strain.

Elongation is a measure of ductility.

Reduction of Area.—With materials that are particularly ductile, a "necking," or local constriction may be noted at the point of rupture in tension. The decrease in area of cross section at this point, divided by the original cross section area, is called the *reduction of area,* and is expressed in per cent. It is also a measure of ductility.

Elongation and reduction of area are the two common methods of measuring ductility. Another method, not so common, is the bend test, which consists of placing a specimen in a specially constructed vise, and bending it through a specified angle until it breaks. It should be stated that neither ductility nor malleability are subject to accurate testing. Sometimes the three ductility tests mentioned will disagree as to the relative degree of ductility of the same material.

Hardness.—Hardness of a material, like ductility, is a very difficult property to measure, yet considerable emphasis is given to its measurement in connection with dental materials. In fact, it ranks among the most important physical properties when materials of different types are compared, particularly dental gold alloys. The term *hardness,* in a dental sense at least, may be defined as the resistance to permanent deformation in the form of indentation or scratching. Naturally, these two quantities are very significant in the study of dental restorations which are constantly subject to attritional forces.

There are many methods of measuring hardness, but only those methods will be described which are commonly used in dental testing, or which are occasionally mentioned in the dental literature.

The Brinell Hardness Test.—In this test, a hardened steel ball of a specified diameter is pressed into a polished surface of a material under a specified load. The area of the surface of indentation is computed, and divided into the magnitude of the load. The quotient is known as the *Brinell Hardness Number,* usually abbreviated B.H.N. This number is an index of hardness as defined above.

The mathematical formula for the computation of the B.H.N. follows:

$$H = \frac{P}{\frac{\pi D}{2}(D - \sqrt{D^2 - d^2})} \qquad (2)$$

Where *H* is the Brinell Hardness Number, *P* the load, *D* the diameter of the ball, and *d* the diameter of the impression.

In practice, the diameter of the impression is measured accurately, and the B.H.N. is found from tables prepared for the purpose.

In the testing of dental materials, the micro-Brinell tester is used. The ball is $\frac{1}{16}$ inch in diameter, and the load is generally 12.61 kilo-

Fig. 3.—A micro-Brinell hardness tester. The specimen is placed on the anvil shown near the top of the figure. The load is applied by means of an oil dash pot, which may be noted near the bottom platform. (Courtesy of the American Instrument Co.)

grams, although 6.3 kilograms is occasionally used for very soft materials. Fig. 3 shows a picture of such an apparatus.

Another instrument which employs much the same principle is the Vickers Hardness Tester. Instead of a steel ball, a diamond, cut in the shape of a square base pyramid is used. The impression is square

3

instead of round, but the method of computing the hardness number is the same as in the case of the Brinell instrument.

Although the Brinell number is a measure of hardness as related to indentation, it is not necessarily a measure of abrasion resistance for all materials. For example vulcanite will have a much lower Brinell number than steel, yet the resistance of the former to certain forms of abrasion is much greater than that of the latter. However, its value in the comparison of various metallic dental restorative materials as to scratching or abrasive resistance is probably quite good.

It has been discovered that the Brinell number is also proportional to the proportional limit and tensile strength of dental gold alloys.[2]

The Microcharacter.—The Brinell test can be used only for those materials which are sufficiently plastic to become indented. If the material is very brittle, such as dental porcelain or tooth enamel, chipping occurs. For such materials, a scratch hardness tester may be used, such as the microcharacter. A carefully cut diamond point is drawn across a polished surface under a certain load and the hardness is determined by making certain computations from the width of the scratch. Space does not permit further discussion of this interesting instrument, except to state that it has been used successfully in determining the hardness of various tooth areas, both in diseased and normal teeth. Data of this nature are needed in connection with dental materials, in comparison with the hardness of the tooth surfaces. This hardness value is not convertible into other types of hardness indices.

Toughness and Brittleness.—*Toughness* is the total work or energy required to rupture a body. The term "work" is used in a physical sense, *i. e.*, force times distance. Toughness is the property of being difficult to break.

Brittleness is generally conceded to be the opposite of toughness. Toughness requires strength and plasticity, whereas brittleness connotes a distinct lack of plasticity, but not necessarily a lack of strength. For example, glass is very strong but extremely brittle, as are both tooth enamel and dental porcelain. However, a material cannot be tough, and at the same time be weak.

Fatigue.—This property, when referring to metals at least, is defined as the "resistance of a material to a load, which is applied and removed, in whole or in part, many times and at short intervals."[3] The structure is placed under an alternating stress, which usually changes from tension to compression, the stresses being produced by transverse loading. This loading and unloading process is repeated many times, usually many millions of cycles being necessary, until the structure breaks. The fracture is progressive in nature; it starts at a certain point, and gradually extends across the structure. It is interesting to note that such induced stresses often may be below the proportional limit, as obtained under static loads.

It was formerly thought that such tests were indicative of the probable life value of the material, when used as a dental restoration. This point has been disputed by Brumfield[4] and others, who claim this test to be worthless in this regard.

The *endurance limit* is the maximum stress which may be introduced into a structure without fracture under repeated loading and unloading an indefinite number of times (10,000,000 cycles or more). That is, if a structure breaks under a fatigue test with a certain induced stress, and if the value of the stress is progressively lowered, a limiting stress value will be found, below which the structure will stand up indefinitely.

These tests are rather difficult and tedious to run, and their dental interpretation is somewhat doubtful. As has been already noted, materials should be selected for dental use, whose proportional limit is greater than the expected masticating stresses; hence, the modulus of resilience is probably a much better property by which to estimate expected life value. In the case of overstress beyond the elastic limit, the degree of ductility is of considerable value in this respect; the greater the ductility of the material the greater will be its life value under overstress.

Thermal Expansion.—It is common knowledge that any form of matter will expand or contract as the temperature respectively increases or decreases. The physical property which designates the amount of thermal expansion (or contraction) of a material is called the *linear coefficient of thermal expansion*, and may be defined as the increase in length per unit length of a body when its temperature is raised through one degree. The unit of length to be selected is immaterial since a ratio is always used, but the coefficient of expansion will, of course, not be the same for different temperature measuring scales; hence either Centigrade or Fahrenheit degrees must always be specified.

The *volume coefficient of expansion* is the increase in volume per unit volume when the temperature of a body is raised through one degree. The linear coefficient of expansion is generally used in connection with dental materials in preference to the volume coefficient; for small temperature changes the latter quantity is very nearly three times the former.

Thermal Conductivity.—Thermal conductivity is a measure of the rate of conduction of heat through a body. The *coefficient of thermal conductivity* is defined as the quantity of heat which passes, in one second, between two opposite faces of a cube of unit size (1 cm.) when the faces are kept at one degree difference in temperature. The rate of conductivity of a body is directly proportional to the time elapsed, the area of the surface exposed, and the difference in temperature between the two surfaces, and is inversely proportional to the thickness of the body.

Specific Heat.—The *specific heat* is the amount of heat required to raise 1 gram of a substance through 1° C. The unit of heat to be used in this book is the calorie which is the amount of heat required to change the temperature of 1 gram of water through 1° C.

Dental Applications of Thermal Properties.—The desirable thermal conductivity of a dental restorative material will vary according to its use. For example, a denture base material should, in general, have a high thermal conductivity, whereas a tooth restorative material should have a low thermal conductivity so as to avoid thermal shock when taking hot or cold foods into the mouth.

The dental applications of thermal expansion are many and varied. For example, in the casting of gold inlays and other restorations, there are various thermal shrinkages involved, which must be compensated for by thermal expansion. Gold alloys, for instance, shrink 1.25 per cent when cooled from the molten state to room temperature; hence, any gold casting will thus be 1.25 per cent too small. In order to produce a casting of the correct size, certain thermal expansions are used to produce a casting mold 1.25 per cent too large at the time the casting is made.

Table II shows the linear thermal expansion coefficients of various

TABLE II[5]

AVERAGE EXPANSION COEFFICIENTS, RANGE 20° TO 50° C.

Material	Linear Expansion Coefficients (° C. × 10[6])
Tooth (root)	8.3
Tooth (across crown)	11.4
Tooth (root and crown)	6.4
Tooth (root and crown)	8.7
Tooth (root and crown)	8.3
Silicate cement	7.1
Silicate cement	8.1
Silicate cement	7.5
Amalgam (H)	26.4
Amalgam (C)	25.0
Amalgam (K)	22.1
Amalgam (P)	24.5
Amalgam (A)	25.4
Amalgam (B)	28.0
Amalgam (L)	24.8
Amalgam (C)	25.0
Amalgam (C)	24.7
Amalgam (C)	28.0
Porcelain (Bayeux)	4.1
Gold	14.4
Platinum	9.0
Silver	19.2
Mercury (linear)	60.6
Zinc	29.2
Tin	22.3
Gutta-percha	198.3
Aluminum	23.1
Steel	11.0

materials of interest to the dentist. An ideal tooth restorative material from the standpoint of thermal expansion is obviously one which will exhibit a dimensional change with temperature comparable to that of the tooth structure. As may be noted from the table, the silicate cements are very good in this respect, since their coefficients of expansion match similar values for tooth structure very closely. On the other hand, the amalgams are very poor in this respect. For example, when eating ice cream, the amalgams will contract linearly two to three times as much as will the tooth structure.

LITERATURE

1. Jeffries, Zay and Archer, R. S., *The Science of Metals*, p. 17. McGraw-Hill Book Company.

2. Taylor, N. O., Paffenbarger, G. C., and Sweeney, W. T., *Inlay Casting Golds: Physical Properties and Specifications.* J. A. D. A., 19: 36–53 (Jan.), 1932.

3. Bureau of Standards Circular No. 101.

4. Brumfield, R. C., *Jelenko Research Bulletin No. 2:* 11–12. J. F. Jelenko and Company.

5. Souder, W. H. and Peters, C. G., *An Investigation of the Physical Properties of Dental Materials.* Bureau of Standards Technologic Paper No. 157, p. 18.

CHAPTER V

DENTAL APPLICATIONS. CRITERIA OF SELECTION.

THE practical significance of the physical properties described in the preceding chapters is very great. Although the terms are applied constantly throughout the succeeding chapters, it might not be amiss, at the present time, to make some general statements as to their uses in dentistry.

Masticating Stresses.—It should be borne in mind that by *masticating stresses* is meant the internal forces within the mouth structures and restorations which resist the external *masticating forces,* or loads.

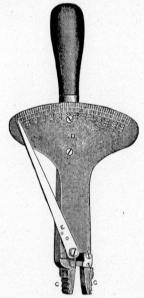

Fig. 4.—Black gnathodynamometer. The teeth are impressed at CC, which actuates lever E which registers the pounds of force on the scale.

The static forces of mastication were first studied quantitatively by G. V. Black. The instrument which he used is shown in Fig. 4, and is called a *gnathodynamometer*. In using the instrument, the opposing teeth are impressed at CC, and the pointer E indicates the force or load exerted in pounds.

Using the opposing molar teeth of a large number of individuals, Dr. Black found the average force exerted in this manner to be **171** pounds. The forces actually exerted by various individuals varied from a minimum of **25** pounds to **275** pounds maximum, the latter value being the limit registered by the apparatus. However, he concluded that the data did not necessarily represent the maximum possible force of mastication, but rather the limiting stresses which might be induced in the mouth structures without pain. He further determined the forces required to crush various foods, notably meats. Such forces varied from 3 pounds for tender boiled tongue to 90 pounds for a tough steak.

It should be noted that the results of the tests are expressed in terms of stress, and not unit stress. Owing to the contour of the tooth cusps, it is very difficult to express the values as unit stresses. The cusps are tapered, and end in small surfaces at the apices which are very nearly pointed. Particularly in the case of the lower posterior teeth, the apices of the cusps must bear considerable of the masticating load which gradually tapers off in magnitude along the inclined planes toward the base. As a conservative estimate of the enormous force involved on the teeth while biting on the gnathodynamometer, let it be assumed that the average masticating force of 171 pounds is distributed over an effective area of 0.01 square inch of the cusp surface.* Expressed in terms of unit stress, the cusp is sustaining the enormous unit stress of 17,000 pounds per square inch.

As explained in Chapter III, the forces of mastication are chiefly impact forces, but the force of 171 pounds exerted by the dynamometer is a static force. Even though such a force is given a comparatively small velocity, the force at impact is probably many times larger than a corresponding static load registered on a gnathodynamometer; hence, the cusp under consideration is certainly a marvel of engineering construction.

Although the impact force cannot be computed, considerations of the energies involved may give additional plausibility to the argument. The energy at impact is entirely energy of motion or *kinetic energy*, as it is designated by the physicist, and it is proportional to the product of the static force value (171 pounds) and the square of the velocity of motion. Under ordinary conditions of mastication, the inelastic resilience of the food bolus plus the elastic resilience of the mouth structures will completely dissipate or absorb this large amount of energy without difficulty or discomfort. However, if the reader has ever had the painful experience of suddenly biting on a bullet when eating wild game, he may readily testify as to the enormous magnitude of the forces involved, even under conditions when no conscious effort is made to exert them. In such a case, most of the impact energy is transmitted to the mouth structures, and a severe pain results. The shot will often be flattened to a disc, and the teeth in some cases are injured permanently. Even under conscious effort, the jaws cannot flatten the bullet, when a static force is used as with the gnathodynamometer.

* That this is a conservative estimate is evident, since 0.01 square inch is equivalent to a square 0.1 inch, or approximately $7/_{64}$ inch, on a side.

It should be evident, then, why the materials used for dental restorations must have sufficient strength. Not only must they be strong, but also they must have a modulus of resilience sufficiently large to absorb the enormous energies involved without becoming permanently deformed. From an engineering standpoint, the construction of an inlay is quite complex in comparison to many of the problems of even the structural engineer. In most cases the latter may increase the bulk of his structures where resilience is needed, but the dentist does not have such an alternative; he must select a material which will be satisfactory for the limited space available.

Criteria of Selection.—Inasmuch as the masticating stresses result from impact forces of unknown magnitude, the question at once arises as to how dental restorative materials may be selected by the dentist upon the basis of physical properties obtained from laboratory tests, which in many cases are not even comparable to mouth conditions. In this respect, the engineer again has an advantage over the dentist, since he knows beforehand what the expected stresses on his structure will be. Furthermore, his structures may be of such a nature that laboratory data may be interpreted directly in terms of each girder and rivet involved.

Since at the present time the dentist cannot follow entirely the methods of the engineer, experience is the first criterion in the selection of his materials, which may be followed by careful laboratory tests. For example, let it be assumed that a gold alloy of a known composition has been worn in the mouth of a patient in the form of a partial denture. If the structure has been found to be satisfactory over a period sufficiently long to demonstrate its utility, the physical properties of this material, such as hardness, proportional limit, moduli of elasticity and resilience, tensile strength, etc., can be determined, and these data may serve as criteria for the selection of other materials for such structures. In other words, any alloy which has physical properties comparable to the proved material should be as satisfactory for such use as is the proved or original material. It is on this basis that dental materials may be selected and rated by the dentist and manufacturer. The American Dental Association Specifications insure that such factors of safety are maintained by the manufacturer, and thus relieve the dentist of considerable difficulty in this regard. If the dentist fails to specify materials for his use which meet such specifications, he is foolishly gambling on unknown factors, and his patients take the losses, if incurred.

Using such laboratory criteria, the manufacturers have been able to improve their products without danger to the patient, who is the ultimate consumer. For example, the gold alloy partial denture mentioned above was probably quite heavy. The manufacturer has been able to make alloys of equal and even superior physical properties, which are considerably lighter than the gold colored alloy, without endangering the health of the patient. However, it must not be thought that perfection has been reached in this regard. While it cannot be denied that such interpretations of laboratory test data into clinical usage have resulted in enormous improvement, and have saved the dentist and patient much time, expense, and ill-health; yet such interpretations necessarily have to be made cautiously and with considerable conservatism. Even at the present time, experience remains the ultimate criterion.

CHAPTER VI*

STRUCTURE OF MATTER. PLASTER OF PARIS: MANU-FACTURE. CHEMISTRY OF SETTING

PLASTER of Paris has been used in various arts for over 2000 years. Its name is derived from a product made from gypsum mined in quarries near Paris.

There is probably no other material which is used more extensively in dentistry than plaster of Paris. It is the basic ingredient of various materials, such as casting and soldering investments, which will be discussed in a later chapter. It is used in taking impressions of the mouth in orthodontia and prosthesis, and occasionally in other dental specialties also. The impression thus obtained is a negative of the mouth parts, and a model may be made by pouring more plaster into the hardened impression. After the latter has set, the impression plaster is trimmed away, and a duplicate form of the mouth parts results. This reproduction is frequently called a cast. According to Prothero,[1] a *cast* is a positive copy or likeness of the object impressed, whereas a *model* is a positive copy of the mouth or some portion of it, used for reproducing a similar positive of itself in metal. A cast usually is employed as a base for the forming of a base plate of some plastic material, which is to be molded or cured. The plasters used for making casts are usually harder than those employed for impressions, and will be discussed separately.

Inasmuch as plaster of Paris is such an important material, its chemical and physical properties will be enumerated at length. Before the material is discussed, a brief review of the states of matter will be given.

Structure of Matter.—Matter, in the ultimate, is composed of positive and negative electrical charges. These electrical particles make up the atom, and the atoms in turn make up the molecules. It is the latter two units of matter with which dentistry is mainly concerned.

The solid state may be further divided into two types, *amorphous* and *crystalline*. Amorphous materials, in general, have a molecular unit structure. The molecules of the amorphous solid tend to have a heterogeneous arrangement, *i. e.*, no definite configuration of the individual molecules with respect to one another. Amorphous solids are sometimes difficult to distinguish physically from liquids. For example, a piece of dental wax will break when bent suddenly at room temperature, yet if it is suspended between two supports, it will

* The author is indebted to Mr. Manvel C. Dailey of the United States Gypsum Company for much of the information contained in this chapter.

42

gradually bend, or flow under its own weight. Obviously the latter property is one generally conceded to liquids. Furthermore, a sharp transition temperature from the solid to the liquid state does not exist in truly amorphous materials. They seem to have no distinct melting point, but rather they soften gradually as the temperature is raised, and finally become fluid. For this reason they are often called *super-cooled liquids*.

The crystalline solids, in contrast to the amorphous materials, all melt at a definite temperature or range in temperature, and do not soften greatly before their fusing point is reached. The atom is the unit usually considered in connection with these materials, and a definite atomic configuration exists, known as a *space lattice*. However, such materials are not necessarily lacking in plasticity, and, as will be pointed out in a subsequent chapter, certain of them exhibit definite properties of flow.

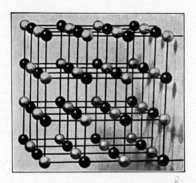

Fig. 5.—Space lattice model for a crystal of sodium chloride. (Courtesy of Central Scientific Co.)

Space Lattice.—A space lattice may be defined as a series of points in space such that every point is situated similarly to every other point. If atoms be located at these points, a model of a crystalline structure will result. Such a configuration is evidenced by x-ray diffraction data, by means of which atomic arrangements are studied. A description of the methods involved in such analyses is not within the scope of this book.

A little thought will show that such an arrangement may be very complicated, and the atoms still be regularly spaced. Fig. 5 shows a model of a simple cubic space lattice of sodium chloride. The spheres represent the sodium and chlorine atoms. It should be noted that each sphere is located at the corner of a cube, and the lattice is therefore known as a *simple cubic* space lattice. If the diagonals on each face of each cube are drawn, and if a sphere is inserted at their points of intersection, a *face centered cubic* lattice results. Now if the simple cubic system is altered by the drawing of diagonals from the four corners of each cube through its geometrical center, and if a sphere is placed at this point, a *body centered cubic* crystal results. Instead of a cube, a hexagonal figure might form the basis of the configuration, or a rhombus, and so on.

Plaster of Paris is a crystalline material belonging to the rhombic system, whereas the ordinary form of gypsum is monoclinic in structure. However, it must not be thought that the entire body of crystalline materials is made up of a single crystal. Such a condition is brought about only under specially controlled experimental conditions. Hardened plaster of Paris consists of individual minute microscopic crystals, interlaced to form the solid. Within each small crystal, a definite space lattice exists, but each crystal may be oriented differently from its neighbor. This interlacing gives the material its solid properties, so far as the crystals themselves are concerned. The principal reason for the strength of the structure is the forces between the atoms themselves.

Setting of Plaster of Paris.—Plaster of Paris, as received by the dentist, is a white powder, which will set to a hard mass when mixed with water. Chemically, the active element is the hemihydrate of gypsum: $(CaSO_4)_2H_2O$. The chemical equation for its reaction with water is usually given as follows:

$$(CaSO_4)_2.H_2O + 3H_2O \longrightarrow 2CaSO_4.2H_2O \qquad (1)$$

The product of the reaction is gypsum.

However, the reaction is probably not as simple as this. There are several theories advanced as to the possible action which takes place, but the so-called *colloidal theory* seems to agree best with the experimental facts.

According to this theory, the hemihydrate (plaster of Paris) dissolves in water to form a saturated solution. Reaction (1) takes place, with an evolution of heat. The dihydrate formed is less soluble in the water than the hemihydrate, and hence, the solution becomes supersaturated with respect to the former.

At this stage, a colloidal sol or gel is formed, in which the gypsum crystallizes in long needle-like forms.

Manufacture of Plaster of Paris.—Until a few years ago, dental plasters were often impure, and a considerable amount of trouble was experienced with mixing consistency and hardening rate. However, improvements in the manufacturing processes have resulted in a uniform product, which does not change appreciably under reasonable care.

The crude materials, as mined and selected for dental plasters, are 95 per cent gypsum. The impurities consist of natural anhydrite $(CaSO_4)$, carbonates, rubidium oxide, and a slight amount of silica. However, such impurities act only as adulterants, and probably have little or no effect upon the physical properties of the material.

The chemistry of the manufacturing process is simply the reversal of equation (1) by heat. However, the temperature must be accurately controlled. If the temperature is allowed to become too high, the hemihydrate may lose its water of crystallization, and be changed to soluble anhydrite, $CaSO_4$. This material is characterized by the fact that it is extremely fast setting. Plasters containing this material in harmful amounts are called "fiery," because of their quick setting properties. If the temperature during calcination is allowed to approach red heat (1000° F. or above), an allotropic change takes place, and *natural anhydrite*, $CaSO_4$, is formed, which is extremely slow setting. This material is identical crystallographically with that found in nature. It is the basic constituent of the *anhydrite stones* to be discussed in a later section. The entire system of reactions may be diagrammed as follows:

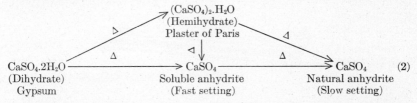

$$(CaSO_4)_2.H_2O$$
(Hemihydrate)
Plaster of Paris

$$CaSO_4.2H_2O \longrightarrow CaSO_4 \longrightarrow CaSO_4 \quad (2)$$

(Dihydrate)	Soluble anhydrite	Natural anhydrite
Gypsum	(Fast setting)	(Slow setting)

A good dental plaster contains the anhydrites in a negligible amount.

The manufacturing process consists of grinding the mined gypsum until fairly fine, and then it is heated in kettles provided with stirring devices. The water of crystallization is driven off, and this is accompanied by a "boiling" of the material at a temperature 235°–250° F. (113°–120° C.), when the hemihydrate is formed. The temperature then is allowed to rise to 300°–330° F. (149°–165° C.), when the kettles are dumped. The plaster of Paris thus formed is very fine grained, and each grain consists of an aggregate of hemihydrate crystals. Such plaster is 90 to 95 per cent hemihydrate of gypsum.

Setting Time of Plaster of Paris.—Obviously, the time during which the reaction between the water and the plaster takes place is of utmost importance to the dentist, particularly in the taking of impressions. The plaster must set rapidly enough so that the patient may not be unduly inconvenienced, yet slowly enough so that the operation may be carried out effectively.

Two setting times are generally recognized, the initial set and the final set. These setting times are both measured from the time the mixing with water is started until the test is completed. The tests are rather arbitrary, and vary somewhat in method.

One such test for time of set is made by means of the Gillmore needles, a set of which is shown in Fig. 6. The smaller needle weighs ¼ pound, and has a point $\frac{1}{12}$ inch in diameter. The large needle weighs 1 pound and has a point $\frac{1}{24}$ inch in diameter. The plaster is mixed with water in certain proportions, and is spread out smoothly in a shallow container. The ¼ pound needle is carefully lowered perpendicularly to the surface, and allowed to rest thereon under its own weight. The time interval, measured from the time when the spatulation was started until the needle makes no appreciable impression on the surface of the plaster, is called the initial setting time.

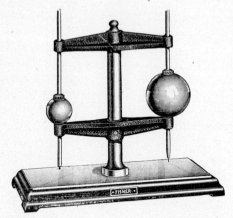

Fig. 6.—Gillmore needles. (Courtesy of Fisher Scientific Co.)

The 1 pound needle is manipulated in a similar manner; the time which elapses from the start of spatulation until no perceptible indentation occurs, is the final setting time.

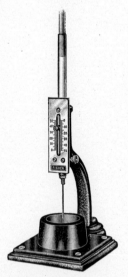

Fig. 7.—The Vicat needle. (Courtesy of Fisher Scientific Co.)

Another method for the determination of the initial set is accomplished by the use of the Vicat needle, which is shown in Fig. 7. This apparatus consists of a rod, weighing 300 grams, to which is attached a needle 1 mm. in diameter, and 5 cm. in length. The rod is supported on a frame, which also supports a scale calibrated in millimeters. A movable pointer is attached to the rod, which acts as an indicator over the scale. The plaster is mixed and poured into a truncated cone-shaped container, which is seated on a glass plate. The needle is lowered until it touches the surface of the plaster, and then released. The time which elapses from the start of spatulation until the needle fails to penetrate to the bottom of the paste, is designated as the initial set. There are other modifications of this method, but such alternative tests are not generally employed in the United States.

Factors Influencing the Setting Time.—The principal factors controlling the setting time are: (1) manufacturing process; (2) amount of spatulation; (3) plaster : water ratio; (4) temperature; and (5) the addition of retarders, accelerators, and other ingredients. Each of these factors will be discussed in turn.

Manufacturing Process.—The manufacturing process outlined in a preceding section generally produces a material of fairly uniform setting qualities. However, if soluble anhydrite is present as an impurity in a considerable amount, the setting time will be obviously decreased.

A few scattered crystals of gypsum are always present in any plaster and they also decrease the setting time, as they provide centers of growth for the crystals which form from the gel. Such minute crystals are called *nuclei* of crystallization. The more nuclei present, the more rapid is the crystallization.

However, these factors are fairly well under control by the manufacturer, and are not of great practical importance to the dentist.

Spatulation.—Within limits, the more the plaster-water mixture is spatulated, the quicker it will set. By amount of spatulation is meant both the time and speed of spatulation, the time element being of greater importance under ordinary conditions. An increase in the speed of spatulation beyond a normal rate very likely tends to increase the rate of solution somewhat, but it is doubtful whether it greatly affects the rate of crystallization, which, in this case at least, is of greater importance in control of the setting time. Although the bulk of the crystal formation occurs as the initial set is approached, yet a few crystals are undoubtedly formed shortly after the water touches the plaster. It may reasonably be assumed that such crystallization is broken up during spatulation, the crystallites then form more nuclei, which accelerate the set. It follows that the longer the mixture is spatulated, more nuclei are thus formed. However, if the mixing is prolonged beyond that period of crystal growth which would normally bring about considerable intermeshing of the crystals, the plaster will be definitely weakened, and the time of initial set, *as determined by the Gillmore or Vicat needle,* will be delayed.

Plaster : Water Ratio.—The less water used in the paste, the shorter will be the setting time. It should be obvious that the more plaster present in a mix, the more nuclei of crystallization there will be; hence, the setting time is decreased.

Temperature.—The higher the temperature of the gauging water, the shorter will be the setting time, *provided the temperature does not exceed 40° C. (104° F.*) which is the temperature of maximum solubility for this material. Although the rate of solution is enhanced, the chemical reaction will be retarded somewhat, since it is exothermic. However, the ultimate result is an acceleration of setting time.

Retarders and Accelerators.—The ingredients added to the plaster are the most effective and important factors in the control of the setting time. As their names indicate, they either accelerate or retard the set.

Some commonly used accelerators are sodium chloride $NaCl$, potash alum $K_2SO_4.Al_2(SO_4)_3.24H_2O$, and potassium sulphate K_2SO_4. The commonly employed chemical retarders are borax $Na_2B_4O_7$, acetic acid $H_4C_2O_2$, and certain citrates. Although many rather involved theories have been advanced in an attempt to account for the actions of these chemicals, the complete explanation of chemical acceleration and retardation of plaster is not known.

Certain materials, such as gelatin, glue, dried blood, althea root, etc., which form colloids in water, have a definite retarding action on the set. Presumably they tend to form a protective colloid about the grains of plaster, and thus prevent the water from reaching them readily.

Setting Expansion.—A linear expansion of 0.15 to 0.30 per cent takes place when plaster of Paris hardens. However, the expansion is only apparent. The specific gravity of the hemihydrate is 2.75, whereas that of the dihydrate is 2.32. Upon calculation, using chemical equation (1), it may be shown that a volume contraction of 7 per cent occurs during the hardening. In the face of such chemical evidence, it is difficult to account for the setting expansion which actually occurs, "apparent" though it may be. This expansion starts at about the time of the initial set as recorded by the Gillmore needle and continues for some hours after. The most logical explanation of this phenomenon is found in the outward thrust of the crystals in the direction of their growth during set.

Naturally, when a plaster model or cast is made which is expected to be an exact reproduction of the mouth parts, such a change in dimension introduces an error which in some cases proves disastrous. For example, when a plaster impression of the upper arch is made, the flanges of the tray prevent the setting expansion from taking place in this direction; hence, the plaster warps in the center, and the vault portion is made deeper than it should be. Such a condition is illustrated in Fig. 8. Furthermore, if a cast is made from such an impression, the error again will be introduced, because of the setting expansion of the cast material as shown in Fig. 9. Therefore, the setting expansion is to be avoided in this case at least.

Fortunately, the setting expansion may be controlled. For example, increasing the water content of the mix will reduce the setting expansion, but unfortunately this prolongs the setting time. Spatulation time also has an effect upon the expansion: within limits, the

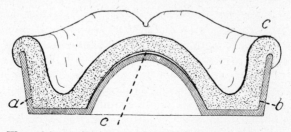

Fig. 8.—Warped impression due to fixed tray flanges. The impression warps at c because the flanges b are fixed, and do not allow lateral expansion. (Prothero, *Prosthetic Dentistry*, Medico-Dental Publishing Co.)

longer the mix is spatulated, the greater will be the setting expansion. It may be controlled chemically, however, in a very practical manner. Potassium sulphate, and some of the other accelerators reduce the setting expansion quite markedly. Potassium sulphate seems to be the best chemical for this purpose, at least for impression plasters. From a practical standpoint, the work of Sodeau and Gibson[2] along this line is most interesting.

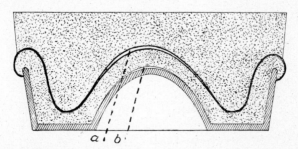

Fig. 9.—Warped cast due to restricted lateral movement. The warpage of the impression shown in Fig. 8 may be seen at b. After forming the cast, warpage of the cast material occurs at a, in addition to that at b, for the same reason. (Prothero, *Prosthetic Dentistry*, Medico-Dental Publishing Co.)

They found that a dental plaster, which normally had an initial setting time of five minutes and forty seconds with a total setting expansion of 0.27 per cent in twenty-three hours, showed an initial set of two minutes and fifteen seconds, with a setting expansion of 0.12 per cent in twenty-three hours when 1 per cent of potassium sulphate was added to the water. It is very evident that, although the setting

4

expansion might be reduced by a further addition of potassium sulphate, the setting time would be too rapid for practical use; hence, borax was added to retard the accelerating action of the potassium sulphate. A series of solutions were made up in this manner, giving varied setting times. A typical solution is: potassium sulphate, 4 per cent; borax, 0.6 per cent; and alizarin S, 0.04 per cent, the remainder of the solution being water. Alizarin S is an aniline dye introduced to color the impression; it has about the same retarding action as borax, and may be replaced by the latter if desired. When 60 cc. of this solution were mixed with 100 grams of plaster, the paste hardened in approximately three minutes, with a total setting expansion of 0.06 per cent in twenty-four hours. However, impression plasters may be purchased on the market which are supposedly balanced, ready for use, and give a minimum setting expansion with the correct setting time. In the latter case, the chemicals are added to the powder instead of the liquid, but the principles involved are the same. Obviously, all dangers of segregation will be removed if the chemicals are dissolved in the liquid.

LITERATURE

1. Prothero, J. H., *Prosthetic Dentistry,* (4th Ed.) p. 450. Medico-Dental Publishing Company.

2. Sodeau, W. H. and Gibson, C. S., *The Use of Plaster of Paris as an Impression Material.* Brit. Dent. Jour., 48: 1089–1115 (Sept. 15) 1927.

CHAPTER VII

PLASTER OF PARIS (Continued). CAST AND MODEL MATERIALS

Ultimate Strength of Plaster of Paris.—The strength of a given specimen of plaster of Paris depends upon the conditions under which it is measured. If the specimen is tested with all the excess water present, the result is called the *wet strength*, but if the specimen is thoroughly dried before rupture, the value obtained is known as the *dry strength*. The dry strength is usually two or more times the wet strength, hence the distinction is very important.

The uncombined water is a very important factor in the determination of strength. For example, 0.1 per cent of excess water by weight will decrease the dry strength 15 to 20 per cent. As described in the last chapter, a gel is one of the products of reaction between the water and plaster. Dailey* gives a theory to account for this difference in wet and dry strength values, on the basis that the residual gel acts as a cementing medium between the interlocked crystals, and it is more effective in this regard when dry than when wet.

Some accelerators and retarders also have a weakening effect. There are many references in the literature to the effect that borax increases the surface hardness, but it definitely decreases the ultimate compressive strength.[1] However, such a decrease in strength is not serious in impression plaster; in fact, it is an advantage to have a comparatively weak plaster for impression work, particularly in partial denture cases, since it will break with a clean fracture when the impression is removed from undercuts, after which the pieces may be accurately refitted.

The less water used in the mix, the stronger the plaster will be. However, thick mixes are not indicated for impressions because of the discomfort or even injury to the patient due to the amount of heat developed during set. The amount of heat generated is not affected by the accelerator,[7] but the latter does increase its rate of formation (see Fig. 10).

Theoretically, only 18.6 per cent of water by weight is necessary to convert the hemihydrate to the dihydrate, but in practice two or three times this amount is necessary in order to obtain a proper consistency for manipulation. Using two parts of plaster to one part of water by weight, Kimball[1] found that the maximum crushing strength occurred in approximately one and one-half hours after mixing, if the excess water was not allowed to evaporate. As the hardened plaster is allowed to dry out, the strength gradually increases.

* Private communication to the author.

51

The wet tensile strength of ordinary dental plaster averages around 200 pounds per square inch, but when dry it should be well in excess of 400 pounds per square inch. The crushing strengths of the respective conditions will be six or more times the tensile strength values.

Temperature has a pronounced effect upon crushing strength of the fully hardened plaster. Kimball[1] found that the higher the temperature, the less is the crushing strength, and that the crushing strength decreases gradually with rise in temperature until a "critical temperature" is reached, when it suddenly decreases markedly. This latter temperature occurs at approximately 245° F. (118° C.), which is the approximate temperature at which the gypsum becomes de-

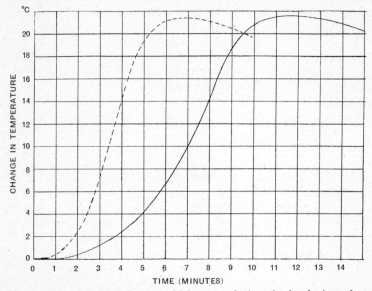

Fig. 10.—Temperature changes which occur during the hardening of model plaster of Paris. The solid line curve represents the temperature change with time, using unaccelerated plaster, whereas the dotted curve shows similar data when 57 cc. of water and 3 cc. of a saturated solution of K_2SO_4 are used. Liquid : plaster ratio of 0.6 used in both cases.

hydrated. Kimball's results are shown graphically in Fig. 11. Curves A, B, and C represent the crushing strengths of three dental plasters, the remainder of the curves showing similar data for a series of artificial stones. As may be noted, all of the products are reduced to essentially the same crushing strength values at the higher temperatures, regardless of their original strengths.

Unless unduly prolonged, an increase in time of spatulation enhances the strength of the plaster. The method of spatulation also affects this property. Obviously, the method of spatulation which produces a mix comparatively free of air bubbles, and homogeneous throughout, will yield a stronger product than would an improperly mixed plaster. Kimball[1] found that if the mix was spatulated mechanically and vibrated when it was poured into the tray or impression, the wet crushing strength was increased 40 per cent over the value obtained by hand spatulation alone without vibration.

Impression Plasters.—As already noted, plaster of Paris may be obtained especially prepared for impression work. Some of these

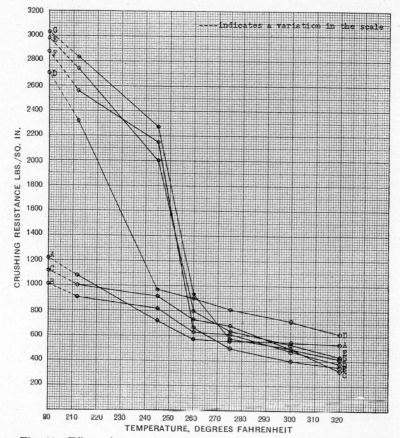

Fig. 11.—Effect of temperature upon the wet crushing strengths of dental plasters and artificial stones, obtained by "vulcanization" at each of the various temperatures for one hour and fifty minutes. (Kimball, Dental Cosmos, December, 1934.)

plasters are colored to facilitate their removal from the cast, and they also may be flavored. Owing to the manufacturing process and the ingredients added (accelerators, retarders, etc.) they are not as strong as ordinary dental plaster, but, as already pointed out, this is somewhat of an advantage.

Soluble Plaster.—"Soluble" plasters are impression plasters to which starch has been added. After the cast or model is poured, the plaster impression is heated in water to a temperature which causes the starch to swell; this disintegrates the impression and allows its ready removal from the cast. Such a disintegrating impression plaster may be made by mixing one part of cornstarch to three parts of plaster by volume. Of course accelerators must be added. Starch is an adulterant, and consequently reduces the strength of the plaster, but not sufficiently to be harmful for impression purposes.

GYPSUM PRODUCTS SUITABLE FOR MODELS AND CASTS

After the impression has been obtained, a model or cast is made. The requisites of an ideal model or cast material are as follows: (1) It should set fairly rapidly, but give adequate time for manipulation. (2) It should set to a very hard and strong mass. (3) It should have a mixing consistency of such a nature that it may be flowed into all parts of the impression easily, with the reproduction of the minutest details. (4) It should neither contract nor expand appreciably while setting. (5) After setting it should not warp or change in shape under any normal conditions of subsequent manipulation. (6) It should not lose its strength to any considerable extent when subjected to vulcanization or any other curing or molding method employed in normal dental practice.

Plaster of Paris as a Model Material.—Plaster of Paris, as ordinarily mixed, is not sufficiently strong for general use as a cast material. The cast is employed usually for the construction of a base plate of vulcanite, for example. During this operation, the plaster, encased in a flask, is exposed to steam under a pressure of approximately 100 pounds (320° F.) for a period of an hour or more. It should be noted that this temperature is somewhat above that at which the dihydrate is changed to the hemihydrate, hence, the strength is considerably lowered, as was discussed in the preceding section, and shown in Fig. 11. In fact the plaster cast may become so weak that the base plate will warp.

Kimball[1] found that the time elapsing between the period when the cast was poured and when it was placed in the vulcanizer, had some effect upon its decrease in strength. However, as may be noted from Table III,[1] there is apparently nothing to be gained beyond a twenty-four hour setting period.

TABLE III

WEAKENING EFFECT OF "VULCANIZATION"

Proportions: 2 parts of plaster : 1 part of water by weight.
Mixing time: 1 minute.

Time elapsing before placing in vulcanizer. (hrs.)	Control. Wet crushing strength. (lb./sq. in.)	Crushing strength after being removed from vulcanizer. (lb./sq. in.)
1	1222	427
24	1220	540
168	1224	533

The average reduction in crushing strength, as shown by the values in column three in the table, as compared with those of column two is 63 per cent. The crushing strengths given in column two were taken with a wet plaster specimen. When thoroughly dried specimens are used, reductions as high as 98 per cent have been reported after vulcanization. Ordinary plaster may be strengthened by decreasing the water content of the mix, but in so doing, the material is likely to harden too rapidly. Johnson and Gibson[3] have developed a solution for use in mixing plasters for casts and models, similar to that described for impression plasters. When such a solution is used, the set is retarded so as to allow more plaster to be mixed with less water, and at the same time the setting expansion is materially reduced. The composition of the solution is: 40 grams Rochelle salt and 2 grams borax, dissolved in 1 liter of water. The recommended mix consists of 100 grams of plaster to 35 cc. of solution. One per cent of gum arabic mixed with ordinary plaster is said to materially increase the strength of the hardened product. Very likely any such increase is caused by the gum arabic acting so as to reduce the amount of gauging water necessary for a given consistency. It also increases the surface hardness.

The behavior of all gypsum products in the vulcanizer is apparently the same. A slight expansion occurs during the vulcanization when the hemihydrate is formed from the dihydrate. If the plaster is allowed to remain in the unopened flask for considerable time after vulcanization, it is often granular and water soaked, presumably due to the rehydration of the hemihydrate. According to Johnson and Gibson,[3] such a condition does not appear when the steam pressure in the vulcanizer is in excess of 100 pounds, possibly because the high vapor pressure prevents the formation of the hemihydrate. Furthermore, a granulation never occurs under "dry heat" under any conditions at ordinary pressures.

Quick Setting Stones.—These materials are usually classified as artificial stones, because of their great hardness and strength after set. The author prefers to classify them as *quick setting stones*, in order to distinguish them from other artificial stones, which are slow setting. The essential constituent of these materials goes under the trade name of "hydrocal," which will be hereafter designated as *alpha gypsum*.

Chemically, there is little difference between alpha gypsum and ordinary plaster of Paris, their chemical formula and reactions being identical. However, there is an important physical difference between the two. As previously noted, the kettle-calcined plaster is a powder whose grains are aggregates of hemihydrate crystals, and they exhibit porosity; whereas the grains of the alpha gypsum product are distinct unit crystals, which are nonporous. The former take up water internally, with the result that additional water is necessary to bring the plaster to a proper working consistency, and this obviously reduces the crushing strength. Inasmuch as the alpha gypsum powder is nonporous, such water absorption does not occur and the necessary gauging water is considerably reduced. This causes the material to set to a very strong and hard mass; dry crushing strengths may be obtained with these products which are two to three times that of ordinary plaster of Paris, the same consistency being used in both cases. In fact, alpha gypsum may be mixed so as to give crushing strengths comparable to that of Portland cement, yet it will gain an initial set in fifteen to twenty minutes, whereas the former may take many hours or even days to harden.

A detailed discussion of the process for manufacturing alpha gypsum cannot be given here. In brief, the mined gypsum is placed in a calciner. Saturated steam is then introduced at 17 pounds per square inch gauge pressure, at a temperature of 253° F. (123° C.). This pressure is maintained for five to seven hours, during which period the hemihydrate is formed. After the steam is released, the material is dried at atmospheric pressure to a temperature of approximately 300° F. (149° C.), in order to prevent a reaction between the residual water and the hemihydrate. The dried material is then mixed with suitable chemicals for the control of setting time and expansion.

The composition of a dental quick setting stone is somewhat as follows:[4]

Rochelle salt	1 to 5 per cent
Pigment	0.5 " "
Retarder	0.1 " "
Alpha gypsum	balance

The retarder used is sodium citrate suspended in silica. A mix of such a product with a water : powder ratio of 0.32 by weight will give a setting expansion of 0.05 to 0.15 per cent, and a dry crushing strength of 7500 pounds per square inch. As may be noted from curves (D), (E), (F), and (G), Fig. 11, page 53, the crushing strength after vulcanization is but slightly greater than that for ordinary plaster of Paris.

The setting reactions for this material are the same as those for plaster of Paris. With the exception of the use of less water in mixing, the same principles apply throughout as previously outlined.

Anhydrite Stones.—If the calcination of gypsum be carried out at an approximate temperature of 1000° F. (540° C.) or higher, a slow setting anhydrite results.* When this material is mixed with water, it sets to a hard mass comparable in strength to that of the alpha gypsum product. The chief objection to these materials is their extremely slow setting time, which is seldom less than two hours when accelerated, and may be twenty-four hours or longer when unaccelerated. Their crushing strength after vulcanization is but very little greater than that of plaster of Paris.

* See equation (2), page 45.

Very little can be found in the literature regarding their chemistry of setting, but very probably they form the dihydrate directly; at least the ultimate product of the reaction is gypsum. Approximately the same powder : water ratio is used as for alpha gypsum.

Since the advent of the quick setting stones, the anhydrite stones are rapidly passing out of use.

Plaster-cement Stones.—Plaster of Paris is sometimes mixed with Portland cement in order to give a stronger mass when hard. One of the most popular products of this nature, according to Gabell,[5] contains plaster of Paris, alum, sand, Portland cement, and citric acid. It exhibits but little setting expansion, and has a comparatively high crushing strength when dry, but it is rather slow in setting. Using a powder : water ratio of 100:28, Mathis[6] found the dry crushing strength of this material to be 2500 pounds per square inch, but after vulcanization, it was 1000 pounds per square inch.

LITERATURE

1. Kimball, H. D., *A Study of the Properties of Plaster of Paris and the Effect of Varying the Manipulation.* Dent. Cos. 76: 1281–1290 (Dec.) 1934.

2. Prinz, Herman, *Dental Formulary*, page 11. Lea and Febiger.

3. Johnson, R. N. and Gibson, C. S., *The Use of Plaster of Paris and Allied Substances for Dental Models.* Brit. Dent. Jour. 50: 681–697 (June 15) 1929.

4. U. S. Patent No. 1,901,054.

5. Gabell, Douglas, *Prosthetic Dentistry*, p. 51. Henry Frowde and Hodder and Stoughton, London.

6. Mathis, E. H., *A Study of the Behavior of Plaster of Paris as an Investment in the Process of Vulcanizing.* J. N. D. A. 6: 432–445 (May) 1919.

7. Harder, O. E., *Modern Dental Metallography*, p. 113. Burgess-Roseberry Company.

CHAPTER VIII

MANIPULATION OF PLASTER OF PARIS AND ARTIFICIAL STONE

Care of Gypsum Products.—Such materials are stored preferably in tightly sealed containers, which are impervious to moisture. The hemihydrate of gypsum is somewhat hygroscopic, and tends to adsorb water vapor. Such adsorbed water does not necessarily act to cause the hydration of the plaster, but rather "deadens" it. Under no circumstances can even a small drop of water be allowed to fall into the dry plaster in storage, without the entire content of the container being endangered. Any plaster spilled on top of the container should be carefully wiped off; dirt and other impurities not only tend to weaken the cast or model, but also they make it unsightly. The mixing bowl and other instruments to be used in manipulation, should be kept spotlessly clean at all times; any gypsum left clinging to a surface with which the mix is to come in contact while setting provides nuclei of crystallization, which accelerate the setting period.

Proportioning.—After mixing, a smooth creamy consistency is necessary for impressions with plaster of Paris. The desirable consistency of such a mix varies according to the opinions of different dentists. Very likely, the average of such opinions will give a consistency such as is obtained by mixing 100 grams of plaster with 60 cc. of water. However, the consistency may vary slightly with different brands of plaster and the water in different localities, as the latter may contain a combination of salts, which, according to their chemical nature, may act as retarders or accelerators. The setting time of impression plasters may be governed largely by the amount of gauging water and mixing time, since strength is not a factor of any moment. Obviously, the temperature of the water will also be a factor in gauging its amount for proper consistency. Many dentists prefer to employ warm water for use with impression plaster, because of the additional comfort it affords to the patient. The *warm* water will, of course, accelerate the hardening rate (see p. 48).

Instead of weighing the plaster, a cup may be provided. For example it has been found by experiment[1] that a two-fluid-ounce measure holds 50 grams of plaster when filled level full without tapping or shaking down. Another measure which holds exactly 30 cc. (1 fluid ounce) may be used for gauging the water. When the two are mixed, enough paste is made for an impression. Many dentists feel that they can gauge the amount of plaster and water by guess, and thus economize on time. While they may be able to do so approximately, nevertheless two successive mixes cannot be made with certainty of control of setting time and expansion. Another factor is the heat evolved during the setting of the plaster while in contact with the tissues of the mouth in impression taking. Many times blisters on the soft tissues may occur due to the use of too thick a mix. It is difficult to understand why a great deal of time is involved in quickly filling a container level full of plaster or water and emptying into a plaster bowl, than using a spoon for the plaster and walking to a tap for the water.

In making casts or models, less gauging water should be used, in order to give the hardened material more strength. As discussed in the preceding chapter, the chief advantage of the quick setting stones is the comparatively small amount of water necessary for mixing them, thus producing a large crushing strength. Usually these latter materials are gauged in the ratio of 100 parts of powder : 30 parts of water by weight; furthermore, because of the shapes of the powder particles, the mix flows readily into the impression, especially under vibration, even though it may appear to be very viscous.

Spatulation of Plaster of Paris and Stone.—As already noted, the mixing equipment must be spotlessly clean. The plaster bowl as usually supplied for mixing is made of rubber which is flexible enough to allow conformation to the spatula. The inner surface of the bowl should be smooth and continuous without sharp angles of any sort. The spatula blade should be stiff, and should be made of some material which will not rust or be attacked in any manner by the chemicals involved. A thin-bladed spatula tends to "drag" and thus prevents proper mixing technic. The end of the spatula should be smooth and rounded, so as to reach into every part of the mixing bowl. The foregoing applies to any type of spatulator, whether for hand or mechanical mixing.

One of the chief obstacles to be overcome during spatulation is the incorporation of air bubbles, which both weaken the hardened product and make the surface of the cast or impression unsightly. All possible precautions should be taken to avoid such a condition. It is for this reason that the water is placed in the bowl first, and the plaster or stone added. The powder should be poured slowly, or, even better, sifted into the water. It may then be gently smoothed over until it is entirely beneath the surface. The mix should be vibrated at this stage by jarring or mechanical vibration; thus any large air bubbles, which would be broken up by latter spatulation, will be brought to the surface and dispelled.

If hand spatulation is used, a rapid stirring motion should be employed, and at the same time all possible surfaces of the bowl should be wiped with the blade of the spatula in order to insure that no plaster settles out. Under no circumstances should the paste be whipped, since such a procedure incorporates air. All lumps should be smoothed out completely. A frequent jarring, turning, and squeezing of the bowl during spatulation is desirable. The spatulation should be completed in thirty to sixty seconds. Prolongation of the spatulation time until the plaster begins to thicken is absolutely contraindicated, since it breaks up the crystal formation and dangerously weakens the final product. After the mix is completed, the bowl is jarred until no more air bubbles come to the surface, and the plaster is poured immediately.

If the paste is too thin or too thick after spatulation, the natural tendency is to add more plaster in the first case, or more water in the second, and continue spatulation. Such procedures are never indicated, since the addition of fresh plaster to a mix which has already been spatulated results in a heterogeneous mass. The first portion of plaster will be partially set before the second portion begins to crystallize, with the net result that the crystal formation is disturbed in both portions of plaster during hydration. In the case of the ultra-thick mix, the very fact that it is too thick signifies that the initial

Fig. 12.—Mechanical spatulators with wall bracket. (Courtesy of Ransom and Randolph Co.)

setting time has been shortened, and that the chemical reaction is well started; thus to add water and to continue spatulation will disturb the crystal formation as previously described. In either case, the only recourse is to throw out the paste and make a fresh mix. Obviously, if the materials are gauged as recommended above, such conditions will not occur.

Mechanical Spatulation.—A mechanical spatulator, shown in Fig. 12, consists of a paddle which is made to revolve in the plaster bowl, either by hand or motor. The paddle should be sufficiently stiff so that it will not bend in the paste, regardless of the consistency of the latter.

The disadvantage of this type of mixer is the likelihood of failure of the paddle to reach all parts of the bowl during spatulation. Many times a paste of thick consistency will be found in the bottom of the bowl after the mix has been poured, which of course indicates that all of the plaster has not been mixed with the water.

However, such a condition can be avoided by proper manipulation. The powder is sifted into the water as before, and if the precaution is taken to stir slowly and carefully with a hand spatula until the water has thoroughly penetrated into the powder before the insertion of the mechanical spatulator, most of the tendency toward subsequent heterogeneity will be avoided, since the agitation of the paddle is sufficient to prevent caking even though the spatulator does not actually wipe around the inside of the bowl by contact.

The same precautions for avoiding air bubbles should be employed as in mixing by hand. The mixing time may be determined by counting the number of turns of the handle, unless a motor is used. The paddle should not turn rapidly enough to churn the material.

Mechanical spatulation has several advantages over hand mixing. It may be employed more uniformly time after time, thus giving greater standardization of the hardened product as to physical properties. Another advantage of this type of spatulation is its ability to give a product with fewer large air bubbles. The hardened material will be stronger, smoother, and superior in every respect.

A description of the actual taking of the impression is not within the scope of this book, but the entire manipulation should be completed before crystallization has proceeded too far.

Construction of the Cast or Model.—The model material is usually very hard when set, and difficult to trim; hence the impression should be boxed with a matrix of wax or a similar material in order that the cast may have a smooth contour. Complete directions for boxing will not be given here, as the specifications vary with different dentists.

A plaster impression must first be painted with a *separating medium*, otherwise it cannot be removed from the cast. The gypsum formation in the impression provides nuclei of crystallization for the model material, thus resulting in cohesion between the two, to some extent at least. Another cause for difficulty in separation is the crystal growth of the model material into the interstices of the gypsum in the impression. Regardless of how smooth the impression appears to the eye, the microscope reveals its crystalline nature, with all its network and minute intercrystalline spaces. The additional gypsum material is thus likely to intermesh with these interstices during setting. Obviously a material may be used to fill up such minute crevices, and thus prevent such union. Such a separating medium must not, however, form a film sufficiently thick that it will change the general dimensions of the model or cast.

Various separating mediums which may be applied are sandarac varnish, collodion, soap, or any other material which will seal the pores of the plaster.

If tooth impressions are present, special precautions must be taken not to entrap air when the artificial stone or model plaster is poured into the impression. The best plan is to place some paste adjacent to such an impression, and vibrate so that it slowly runs down the wall and across the occlusal or incisal surface, thus constantly pushing the air ahead of itself and completely filling the space.

After the model material has thoroughly hardened, the boxing is removed and the impression is trimmed carefully from the model or cast, without injuring the latter. There are several methods for the accomplishment of this, but at best, it consists of a careful dissection of the impression plaster from the cast. It is at this stage that the use of "soluble" impression plaster, described on page 53, is helpful.

The cast, as obtained in this manner, should be smooth and accurate in its reproduction of the mouth parts. If the model material has a large setting expansion, it will, of course, warp in the same manner as shown on page 49, Fig. 9. Therefore a low setting expansion value should be required for an artificial stone, as well as strength.

LITERATURE

1. Sodeau, W. H. and Gibson, C. S., *The Use of Plaster of Paris as an Impression Material.* Brit. Dent. Jour., 18: 1089–1115 (Sept. 15) 1927.

CHAPTER IX

MODELING COMPOUND: COMPOSITION AND PHYSICAL PROPERTIES

OTHER types of impression materials, as distinguished from plaster of Paris which hardens by chemical action and crystallization, are those which are rendered plastic by heat, and solidify upon cooling. To this classification belong the so-called *modeling compounds*.

Modeling compounds should ideally show the following properties:

1. They should harden completely at, or slightly above mouth temperature.

2. They should be plastic at a temperature which is sufficiently low so as not to injure the mouth tissues, and which will not be unduly uncomfortable to the patient.

3. They must be free of poisonous or irritating ingredients.

4. They should harden uniformly, without warpage or distortion, of any sort.

5. They should be sufficiently cohesive, with a consistency which will enable them to reproduce all details of crevices and other small markings, and retain such detail after solidification. However, they should not be adhesive in nature.

6. They should not be permanently deformed or fractured while removing from the mouth, yet they should reproduce all unyielding undercuts, dovetails, etc., in the withdrawn impression.

7. They should not be subject to dimensional changes of any sort.

8. They should exhibit a smooth glossy surface after flaming.

9. They should not flake when they are trimmed at room temperature.

10. They should maintain their shape and dimensions indefinitely at normal room temperature and humidity under reasonable care.

Composition. The formulae for these materials have been kept a secret by their manufacturer, and consequently any discussion of their composition will be somewhat speculative in nature. Prinz[1] gives five different formulae, three of which are as follows:*

Material	Parts by weight
1	
Stearin	25
Dammar resin	50
Powdered soapstone	85
Carmine, enough to color.	

* All formulae are given as examples only. No data as to physical properties of these compounds are at hand, and nothing can be stated as to their quality.

Material	Parts by weight

2

Stearic acid	20
Oleic acid	4
Gum copal	19
Krapplac	17
Powdered soapstone	40

3

Best light-colored rosin	50
Gum copal	2
Yellow ceresin	8
Gum turpentine	5
Powdered soapstone	50
Menthol	$\frac{1}{2}$
Fresh slaked lime	10

Coloring: Red: Florentine lake. Brown: Crocus martis (iron hydroxide).

A number of formulae are given in a patent specification,[2] a typical example of which is:

Shellac	About 45 per cent by weight
Filler (talc, French chalk, etc.)	" 30 " " " "
Glycerin	" 2.5 " " " "
Fatty acids (from Japan wax, palm oil, and tallow) and coloring matter	Remainder

It should be noted that all of the formulae contain an inert filler of some nature (talc, French chalk, powdered soapstone, etc.), which probably is incorporated in order to give the softened material a working plasticity. With the exception of the fatty acids, most of the materials which soften at the working temperatures are amorphous in nature.

If some softened impression compound is wrapped about the bulb of a thermometer, and the temperature noted at definite intervals during cooling, a temperature will be found, which is maintained constantly for several minutes. If the temperature data are plotted as a function of the time, a curve similar to that shown in Fig. 13 will result, and the period of constant temperature will appear as a "plateau" in the curve. Such a plateau is indicative of a solidification of some ingredient in the compound. The temperature at which this occurs in these materials is frequently referred to in the literature as a "hardening point," but the term is, in one sense, a misnomer in most compounds, as the materials are usually plastic at this temperature. However, such data are of value in the determination of the temperature at which this solidification occurs. Since a constant solidification temperature is usually characteristic of crystalline compounds or elements, it may be assumed that the plateau shown in the curve (Fig. 13) is caused by a crystallization. Such crystallization undoubtedly contributes to the strength of the hardened material; hence it naturally follows that any disturbance of the crystals during growth, or fracture after growth, will weaken the impression. Such a condition will occur if the crystallization occurs in the range of working plasticity of the compound. Furthermore, if such a solidification occurs below mouth temperature, it would be of no help in strengthening the impression before removal. Ideally, it should occur at or slightly above mouth temperature. At temperatures above their normal working range, the compounds usually become sticky and difficult to handle, which is probably caused by the resinous materials present.

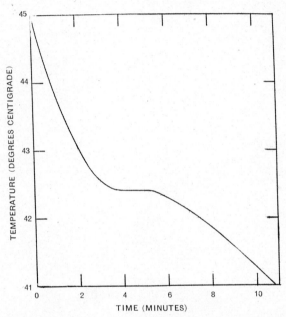

Fig. 13.—Time-temperature cooling curve for modeling compound.

Thermal Properties.—The thermal conductivity of these materials is very low. When immersed in a water bath at their working temperatures, they will soften on the outside, and yet may be quite hard at the center. Patience and time are required to soften as well as to chill them.

From a practical standpoint the thermal contraction of compound is most important. The average linear thermal contraction of modern compounds from mouth to room temperature (77° F. or 25° C.) is probably 0.3 to 0.4 per cent. This means that an impression is 0.3 per cent smaller in all dimensions at room temperature than it was in the mouth. If the room temperature is higher or lower than this value, obviously the shrinkage will vary accordingly. In any event, such a shrinkage introduces a variable which tends to give the finished denture or casting an error of this amount unless it is compensated.

5

Fig. 14 shows a curve which demonstrates the amount of contraction of a well-known modeling compound at various temperatures from 40° to 20° C. (104° to 68° F.).

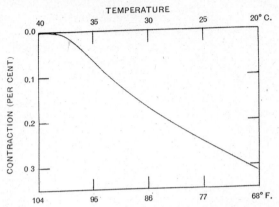

Fig. 14.—Thermal contraction curve of a modeling compound.

Flow.—Inasmuch as considerable of the principal ingredients in these materials are amorphous in nature, a certain amount of plas-

Fig. 15.—Flow micrometer for determining the plastic flow of modeling compounds and inlay waxes. (Taylor, Sweeney and Paffenbarger, Jour. Amer. Dent. Assoc., Jan., 1931.)

ticity may be expected. A little thought will show that if the compound flows plastically in any degree under the forces exerted when an impression is removed from the mouth, the impression will be imperfect. This effect is most noticeable in the case of impressions of cavity preparations in operative dentistry.

In the testing of flow, a cylinder of compound is placed under a load of 2 kg. for a definite time and temperature, and the amount of shortening is determined and expressed in per cent. The equipment used for this test is shown in Fig. 15. The compound is melted and poured into a cylindrical mold 10 mm. in diameter and 6 mm. high, where it solidifies. The compound cylinders thus prepared are placed under the 2-kg. weight for ten minutes in a water bath at the desired temperature. The lowest temperature usually employed is 35° C. (95° F.), at which temperature the specimen must not shorten more than 2 per cent in order to be acceptable for use.*

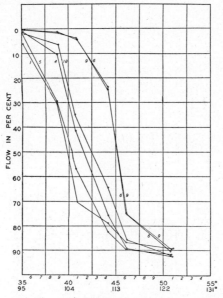

Fig. 16.—Flow of impression compounds under pressure. (Taylor, Sweeney and Paffenbarger, Jour. Amer. Dent. Assoc., Jan., 1931.)

The temperature is then raised by arbitrary amounts, and the test is repeated each time with a new specimen, until 100 per cent flow is realized during the ten-minute interval. If the percentage flow at the various temperatures is plotted as a function of the temperature, some interesting data may be obtained. Fig. 16 shows the flow curves for six different compounds,[3] obtained by the Dental Research Group at the National Bureau of Standards. These investigators arbitrarily established the "softening point" as the temperature at which a 10 per cent flow occurred, and the "working range" as the temperature at which the flow is 85 per cent. The working range is

* American Dental Association Specification No. 3. See Appendix, page 385.

TABLE IV

PROPERTIES OF MODELING COMPOUNDS[3]

Compound No.	Hardening point from cooling curve. (°C.)	Flow per cent.				Working range from flow curve. (°C.)	Tensile strength (lbs./sq. in.)	Shrinkage from 40° to 25° C. (%)	Determined by committee.	
		35° C. (95° F.)	40° C. (104° F.)	45° C. (113° F.)	50° C. (122° F.)				Working range (°C.)	Classification of compounds.
1	40.0	5.0	53.0	82.0	89.0	50–55	450	0.35	50–60	Good all-round.
4	43.5	1.0	30.0	81.0	92.0	45–50	480	0.60	50–55	Good low heat.
5	41.5	2.0	46.0	86.0	91.0	45–50	480	0.45	45–55	Doubtful value.
6	43.0	0.5	3.0	45.0	88.0	50–55	490	0.30	55–60	Good high heat.
9	43.0	0.5	3.0	45.0	87.0	50–55	420	0.45	50–60	Doubtful value.
18	42.5	2.0	24.0	73.0	91.0	50–55	420	0.55	50–55	Good low heat.

understood to be the temperature at which the compound is inserted in the impression tray, and not the temperature at which it is inserted in the mouth. The data from which these curves were plotted are shown in columns 3 to 6 inclusive in Table IV.

Specifications.—American Dental Association Specification No. 3, see Appendix, page 385.

LITERATURE

1. Prinz, Herman, *Dental Formulary* (4th Ed.) pp. 42–43, Lea and Febiger.
2. U. S. Patent No 1,889,622.
3. Taylor, N. O., Sweeney, W. T., and Paffenbarger, G. C., *A Specification for Dental Impression Compound.* J.A.D.A., 18: 53–62 (Jan.) 1931.
4. Souder, W. H. and Peters, C. G., *Investigation of the Physical Properties of Dental Materials.* Bureau of Standards Technologic Paper No. 157 (1920).

CHAPTER X

MANIPULATION OF MODELING COMPOUND. ELASTIC IMPRESSION MATERIALS

Softening of Modeling Compound.—The compound may be supplied in cakes or sticks. The cakes are used for large impressions, and the sticks are employed for obtaining impressions of cavity preparations in operative work, and for making additions, corrections, and tracings on large impressions. The material is preferably softened in a water bath. If it is softened in a flame, great care must be taken that none of the constituents are volatilized in the process. A few of these materials are quite critical as to softening temperature; if they are not heated sufficiently they exhibit a "grainy" appearance, and if the temperature is raised only a few degrees above their softening point, they become adhesive and very difficult to handle.

In general, the compound should be softened at the highest temperature possible without its becoming sticky. Failure to do this is a general fault of the beginner, and his impressions are apt to be rough, which results in a roughened surface of the cast or model. However, if the highest practicable softening temperature is used, the temperature gradient between the interior and the outside will be such that the surface roughness will not occur if the work is done skilfully, yet by the time the tray is inserted in the mouth, the temperature of the compound will be low enough so as not to be unduly disagreeable to the patient, and a smooth impression will result, with full reproduction of all details.

For most compounds, which meet the American Dental Association Specification No. 3, the correct temperature of the water bath is approximately 55° C. (131° F.). A thermometer is very desirable for the measurement of this temperature until experience enables other methods to be used. Thermostatically controlled water baths may be obtained which will maintain the correct working temperature at all times.

If a water bath is employed for softening the compound, the floor of the container should be lined with a towel or paper to prevent the compound from sticking should the temperature become too high. The compound is placed in the bath, and allowed to become plastic. Because of the low thermal conductivity of the material, the outside will soften before the interior. If it is worked with wet fingers as soon as it becomes at all plastic the softening will be hastened; this may be accomplished by working it with both hands, holding it so that the wrinkles may be folded under with the thumbs, and at the

70

same time smoothing it above with the fingers. In this fashion, it will gradually form into an egg-shaped mass. It should be returned to the bath frequently, and the working repeated until a smooth soft homogeneous mass results.

Preparing the Impression.—When an upper impression tray is used, the ball of plastic compound is placed on the vault portion, smooth side uppermost, and worked laterally, with the thumbs, over the floor and flanges of the tray, to form a general reversed contour of the mouth parts. A conically shaped portion of the material is left in excess on the vault portion. The lower tray is filled by making a rope of the material, and working it from the floor to the flange walls.

It should be noted that the compound is always worked toward the periphery of the tray. This is done in order to prevent wrinkling, which always occurs if the material is worked toward the center. Furthermore, the compound should be contoured so that it moves outward toward the tray periphery while the impression is being taken. The technic of impression taking should largely prevent any of the material from exuding at the posterior portion.

Obviously, all of this procedure must be done in a short time in order that the compound will not become too rigid. The surface of the compound in the tray is passed quickly through a flame several times until it becomes glossy, in order to insure additional smoothness and to prevent surface crystallization, then it is dipped in the water bath and inserted in the mouth. As in the case of plaster impressions, the detailed method of impression taking is not within the scope of this book, only to caution the operator to hold the tray rigidly while the compound is chilled, and, at least in complete denture prosthesis, not to remove the impression until the compound is *thoroughly hardened.*

Making the Cast or Model.—The model material is mixed and poured in the same manner as described for the plaster impressions, and the same precautions are to be observed as before to avoid the entrapping of air.

There is little or no danger of the vault portion warping because of confinement as described for plaster impressions. The model material usually generates so much heat during setting, particularly when the quick setting stones are used, that the compound becomes sufficiently soft to allow the setting expansion of the cast material to occur unimpeded.

In fact the compound may become sufficiently soft at this stage to allow the removal of the impression from the cast; however, it should be done cautiously, particularly if tooth forms are present. The safest method for removal of the impression is to place the hardened cast and impression in *warm* water until the compound is sufficiently soft to allow its separation.

ELASTIC IMPRESSION MATERIALS

One of the disadvantages of modeling compound and plaster of Paris as impression materials is their inability to reproduce undercuts and dovetails, formed by arch malformations and interproximal spaces between the teeth. Neither of these materials are elastic to an appreciable extent, and they may either fracture or flow when the impression is withdrawn. Within the last five or six years, impression materials have appeared which are elastic in character, and which are designed to overcome such difficulties. The exact composition of these materials has been carefully guarded by the manufacturers. Furthermore their physical properties have not been investigated thoroughly; hence, some of the discussion which follows must be rather speculative.

Superficial examination of the materials indicates that there are two types. One type is very evidently a colloidal gel, whereas the other type appears to be a mixture of colloids, waxes, and oils.

Colloids.—The colloidal properties of matter depend upon its particular state of aggregation or degree of subdivision, intermediate between units or aggregations which can be observed with the naked eye or microscope, and the molecular condition. For example, crystals of copper sulphate are solid, yet when they are dissolved in water they form a solution. In this condition, the ion or molecule is the unit; the solution will obey all laws of diffusion and similar phenomena characteristic of liquids. On the other hand if agar agar is dissolved in water, although the solution appears to be the same as before, it will not diffuse through a parchment membrane, for example, as will the true solution. A solution of the latter type is said to be a *colloid*, or *colloidal sol*. The difference between the sol and the solution of copper sulphate lies in the fact that the former is composed of aggregations of molecules (*dispersed phase*) dispersed in the water (*dispersion medium*); *i. e.*, it consists of droplets of liquid dispersed in the water. Such a colloid is called an *emulsion*. Had the particles been solid, the sol would have been called a *suspension*.

If the above agar agar sol is cooled to a sufficiently low temperature, it will form a jelly, or *gel*. This process is reversible, and it will again become liquid when the temperature is raised. In gelation, it is believed that the particles coalesce to form a network of some sort. This "setting" may be retarded or accelerated by certain chemicals, although such an effect may be rather one of increase or decrease of the temperature of gelation, which is not critical. For example, the anions, acetate, tartrate, citrate, and sulphate are progressively more effective as accelerators, and the chloride, chlorate, nitrate, bromide, iodide, and thiocyanate radicals are progressively more efficient as retarders for most gels.[1] This type of colloid also exhibits the property of swelling when in contact with water, gelatin being a well known example. This phenomenon is known as *imbibition*. The more concentrated gels are surprisingly elastic.

Gel Impression Materials.—These materials are essentially gels of agar agar which are probably 80 per cent water. One manufacturer states that his material contains agar agar, rubber latex, cellulose fiber, wax, and water. The cellulose fiber is added for strength, and the wax to give added plasticity, the latex and agar agar being the colloids. The manufacturers of similar materials without the cellulose fibers claim that the latter prevent a clean fracture in the event that the material breaks upon the removal of the impression.

Very little is known, so far as the dentist is concerned, about the physical properties of these materials. Like most gels, they probably have an elastic limit and modulus of elasticity. They are low in thermal conductivity, and show little or no thermal contraction between mouth temperature and room temperature after setting.

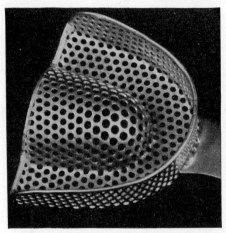

Fig. 17.—A perforated tray for use with colloidal impression materials. (Courtesy of L. D. Caulk Co.)

Like all colloids of this type, if they are allowed to remain in unsaturated air at room temperature, dehydration occurs together with a serious shrinkage. Impressions will shrink in this manner to about one fifth of their original size, hence it is imperative that the impression be kept entirely moist until the cast is made. As previously mentioned, these colloids are reversible in nature, but rehydration occurs very slowly at room temperature. A dried specimen of this material, which was kept in water at room temperature for three months, recovered approximately one third of its former volume during the period; of course the rehydration would occur more rapidly at higher temperatures.

These materials exhibit no adhesion whatever to the impression tray, hence, some other means must be provided for retention. A special type of tray may be used, or else a preliminary impression in modeling compound should be taken, which is then carved so as to provide retention, after which a second impression is made with the gel. The special perforated trays for use with these types of materials are illustrated in Fig. 17. The soft material penetrates through the perforations and is thus retained after setting.

In the manipulation of the material, the manufacturer's directions must be carefully followed. It is very important that the sol be completely homogeneous when it is poured into the tray. A mixing "gun" seems to be essential for such a condition; such a device is shown in Fig. 18. The material is usually supplied in cylinders which fit into the barrel. The cap of the barrel is screwed into place, and the gun is placed in boiling water until the gel has become liquefied. The portion of the piston, to which the loops are attached, is fastened to a flat plunger which is perforated with large holes. This is worked back and forth frequently; this breaks up the gel and increases the rate of liquefaction. After the sol is formed, the gun is removed from the boiler, and cooled to approximately 50° to 54° C. (120°–129° F.) so that the material will not be uncomfortable to the patient. The cap is then removed from the barrel, and the gel is exuded onto the tray.

Fig. 18.—A mixing "gun" for colloidal impression materials. (Courtesy of L. D. Caulk Co.)

The impression is made and the tray is held rigidly in position while the material is cooled. The latter precaution is very important, for if the gel is distorted or broken while setting, it will neither return to its original position nor grow together again. Twenty-two to twenty-five degrees centigrade (72°–77° F.) appears to be the gelation temperature of the materials, hence water below these temperatures should be used in chilling, in order not to unduly prolong the setting time. Three to five minutes is usually required, unless ice water is used which will obviously shorten the time considerably.

The impression is removed carefully and kept moist until the cast is made, as previously stated. The cast is made as described for other impression materials.

Other Elastic Impression Materials.—To all appearances, the other type of elastic impression materials is simply modeling compound whose formula has been altered by the addition of certain colloids and oils. No scientific data are at hand as to the physical properties of these materials, but superficial examination seems to indicate that many of them are subject to considerable flow, even at room temperature.

As to the ingredients used in the compounding of these materials, at least two approximate formulae[2] may be given, but it is not known whether or not they are typical.

FORMULA 1

Ingredients	Percentage by weight
Paraffin oil	18
Boiled linseed oil	18
Beeswax	10
Paraffin	10
Aluminum stearate	30
Glycerol	1
Starch	10
Sulphur	3

Flavoring and scenting material.
Cotton lint or other fibrous material may be added to give strength.

FORMULA 2

Ingredients	Percentage by weight
Rubber	22.0
Balata	40.0
Gelatin	12.5
Flaked aluminum	8.0
Glycerol	5.0
Stearic acid	4.0
Paraffin wax	4.0
Water	4.0
Methyl salicylate	0.5

The manipulation of these materials is very similar to that of modeling compound; no mixing gun or special impression tray is necessary.

Zinc Oxide Impression Pastes.—These materials are said to have merit for impression purposes. They consist of a powder which is mixed with a liquid to form a paste, which hardens in the mouth. According to Ross,[4] if a powder composed of zinc oxide, 85 parts, and white powdered rosin, 15 parts by weight, is mixed with a liquid of composition—oil of cloves 60 parts, Canada balsam, 35 parts, and balsam of Peru, 5 parts by weight, a satisfactory material of this nature results. This material is also said to be useful for the purpose of the temporary rebasing of dentures.[5]

LITERATURE

1. Findlay, Alexander, *Introduction to Physical Chemistry*, p. 464. Longmans, Green and Co.
2. U. S. Patent No. 1,897,034.
3. U. S. Patent No. 1,920,857.
4. Ross R. A., *Zinc Oxide Impression Pastes*, J.A.D.A., 21: 2029–2032 (Nov.) 1934.
5. *Accepted Dental Remedies*, p. 158. American Dental Association (1934).

CHAPTER XI

DENTURE BASE MATERIALS. VULCANITE

NONMETALLIC denture base materials may be classified as *thermocure* and *thermoplastic*. Thermoplastic materials are those substances which soften under heat and mold into form under pressure, whereas thermocure materials change chemically while being subjected to heat and pressure.

The perfect denture base material should probably meet the following requirements:

1. It must be easy to manipulate.

2. It must have sufficient strength and resilience at mouth temperature to resist all normal masticating stresses.

3. It should be easy to repair, and should neither shrink nor expand during the fabrication of the denture.

4. It should have sufficient impact strength to resist unavoidable accident.

5. It should have a relatively high thermal conductivity.

6. It should be impermeable to mouth fluids, and resist bacterial action and growth.

7. It should harmonize with the soft tissues in color and translucence, and should retain such properties in the mouth indefinitely.

8. It should be tolerable to the mouth tissues, and should be both odorless and tasteless.

9. It should have a low specific gravity.

10. It should maintain its shape whether in or out of the mouth.

Vulcanite.—Needless to say, the ideal denture base material has not been found. However, the nonmetallic base material which has withstood the test of time is *vulcanite*, also known as ebonite or hard rubber. It is thermocure by classification, since its fabrication is the result of a chemical reaction between sulphur and rubber, called *vulcanization*. Its chief disadvantages are its lack of esthetics, low thermal conductivity, lack of resistance to bacterial growth, continued shrinkage upon revulcanization, and the bulk necessary to provide sufficient strength. Hence, it meets only half the number of requirements for an ideal material.

In dental prosthesis, the procedure of vulcanization of a denture base is, in brief, somewhat as follows: a wax model, or pattern, in which the teeth have been set up, is constructed on the cast, which is imbedded in the lower half of a vulcanizing flask, and surrounded by plaster or artificial stone. A separating medium is applied; the upper half of the flask is placed in position above the lower half, and filled with plaster or stone. After the final set of the plaster material has occurred, the halves are separated, and the wax is removed by flushing with hot water. The sulphur-impregnated rubber is then packed into the space left by the wax, and the flask is again closed. It is then placed in the vulcanizer, which is essentially an air-tight water boiler. The temperature is raised to the desired point and held for a stated time. After it has cooled, the flask is opened, and the vulcanized denture base is removed. The procedure will be given in more detail in the next chapter.

In its entirety, the chemistry of vulcanization is still somewhat of a mystery, and no attempt will be made to go very deeply into the subject. However, a few facts which are known definitely will be of practical interest. In order to appreciate the chemistry of vulcanization fully, a short résumé of the chemistry of rubber itself is necessary.

Chemistry of Rubber.—Rubber, or *caoutchouc* as it is often called, is the product of the dried milky juice or *latex* of various trees and plants. The common milkweed and goldenrod in this country are two examples of plants which furnish such an exudate, but the use of these sources for the production of rubber is not commercially profitable. The tropical tree, *Hevea brasiliensis*, furnishes practically all latex commercially.

Latex is a colloid, the caoutchouc being the disperse phase, and a peptizing serum the dispersion medium. The size of the colloidal particles varies from 0.1 to 5 microns, with an average size of 1.5 microns. The chemical composition of the latex is 35 per cent rubber, 5 per cent nonrubber constituents, such as proteins, resins, sugar, and certain inorganic salts, and 60 per cent water.[1] It is neutral in chemical action when fresh. The rubber may be coagulated by acidifying the latex, after which it is milled into sheets and dried.

Rubber is an extremely elastic material. It further shows the remarkable property of contraction when heated. Its molecular weight is not known, but it is undoubtedly very large. In the unstretched condition it is amorphous in character so far as can be determined, but when stretched 80 to 100 per cent, it takes on a fibrous structure.

The molecular formula of pure rubber is usually given as *isoprene* C_5H_8, and its formula is often written as $(C_5H_8)_n$. The exact form of the rubber molecule is somewhat open to question. X-ray[2] and other evidence seem to indicate that the molecule is a long chain hydrocarbon, perhaps spiral in shape, which may uncoil, similar to a spiral spring, when the rubber is stretched.

Chemically, rubber is quite active, since it is an unsaturated compound as may be noted from the structural formula of isoprene:*

* For the benefit of readers who may not be familiar with organic chemistry, perhaps the significance of some of these terms should be given. In the isoprene formula, each carbon atom has a valence of 4. As may be noted, there are two valences between some of the carbon atoms; such a compound is therefore said

$$
\begin{array}{c}
\text{H} \quad \text{H} \quad \ \ \text{H} \\
| \quad \ | \qquad | \\
\text{H—C=C—C=C—H} \\
| \\
\text{H—C—H} \\
| \\
\text{H}
\end{array}
$$

In comparison, the formula of the rubber hydrocarbon may consist of thousands of isoprene groups joined as follows:

$$
\begin{array}{c}
\text{H} \\
| \\
\text{H—C—H} \\
\text{H} \quad \text{H} \qquad \text{H} \quad \text{H} \qquad | \qquad \text{H} \\
| \quad \ | \qquad \ | \quad \ | \qquad | \qquad | \\
\cdots\cdots\ \text{—C—C=C} \quad \text{—C—C—C=C—} \quad \text{C—}\ \cdots\cdots \\
| \quad \ | \qquad \ \ \ | \quad \ | \quad \ | \qquad | \\
\text{H} \quad \text{H—C—H H} \quad \text{H} \quad \text{H} \qquad \text{H} \\
| \\
\text{H}
\end{array}
$$

The uses of pure rubber are extremely few. Priestly, famous for his discovery of oxygen, in 1770 discovered its use for the erasing of pencil marks; hence, the term "rubber" is used in all English-speaking countries. Articles, particularly wearing apparel, made from raw rubber become hard and brittle in cold weather, and are soft and sticky at temperatures reached during the summer season of even moderate climates. Rubber became generally useful only after the discovery of the vulcanization process by Charles Goodyear in 1839.

Vulcanization of Rubber.—In the "hot" process of vulcanization, some sort of a reaction takes place between the rubber and sulphur* which produces a material differing in many respects from the crude rubber. The vulcanized product is much less subject to chemical action and changes in temperature and humidity. Its strength is many times greater, and, by a proper compounding, it may be made as much more or less elastic than the crude product as is desired; rubber bands may be stretched many times their own length, whereas dental vulcanite is considered inelastic in comparison.

The exact nature of the action of the sulphur upon the rubber is unknown, but such research as has been done in rubber chemistry seems to indicate that an additional reaction occurs between the sulphur and the rubber, perhaps accompanied by *polymerization*.†
The reaction cannot be a combination by substitution, as the latter

to be *unsaturated,* that is, all of the valences are not occupied by hydrogen, carbon, or other atoms. In compounds where none of these *double bonds* occur, the material is said to be *saturated.* Any substance which reacts with an unsaturated compound so as to saturate a double bond, forms an *addition product.* On the other hand, if the reaction occurs so that one of the hydrogen atoms is replaced, the reaction would occur by *substitution.* The latter type of reaction is similar to that which ordinarily occurs in inorganic chemistry.

* Other chemical elements have been found which produce similar effects with rubber, but so far as is known they are not used in dental vulcanite.

† A molecular change which involves a change in molecular size by the combination of several molecules in a regular manner. Polymerization must not be confused with *aggregation* in which the molecules group together haphazardly.

would undoubtedly result in considerable evolution of hydrogen sulphide. If such a substitution reaction did occur, Rippon[4] calculates that for every ton of vulcanite cured,* 2000 gallons of gas would be evolved. In other words, for every gram weight of vulcanite used in a denture, approximately 10 cc. of gas would be given off during vulcanization at the usual temperatures employed. That such a condition does not exist is evident to anyone who has ever manipulated the material. It is true that the odor of hydrogen sulphide always occurs to a slight extent, when a vulcanizing flask is opened, but this is thought to be due to a substitution reaction which occurs between the sulphur and the small amounts of nonrubber constituents present, such as proteins and resins. When the odor of the gas is present to a considerable degree, it is an almost sure sign that "something is wrong," and almost invariably the product will exhibit internal porosity. Such a condition is usually attributed to a too rapid reaction between the rubber and sulphur, and in this case substitution reactions may possibly occur. The importance of control of this rate of reaction during vulcanization cannot be overemphasized.

A Chemical Theory of Vulcanization.—The exact form of the rubber molecules and their configuration after vulcanization is not clear. Weber is of the opinion that for possible vulcanization the lower limit of sulphur in the mixture is 2 per cent, which results in a chemical formula $(C_5H_8)_{20}S$, and the upper limit is 32 per cent sulphur, with the formula $(C_5H_8S)_n$. The lower limit represents soft elastic rubber, and there is a gradual change to vulcanite as the upper limit is approached. However, quantitatively this theory has so many faults, that its validity is distinctly questionable at the present time. According to Clark,[5] with the lower sulphur content vulcanized rubbers a sulphur bridge formation takes place between the spiral chains previously mentioned, the unit "crystal" being the same as that of the pure rubber. As the sulphur content is increased, a loss of elasticity occurs because of the production of a "net formation," which occurs in vulcanite.

Such a view is compatible with a recent theory of vulcanization propounded by Boggs and Blake,[6] which is entirely chemical in nature. The theory assumes that the rubber molecule is a straight chain molecule with a spiral configuration, composed of isoprene molecules joined together through their end carbon atoms, with the loss of a double bond for each union, thus:†

Isoprene molecules

$$C{=}C{-}C{=}C \qquad C{=}C{-}C{=}C \qquad C{=}C{-}C{=}C \qquad C{=}C{-}C{=}C, \text{ etc.} \qquad (1)$$

Rubber molecule

$$C{=}C{-}C{-}C{=}C{-}C{-}C{-}C{=}C{-}C{-}C{-}C{=} \ldots \ldots C{-}C{-}C{=}C \qquad (2)$$

* The process of vulcanization is often spoken of as "curing." These calculations are based on previous computations by Weber.

† The hydrogen atoms and CH_3 groups have been omitted for purposes of simplification. Compare with the formulae on the previous page.

The theory offers a unique explanation of the differences between soft vulcanized rubber and vulcanite, based upon observed tensile strength values for different rubber-sulphur combinations. A curve which presents the relation between tensile strength and combined sulphur is shown in Fig. 19.[6] The first strength maximum is reached at approximately 5 per cent combined sulphur, and marks the soft rubber region. As the sulphur content increases, the tensile strength decreases to a constant value, until approximately 26 per cent sulphur is reached, when it again increases. The region of minimum tensile strength is known as "medium hard rubber," the compounds of which

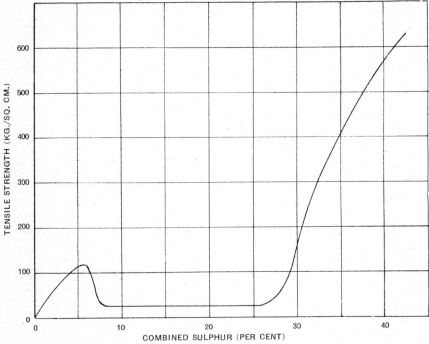

Fig. 19.—Tensile strength of rubber-sulphur compounds.

are metastable; they are leather-like materials and are lacking in strength and aging ability. Vulcanite begins to form at approximately 30 per cent sulphur and increases in strength as the sulphur content increases up to approximately 47.1 per cent, an amount above which a substitution reaction may take place with any excess sulphur.

Such a curve may be explained upon a purely chemical basis. Noting formula (2) above, it may be seen that the end carbon atoms are attached to a double bond. It is a common observation that the end atoms of a chain compound are chemically the most active; hence the addition of sulphur to these atoms is most likely to occur first, before the other double bonds are filled. The authors of this theory, therefore, postulate that the formation of soft rubber entails the saturation of the end double bonds only; hence, formula (2) becomes as follows for soft rubber:

Soft vulcanized rubber

$$C-C-C-C=C-C-C-C=C-C-C-C= \ldots \ldots C-C-C-C \quad (3)$$

As the vulcanization proceeds, the center bonds begin to fill, which disrupts the atomic forces and makes for less strength. When they are completely filled, the strength becomes comparatively large and vulcanite is formed. Formula (3) becomes as follows:

Vulcanite

$$C-C-C-C-C-C-C-C-C-C-C-C \ldots \ldots C-C-C-C \quad (4)$$

That is, vulcanite is a saturated compound of rubber; hence, vulcanite is not thoroughly cured until all of the double bonds are filled. From a dental standpoint, *failure to complete this process results in part of the molecules being of the nature of medium hard rubber, with unsaturated double bonds, which may unite with oxygen and possibly certain other chemical elements in the mouth; this results in a greatly shortened life of the restoration and a general unsanitary condition.* On this basis, there is no mystery about the chemical difference between hard and soft rubber, as the latter is a natural formation during the curing of the former.

Optimum Cure.—There is no fixed temperature at which vulcanization begins. In this connection Furnas[7] states: "Sulphur will unite with rubber at ordinary temperatures; however, in direct ratio as the temperature is increased, the time necessary for vulcanization is shortened." The first statement is of great practical importance as it indicates that the rubber mixture supplied to the dentist for packing his case has a shelf life; that is, it may gradually vulcanize at room temperature.

As previously mentioned, the time, temperature, and pressure during cure must be accurately balanced in order to control the reactions. As noted above, the higher the temperature, less time will be necessary, but if the rate is too rapid, the vulcanite will be of poor quality, since it will exhibit internal porosity especially in thick pieces. The consensus of opinion is that the reactions are more readily controlled by the employment of a lower temperature and a longer time of vulcanization.

If the vulcanite is undercured, it will be soft and weak, and permeable to mouth fluids. If overcured, it will be brittle and it will exhibit considerable shrinkage. It is very evident that a time, temperature, and pressure may be selected which will give an *optimum*

6

cure, which will give a product of best possible properties. As will be shown later, the optimum curing time for dental vulcanite is not critical, once the undercured stage has been passed, and hence, the danger of overcure is much less than that of undercure, provided gas is not evolved. The selection of optimum curing conditions will depend upon the composition of the vulcanite and the size and shape of the article to be vulcanized.

In the manufacture of soft rubbers, accelerators are used which hasten the curing time. When used in vulcanite, they hasten the formation of the soft rubber stage, but have little or no effect upon the rate of the formation of vulcanite, the latter being proportional only to the amount of sulphur present and the concentration of the soft rubber. They should be used sparingly in dental vulcanite, because of the dangers of scorching, porosity, surface discoloration, and brittleness in the final product.[8]

Dimensional Changes During Vulcanization.—The vulcanization of dental vulcanite is accompanied by an expansion as the temperature rises to a certain value, after which a small contraction takes place. Upon cooling, the thermal contraction is very nearly the same as the original expansion.

The studies of Gysi,[9] in this regard, are most interesting. He made a pile of air-free dental rubber specimens, which were placed one above the other and separated by plates of aluminum. The pile was encased in a specially constructed flask, leading out of the top of which was a glass tube, calibrated in cubic centimeters. Glycerin was poured into the flask, thus surrounding the rubber; hence, any change in volume of the rubber would be indicated by a rise or fall of the glycerin in the glass tube. The flask was immersed in a glycerin bath, the temperature of which could be accurately controlled.

As nearly as can be judged from the data as presented in the report, a total volume expansion of approximately 30 per cent occurred from room temperature to 280° F. (138° C.), after which a volume contraction of approximately 7 per cent took place which continued to the maximum temperature reached (320° F. or 160° C.). Upon cooling, a contraction of 30 per cent occurred. Since the total contraction was 37 per cent, and the total expansion was 30 per cent, the vulcanite was obviously 7 per cent smaller in volume than the original rubber.

The first expansion and the final contraction are very evidently thermal; but the first contraction must be due to some change in form, chemical or otherwise, and may be termed a *reaction shrinkage.*

It should be noted that the above data are for vulcanization without pressure; in practice, the results are somewhat different, due to the pressure involved. This will be discussed later.

Both the expansion and contractions are extremely troublesome in practice. Unless proper precautions are taken, the expansion will often crush the investing medium, thus causing warpage of the case.

Not only does the contraction cause further warpage, but also the vulcanite tends to pull away from the teeth.

Revulcanization causes further shrinkage.   Furnas[10] revulcanized a strip of red dental vulcanite six times at 320° F. (160° C.) for one hour and twenty minutes each time.   The total shrinkage was 3.2 per cent, or approximately 0.5 per cent for each vulcanization.

LITERATURE

1. Hauser, E. A., *The Colloid Chemistry of Rubber,* pp. 23–24.   Oxford University Press.

2. Clark, G. L., *Applied X-Rays,* (2nd Ed.) p. 449.   McGraw-Hill Book Company.

3. Reference (1), p. 22.

4. Rippon, Charles, *Vulcanite and Vulcanization.*   Brit. Dent. Jour., 34: 965–975 (Sept. 15) 1913.

5. Reference (2), p. 450.

6. Boggs, C. R. and Blake, J. T., *A Theory of Vulcanization of Rubber.*   Ind. Eng. Chem., 22: 748–755 (July) 1930.

7. Furnas, I. L., in Turner and Anthony, *The American Textbook of Prosthetic Dentistry* (6th Ed.) p. 456.   Lea and Febiger.

8. Kemp, A. R. and Malm, F. S., *Hard Rubber (Ebonite),* Ind. Eng. Chem., 27: 141–146 (Feb.) 1935.

9. Gysi, A., *Controlling the Shrinkage of Rubber During Vulcanization.* Dent. Digest, 27: 286 (May) 1921.

10. Reference (7) p. 458.

CHAPTER XII

COMPOSITION AND MANIPULATION OF DENTAL VULCANITE. DENTAL VULCANIZERS

Composition.—The dental vulcanite formulae of Dr. Wildman quoted in various textbooks on Prosthetic Dentistry are given in Table V.*

TABLE V
FORMULAE FOR DENTAL VULCANITE

Constituent.	Dark brown.	Red.	Dark pink.	Gray-ish white.	Black.	Jet black.	Ma-roon.
Caoutchouc..........	48	48	48	48	48	48	48
Sulphur..............	24	24	24	24	24	24	24
Vermilion............	..	36	10	..	..	..	30
Zinc oxide (white).....	..	..	30	96			
Ivory or drop black ...	..	..	..	..	24	48	6

It should be noted that the sulphur content is exactly 50 per cent that of the rubber content in all cases. The vermilion is added for coloring purposes. The materials other than rubber and sulphur are known as *fillers*. In soft rubbers, many of these fillers are very active in the promotion of increased strength, resilience, and resistance to abrasion, but they tend to weaken vulcanite. The pink vulcanites are called *veneer rubbers* because of the fact that they are used as a veneer on labial and buccal surfaces of the denture for esthetic purposes. The remaining materials are *base rubbers*, and give strength to the denture.

The Vulcanizing Flask.—The container in which the denture is vulcanized is called a *flask*, which is illustrated in Fig. 20. It is constructed of metal, and has three parts: a lower half, an upper half, and a cover, all of which are separable.

Investing the Cast.—A model of the denture base is constructed with wax on the cast.† The latter is then invested in the lower half of the flask with the use of plaster or, preferably, artificial stone. After the plaster has thoroughly set, a separating medium is applied and allowed to dry. The upper half of the flask is then placed in position, and filled with plaster or artificial stone, after which the cover is placed on and the plaster is allowed to harden thoroughly.

* Other formulae are given on page 108.

† Mention of the insertion of the teeth has been omitted, as it contributes nothing to the discussion.

84

The two halves are then separated. This is best done by placing the flask in a pan of cold water, and gradually raising the temperature of the latter until the wax is softened. The temperature can be gauged by placing a piece of the wax on the cover of the flask. When it shows signs of being melted when rubbed over the metal surface, the wax inside is usually soft enough to allow separation, provided that the temperature has been raised with sufficient slowness. It should be remembered that the plaster is a poor conductor

Fig. 20.—A vulcanizing flask for use with clamp or compress. (Courtesy of the Buffalo Dental Mfg. Co.)

of heat and the metal a good conductor, hence, if the rise in temperature is too rapid, the flask itself may be quite warm, yet the interior may be barely above room temperature. The wax must be softened before the flask is opened in order to prevent fracture of the cast or matrix, and possibly a loosening of the porcelain teeth if present.

Under no circumstances should the wax be allowed to melt in the flask. This is extremely important, due to the tendency of the liquid wax to seep into the pores of the cast so that it cannot be removed. During the vulcanization process such entrapped wax is likely to boil up into the semiliquid vulcanite, thus ruining the surface, or causing porosity.

The two halves of the flask are then separated, and the wax carefully removed.

As previously mentioned, an expansion of the vulcanite occurs during vulcanization. As will be shortly described, the rubber is packed so as to fill completely the space formerly occupied by the wax, and during the vulcanization process, the rubber expands with great force. If a channel for the excess rubber is not provided, the force of the expansion may crush the cast and matrix. Hence a small channel is usually cut around the periphery of the cast with V-shaped waste gates which extend from the channel to the denture mold. During vulcanization, the excess vulcanite exudes through the waste gates into the channels.

Flushing.—The case is now flushed thoroughly with boiling water in order to remove any bits of plaster or wax which may cling to various portions of the mold. The addition of a tablespoonful of washing soda to 2 quarts of flushing water[1] greatly facilitates the flushing process.

The surfaces of the mold may now be treated in some manner to prevent the plaster or stone from adhering to the vulcanite after vulcanization, thus greatly simplifying the cleaning and polishing of the vulcanized denture. Tin foil is commonly used for this purpose. The tin foil is carefully burnished and smoothed over all the surfaces, and held in position with varnish.* However, the use of tin foil on the maxillary and ridge surfaces of the casts is likely to decrease the adaptation of the finished denture, because of the thickness of the foil coating. There are certain liquid paints on the market which are said to be as efficient as tin foil in this respect, and do not have the disadvantage of bulk.

Packing.—The sulphur-impregnated rubber is usually supplied in sheets, which are extremely flexible and "sticky"; hence, they must be kept absolutely clean and free from particles of plaster, wax, etc., which adhere to them quite readily.

The sheets are cut into various sizes and shapes for packing, and laid on a clean towel. Since the rubber must be packed warm in order that it may be of a soft consistency, either the mold or rubber, or both, must be heated before packing. One method of doing this is to place the rubber and flask on a towel supported over boiling water, or the flask may be heated over a Bunsen burner, so that the rubber will be heated sufficiently when it comes in contact with the heated mold. If the latter method is used, great care must be taken to heat the flask gradually so as not to disintegrate the plaster, or

* There is some advantage to be gained by thus treating the cast and wax model before flasking.

even explode the contents. Furthermore, if rubber or vulcanite is already present, excessive heat will scorch it.

The rubber is packed into place bit by bit until the case is filled. A wax spatula or similar instrument may be used in packing. Great care must be taken to obtain as nearly a homogeneous mass as possible. Under no conditions should bits of wax or plaster be allowed to become impregnated in the rubber while packing. At the vulcanization temperatures generally employed, the wax will volatilize and the plaster will give up its water of crystallization, both of which will cause bubbles and regions of weakness.

Testing.—Because of the expansion of the vulcanite during vulcanization, the case is usually tested. A piece of clean linen cloth, or a colored sheet of cellophane is laid over the packed rubber. The flask is then closed with light pressure and placed in boiling water for ten or fifteen minutes. At this temperature the vulcanite expands over the edges of the mold. The excess is trimmed away, and the process repeated, gradually closing the flask tight shut, until no more excess rubber appears. The flask is finally closed tightly in a screw press without the cloth, and then preferably placed in a spring clamp, or, if a bolted flask is used, the parts are firmly bolted together. The case is now ready to be vulcanized.

The Dental Vulcanizer.—The dental vulcanizer is essentially a steam boiler. Fig. 21 shows such an equipment. The boiler is usually lined with seamless copper, reinforced with brass or bronze. The heat is supplied by means of gas or electricity, the supply being regulated automatically by some means.

As was discussed in the previous chapter, the rate of vulcanization is governed by the time and temperature during vulcanization, pressure being necessary as well. In dental vulcanizers, the temperature is governed by steam pressure within the boiler.

The theory behind this phenomenon relies upon the fact that the boiling point of the water, or any liquid for that matter, depends upon the pressure. For example, if water boils at 212° F. (100° C.), the atmospheric pressure will be 14.7 pounds per square inch. It is a well known fact that a "three-minute egg" boiled on Pike's Peak, for example, is only slightly coagulated, whereas if the same egg is boiled for three minutes in a pressure cooker, it will be completely coagulated. Obviously, the three minutes of boiling time applies to conditions of normal atmospheric pressure; on Pike's Peak, the air pressure is less than 14.7 pounds per square inch; hence, the boiling temperature is lower, whereas in the pressure cooker, the steam is confined, and *by its own pressure,* it raises the boiling temperature of the water.

Another point that should be noted is that the temperature of an open kettle of boiling water is independent of the rate at which the heat is supplied. That is, regardless of how hot the fire under the kettle, the temperature of the water will remain constant, although it may boil violently, *i. e.*, bubbles of steam will come to the surface with great rapidity. The reason for this is that the heat is used up in converting the water into steam. As a matter of fact 538.7 calories of heat are required to change 1 gram of water into steam at 212° F. (100° C.) under normal atmospheric pressure. The amount of heat required to change 1 gram of a liquid into vapor is called the *heat of vaporization.*

If the boiler is closed, the boiling point will be raised, since the pressure increases. The steam pressure will increase until equilibrium is established, that is, the rate at which the boiler receives heat is

Fig. 21.—A dental vulcanizer with gas and time-regulator attachments. (Courtesy of the Buffalo Dental Mfg. Co.)

exactly equal to the heat losses. At this equilibrium temperature, the steam is said to be *saturated*, that is, just as many molecules of water are leaving the liquid as are entering it. If the temperature is lowered, more steam will condense than is formed, until equilibrium is again established. On the other hand, if the temperature is raised, more molecules leave the liquid than enter, until equilibrium is again established. However, it should again be noted *that the higher the temperature, the greater is the pressure.* The necessity of careful regulation of heat during vulcanization is therefore evident. Obviously the operator of a vulcanizer cannot afford the time to regulate the temperature manually over the period of vulcanization (one to three hours); hence, an accurate gas or electric temperature regulator is second in importance only to an explosion-proof boiler construction. Table VI shows the variation of steam pressure with

TABLE VI

Steam Pressure at Various Temperatures*

Temperature (° F.) (° C.)		Pressure (lbs./in.²)	Pressure gauge reading (lbs./in.²
212	100	14.7	0.0
220	104.4	17.2	2.5
230	110.0	20.8	6.1
240	115.5	24.9	10.2
250	121.0	29.7	15.0
260	126.5	35.2	20.5
270	132.0	41.6	26.9
280	137.7	49.0	34.3
290	143.2	57.3	42.6
300	149.0	67.2	52.5
310	154.4	77.7	63.0
320	160.0	89.6	74.9
330	165.5	102.8	88.1
340	171.0	117.6	102.9
350	176.5	134.0	119.3
360	182.0	152.1	137.4
370	187.8	173.2	158.5
380	193.2	194.9	180.2
390	199.0	220.6	206.2
400	204.5	247.3	232.6

* Calculated from the Smithsonian Physical Tables, pp. 298–303.

temperature. The third column gives the absolute pressure within the vulcanizer, and the fourth column the pressure as indicated on the steam pressure gauge. It should be noted that these latter values are 14.7 pounds per square inch less than the values in the third column.

If dry air were used in the vulcanizer instead of steam, the pressure would vary approximately with the change in temperature, since the volume is constant,* but the relation between saturated steam pressure and temperature is not so simple as this. In Fig. 22, the absolute saturated steam pressure has been plotted against the corresponding temperature values. As may be noted, the curve is by no means a straight line. In fact, the higher the temperature, the greater the rate of change in pressure becomes; hence, the great importance of accurate control of the heat source during vulcanization.

* This is absolutely true only in the case of a "perfect gas." The relation is given by the well known gas law: $PV = RT$, where P is the pressure, V the volume, T the temperature in degrees absolute, and R is the gas constant. In the system considered, the volume is constant; hence, for all practical purposes, the pressure of a gas will vary directly with the absolute temperature.

Although the pressure gauge theoretically indicates the temperature of the vulcanizer as well as the pressure, its readings should usually be checked by means of a thermometer. As a general rule,

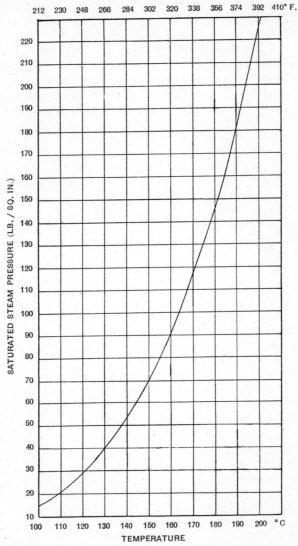

Fig. 22.—Variation of saturated steam pressure with temperature.

the bulb of the thermometer is placed in contact with the outside of the boiler by inserting it in a mercury well, the mercury being in contact with the top of the boiler. Obviously, the temperature indicated by the thermometer in this position is lower than that on the interior of the vulcanizer, due to heat losses from the surface of the boiler. Nevertheless its use for purposes of comparison is of value.

For example, there is a possibility of the correct pressure being maintained, yet the temperature being at the same time alarmingly high. It may be noted in the preceding discussion, that it has been tacitly assumed that the pressure is due to saturated steam. In order to maintain such a condition, there must be water present in the vulcanizer at all times. If insufficient water is placed in the boiler at the start, so that all of the water is converted into steam, or if the steam leaks out because of faulty sealing of the boiler, so that the latter becomes dry, *super-heated* steam results, that is, unsaturated steam. Super-heated steam is essentially a gas, and obeys the gas law as the temperature is raised. As may be noted from Fig. 22, with saturated steam, the rise in pressure is by no means directly proportional to the temperature, but changes very rapidly as the temperature is raised. As already noted, when the volume remains constant a gas changes pressure directly in proportion to the temperature; hence, in the latter case, the change in pressure with temperature is much less than a similar change with saturated steam. Therefore, if super-heated steam is used for vulcanization, the pressure gauge as a temperature indicator in accordance with Table VI is in error. If the thermometer is not present to warn of such a condition, the case will be completely ruined, because of the high temperatures involved. There are instances on record of violent explosions occurring under such conditions.

The Blow-off Valve.—All vulcanizers are equipped with a manually operated blow-off valve. The valve is left open until the water starts to boil, as evidenced by steam pouring through it. In this manner the air is expelled from the boiler, being driven out by the steam. The valve is tightly closed after the boiling temperature is reached.

Although the presence of the air in the boiler does not appreciably affect the temperature and pressure during vulcanization, yet it is commonly exhausted in dental practice. The presence of considerable air in the vulcanizer probably decreases the rate at which equilibrium conditions are established between the saturated vapor and the water. The air and steam molecules must be visualized as constantly colliding with each other and the walls of the boiler; the higher the temperature the greater will be their energy. The presence of air molecules will decrease the rate at which the molecules of water may be converted into steam and diffuse throughout the space provided in the boiler. Hence, the absence of air possibly may allow a more accurate control of the time, temperature, and pressure variables.

The Safety Valve.—This consists of a valve which opens directly into the boiler. The valve is sealed with a thin disk of metal such as copper, which will break at a pressure well above the vulcanization pressures, yet low enough so that the ultimate strength of the boiler will not be approached. As a safety device it is a very important unit in the construction of the vulcanizer.

The Gas Regulator.—Gas regulators are of two types, one of which is controlled by the temperature of the vulcanizer and the other by the steam pressure.

From the previous discussion, it may be concluded that the regulator activated by temperature may be safer under certain unforeseen conditions than the other type. Such a regulator usually consists of a metal rod which regulates the gas flow by thermal expansion or contraction.

The regulator controlled by steam pressure consists of a diaphragm which moves up or down as the pressure increases or decreases, thus automatically decreasing or increasing the rate of gas flow through a valve system as in the other case.

In either case a calibrated screw arrangement is provided, so that the operator may set the regulator at any desired temperature and pressure, and be certain that the quantities will be maintained without further attention. However, all too frequently, either type of regulator will get out of adjustment with continued use, thus requiring recalibration or resetting.

Time Regulators.—The time of vulcanization may be automatically controlled by the use of a clock placed in the gas or electric line, which may be set so as to shut off the fuel at a certain predetermined time. Hence, if all the parts of the vulcanizer are in working order, it may be noted that the total operation may be accomplished automatically. The operator places the flasks in the vulcanizer, closes the door, and lights the gas. After the blow-off valve is closed, the time and gas regulators are set, and the work forgotten until the case is vulcanized.

LITERATURE

1. Prothero, J. H., Prosthetic Dentistry (4th Ed.) p. 814. Medico-Dental Publishing Co.

CHAPTER XIII

VULCANIZATION PROCEDURE. POROSITY. PHYSICAL PROPERTIES OF DENTAL VULCANITE

Vulcanization Procedure.—The vulcanizer must first be inspected as to whether there is sufficient water; most vulcanizers require about 8 fluid ounces. After the flask is placed in the vulcanizer, the pressure regulator is set at the desired temperature, the blow-off valve opened, and the gas supply lighted or the electricity turned on. When the steam begins to escape freely, the blow-off valve is closed. The temperature and pressure should reach the desired value in approximately twenty to thirty minutes, after which the time regulator is set.

After the case is vulcanized, the safest method of cooling is to shut off the gas and allow the boiler to cool gradually. Under no conditions should the blow-off valve be opened before the steam gauge registers zero pressure. The force exerted on the flask during vulcanization is enormous, since at 75 pounds gauge pressure, for example, there are 75 pounds of force exerted on *each square inch* of flask surface. If the total surface of the flask is 50 square inches, this means that a total force of approximately 3750 pounds is distributed over the entire surface of the flask. If such a force is suddenly released, the effect upon the vulcanite, which is still comparatively soft, can well be imagined. Economy of time may sometimes require that the boiler be cooled by water or compressed air, but in doing so, the operator is running a risk of warpage of his case.

When the gauge registers zero, the blow-off valve may be opened. This must always be done before the door of the vulcanizer is opened because of the danger from residual steam. Serious burns have occurred because this precaution was neglected.

The flask should not be opened until the vulcanite is thoroughly hard if warpage is to be avoided. The general rule to follow in this regard is to delay the opening until the flask is cool enough to be held in the hands with comfort.

Vulcanite is polished according to the rules given in Chapter XV.

Dimensional Changes During Vulcanization.—In a practical denture case, the changes in dimension during vulcanization are somewhat different from those given on page 82 for the freely expanding material. However, an expansion to approximately 280° F. (138° C.), followed by a contraction may be expected under any conditions. The chief difference lies in the action of the pressure to which the practical case is subjected. As previously noted, during expansion the rubber is forced out through the waste gates, the amount being equal to the total expansion; obviously, this excess material will not return to the mold during the ensuing contraction, hence, the volume of the depleted denture will be less by this amount, in addition to the normal reaction contraction.

By means of some ingenious experiments, Gysi[6] has been able to estimate the loss as well as the reaction shrinkage under practical conditions. His results indicate that the reaction shrinkage for base rubber may be from 2.5 to 4 per cent, and that from loss through the waste gates to be 6 to 10 per cent. This is obviously equivalent to a total shrinkage of 8.5 to 14 per cent in volume. The shrinkage of veneer rubbers is considerably less.

Such shrinkages cannot be avoided or compensated for completely by any method known at the present time. Gysi[7] is of the opinion that the reaction shrinkage may be directed to regions of little consequence by the use of tin foil. He demonstrated that this shrinkage takes place more readily on smooth surfaces than on plaster, for example. He therefore advocates that tin foil be burnished over the lingual surface of an upper case before vulcanizing, with the expectation that most of the shrinkage will occur adjacent to the tin foil, rather than on the palatal surface adjacent to the plaster.

Some authorities advocate that waste gates and channels be dispensed with. Theoretically, this idea is sound, especially if the flask is placed in a spring clamp during vulcanization. According to the theory, the spring should allow the flask to open slightly during the expansion period, and then gradually close during the subsequent contraction. Unfortunately, in practice this does not happen. Gysi[8] describes the effect in connection with a similar method as follows:

"When the rubber expands and opens the flask, . . . then the metal borders all around the flask are no more in contact, so that the upper half of the flask is swimming in an unstable equilibrium on the soft rubber. . . . If, now, the force . . . is not accurately centered over the flask, which can never be done, . . . then the upper half of the flask will tilt over toward the side of least resistance until the metal borders of the flask touch on this side, whereby the metal borders on the opposite side of the flask separate more than the rubber expansion accounts for. . . . The halves of the flask are kept tilted in this position, producing on one side a deeper articulation and on the other side a higher articulation."

On the other hand, if the flask is bolted instead of being placed under spring pressure, the rubber can only displace or fracture the investing medium while it is expanding.

Time and Temperature of Vulcanization.—No set rules can be given as to time and temperature of vulcanization, as they vary both with the composition of the vulcanite and the size (particularly thickness) of the piece. As has been so frequently emphasized, a low temperature and a long time are preferable to a high temperature and a short time. A thin case may be safely vulcanized at a higher temperature and shorter time than a thick one. An ordinary base plate may be vulcanized safely at a temperature of 338° F. (170° C.) and 100 pounds gauge pressure for one hour, but when a thick ridge is placed on the base, a longer vulcanization time at a lower temperature is required.

As has been repeatedly emphasized, too rapid vulcanization inevitably leads to porosity. Inasmuch as this is the greatest single evil to be avoided, and occurs so frequently in "perfectly vulcanized" cases, it will be considered in detail.

Internal Porosity.—Fig. 23 shows a denture with internal porosity. It should be noted that it occurs in the thick ridge portion. Such a condition rarely occurs in thin portions; furthermore, it never occurs in pink veneer rubber. Such a condition is generally attributed to overheating which causes a substitution reaction to occur between

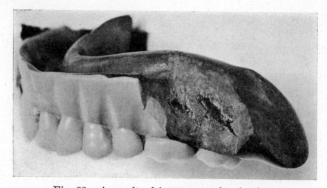

Fig. 23.—A result of improper vulcanization.

the sulphur and rubber as described in Chapter XI. At first thought, such a condition could not exist, since the entire denture shown in the illustration was vulcanized in one piece, and was presumably at the same temperature throughout; hence, one portion should be theoretically as liable to exhibit porosity as another.

The answer to this apparent dilemma lies in the facts that vulcanite is a poor conductor of heat and exhibits a large heat of reaction during vulcanization. Blake[1] has shown that 300 calories of heat per gram are given off during the vulcanization of rubber containing 32 per cent sulphur, when cured at a temperature of 160° C. (320° F.). Table VII shows the approximate increase in temperature found by various investigators[2] when hard rubber cylinders were vulcanized.*

* 3.5 cm. cylindrical specimens were used. Presumably the bulk of the denture would be less than this with a correspondingly lower increase in temperature.

TABLE VII

INCREASE IN TEMPERATURE DURING VULCANIZATION AT VARIOUS VULCANIZING TEMPERATURES

Vulcanizing temperature		Increase in temperature	
° C.	° F.	° C.	° F.
160	320	> 100	> 180
145	293	60	140
135	275	10	18

Assume that the temperature of vulcanization for the denture shown in Fig. 23 was 320° F. (160° C.) for a time of one hour; then the increase in temperature due to the heat of reaction would carry the cure to a higher temperature than that registered by the gauge or thermometer. The substitution reaction between sulphur and rubber normally begins at approximately 347° F. (175° C.),* hence, a relatively small increase in temperature (27° F. or 15° C.) would likely start the formation of gas in the denture. Since the actual increase in temperature is probably greater than this, the occurrence of internal porosity is not to be wondered at. The thinner portions of the denture can effectively dissipate this heat of reaction into the investing medium, but because of the low thermal conductivity of the rubber, the central portions of the thicker pieces do not lose heat rapidly enough. This also explains the "case hardening" effect often seen in large pieces of vulcanite. The external surface will be to all appearances perfectly normal, and give no hint as to the internal porosity. Obviously the external layers dissipate the heat of reaction as do the thin vault portions. Furthermore the external portion hardens and entraps the gas. If the pressure of the gas is not sufficient to force an opening through this hard layer, the external surface will be smooth and unblemished.

The filler in the pink vulcanite very likely increases the thermal conductivity sufficiently so that the heat of reaction is conducted from the interior with sufficient rapidity to prevent the occurrence of the gas formation.

As may be noted from Table VII, the lower the temperature of vulcanization, the less is the observed heat of reaction, which is in accord with the general principle so often quoted: "Vulcanize at a lower temperature for a longer time."

Another method for the prevention of porosity is to place old vulcanite in the center of the thicker portions. In the rubber industry the vulcanite is usually added in the form of a powder. Aluminum or tin powder is sometimes used for this purpose instead of vulcanite. In either case the ultimate result is the same as though any other type of filler had been added.

* In the experiment described on page 82, Gysi established this temperature as being 300° F. (149° C.), which is in fair agreement with the value given, considering the type of apparatus which he used.

Repair of Vulcanite Dentures.—Vulcanite can be easily repaired in case of breakage. A cast is constructed, and the edges of the fractured pieces are cleaned and prepared for joining with new vulcanite. The fractured denture is assembled on the cast,* the pieces waxed together, and the cast and assembled denture are flasked as described on page 84. The wax is flushed out and the rubber packed into the joint, which is followed by vulcanization in the usual manner. However, the repaired denture seldom exhibits the strength and wearing qualities of the original.

Physical Properties of Vulcanite.—The specific gravity of dental vulcanite is only slightly greater than that of water, its exact value being dependent upon the ingredients. Turner[3] gives the specific gravity of black vulcanite, probably containing carbon, as 1.2019, whereas a rubber containing vermilion was found to be 1.7263. McPherson[9] found the specific gravity of a vulcanite of composition 68 per cent rubber and 32 per cent sulphur to be 1.172. That the use of tin foil does not increase the density or specific gravity of vulcanite, as claimed by some authorities, is shown by an experiment performed by the author. Two samples each of certain popular brands of veneer and base rubber were packed in a flask. One of each of the two types was wrapped in tin foil, and the others were flasked in the usual manner without tin foil. They were vulcanized in the same vulcanizer for one hour at 338° F. (170° C.). As may be seen from Table VIII, there was no difference in specific gravity of any practical importance. The high specific gravity of the gum pink vulcanite should be noted as being due to the ingredients, probably vermilion and zinc oxide.

TABLE VIII

EFFECT OF THE LINING OF A MOLD WITH TIN FOIL UPON THE SPECIFIC GRAVITY
OF VULCANITE

	Base vulcanite (sp. gr.)	Pink vulcanite (sp. gr.)
Flasked without tin foil	1.2092	2.4550
Flasked with tin foil	1.2090	2.4750

The tensile properties of dental vulcanite have not been studied as much as they should be. The curves in Fig. 24 show the changes brought about by increase in vulcanization time, the temperature held constant at 320° F. (160° C.).† As may be noted, all of the curves are lacking in a sharply defined proportional limit;‡ in fact, there is no portion of the curves which might be called a straight line. Such a condition indicates a plastic flow under all stress values.

* The cast is made from the denture, not from an impression of the mouth.
† The author is indebted to Mr. P. B. Taylor of Western Reserve University for supplying these curves.
‡ Compare with the stress-strain curve on page 25, Fig. 2.

7

It is suggested that the mouth tissues not only adapt themselves to the denture while it is in use, but that there may also be an adaptation of the denture itself to the mouth by a slight flow, particularly in the thin vault portions.

A tendency toward less plasticity is generally noted as the vulcanization time is increased. This is in agreement with the work of

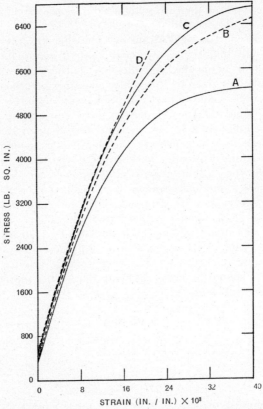

Fig. 24.—Stress-strain curves of dental vulcanite. All specimens cured at 160° C. (320° F.) for times: curve A, one-half hour; curve B, one hour; curve C, one and one-half hours; curve D, two hours.

Davies,[4] who studied the tensile properties of a hard rubber of the following composition:

Pale crepe rubber........................ 100 parts
Sulphur................................ 50   "
Zinc oxide.............................. 5   "
Accelerator............................. 0.01 mol./100 g. rubber

He vulcanized his specimens for the various periods at a gauge pressure of 40 pounds per square inch and a temperature of 142° C. (288° F.). His results are shown in Table IX, which are plotted in

TABLE IX

Tensile Strength and Elongation of Vulcanite at Different Vulcanizing Times

Vulcanization time (hrs.)	Tensile strength (lb./sq. in.)	Elongation (per cent)
1	3610	6.20
1½	6330	2.39
2	7150	2.46
3	7460	2.50
5	7460	2.155

Fig. 25; the solid curve represents the change in tensile strength with time of vulcanization and the dotted curve shows the change in elongation with time. It should be noted that the elongation drops

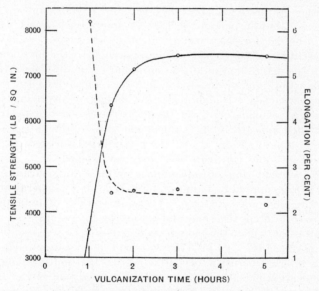

Fig. 25.—Variation of tensile strength and elongation of vulcanite, with time of vulcanization. Dotted curve for elongation.

to a fairly constant value before the maximum strength is reached; also the tensile strength reaches its maximum in approximately three hours of vulcanization time, and remains constant for longer periods.

The ingredients in the vulcanite greatly alter its strength. For example, Barber[5] found olive base vulcanite to have a tensile strength of 7100 pounds per square inch whereas that of maroon base vulcanite was 6100 pounds per square inch. Gum pink vulcanite has a tensile strength as low as 2500 pounds per square inch. The olive base vulcanite probably contains little or no filler, whereas the other two do. It is very evident from these data why gum pink vulcanite is used only as a veneer for esthetic purposes.

Optimum Cure.—As noted in Chapter XI, the optimum cure of rubber is the treatment which gives it the best physical properties. Criteria for selection of such a cure might be based on tensile strength, proportional limit, modulus of elasticity, ductility, and resilience. As may be noted from the stress-strain curves, the elastic properties are not at all critical as the vulcanization time is increased. It is very simple to determine the points of undercure, since the strength increases quite rapidly to a constant maximum, yet at the same time the ductility is decreasing to a constant minimum with change in time of vulcanization. It is probably true that if a vulcanization time and temperature were selected which would show a ductility greater than the minimum, the strength would be low and the vulcanite would not be sufficiently resistant to the mouth fluids.

The total resilience of the specimens may be estimated by the determination of the total areas between the stress-strain curves and the abscissa, but inspection of Fig. 24 shows such areas not to be greatly different for the various vulcanization times. So far as the data presented are concerned, ultimate strength is the most important factor in the determination of the optimum cure; this factor certainly determines the limit of undercure, but does not show when the overcure is approached. Undoubtedly the danger of overcure is not as great as that of undercure, yet the disastrous results of overcure are demonstrated repeatedly by clinical evidence of breakage after repair, for example. More study along this line is needed before conditions of optimum cure can be clearly established.

At the present time, an optimum cure of dental vulcanite can be defined as the minimum value of both time and temperature which will give a maximum strength. The safe method of obtaining such a cure is to prolong the time and lower the temperature so that the temperature at which the substitution reaction between sulphur and rubber begins (347° F. or 175° C.) will not be approached, thus avoiding internal porosity. In other words, the limiting temperature of vulcanization is below 347° F. (175° C.), and the thinner the case, the closer this temperature may be approached, thus shortening the time; conversely, the thicker the case, the lower must be the temperature of vulcanization and the longer must be the time involved, in order to obtain an optimum cure.

LITERATURE

1. Blake, J. T., *Studies in the Vulcanization of Rubber*. Ind. Eng. Chem., 22: 737–740 (July) 1930.

2. Kemp, A. R. and Malm, F. S., *Hard Rubber (Ebonite)*. Ind. Eng. Chem., 27: 141–146 (Feb.) 1935.

3. Turner and Anthony, *American Textbook of Prosthetic Dentistry* (6th Ed.), page 459.

4. Davies, *The Stress-Strain Relationship in Ebonite*. Trans. Inst. Rubber Ind., 9: 130–149 (1933).

5. Barber, Ronald, *Preliminary Tests of Some of the Newer Denture Materials.* J.A.D.A., 21: 1969–1985 (Nov.) 1934.

6. Gysi, A., *Controlling the Shrinkage of Rubber During Vulcanization.* Dent. Digest, 27: 284, 285, 405 (1921).

7. *Ibid.*, p. 349.

8. *Ibid.*, p. 407.

9. McPherson, A. T., *Density of Rubber-Sulphur Compounds, Part I.* Bur. of Standards Sci. Paper No. 560.

CHAPTER XIV

ARTIFICIAL DENTURE MATERIALS OTHER THAN VULCANITE

NONMETALLIC MATERIALS

EVER since Nelson Goodyear introduced vulcanite for the construction of dentures in about the middle of the nineteenth century, the dentist has been searching for a better material. The chief objection to vulcanite is its inability to match the gum tissue due to its lack of translucence. In the cases of those unfortunate denture wearers who habitually show their gums when smiling or laughing, a vulcanite denture is indeed hideous. The search for new materials has centered around this particular property, together with sufficient strength, permanence of form and color, nonabsorption of fluids, cleanliness, and tissue adaptation.

Although the ideal material has not yet been found, considerable progress with vulcanite substitutes has been made, and 50 or more different commercial brands are on the market at the present time.

The nonmetallic artificial denture materials other than vulcanite may be classified in two divisions:

1. Celluloids.
2. Synthetic resins.

The celluloid materials were first placed on the market soon after dental vulcanite was introduced, but they fell into disuse. In Germany, during the World War, and in America after the War, their use again became widespread, but even in their improved form, they are gradually fading from the scene, since they have been found quite unsatisfactory.

The introduction of the synthetic resins on an industrial basis by Baekeland in 1909 has opened up many heretofore unheard of inventions. They are coming to mean as much in human comfort as rubber. Scheiber and Sändig[1] list 220 different uses for these products, which vary from ornamental objects to cogwheels, yet their use for prosthetic purposes is not even mentioned.

The synthetic resins may be classified as (1) *polymerization resins* and (2) *condensation resins*.

Polymerization resins, as the name indicates, are formed as the result of polymerization brought about by heat or other means, starting with a single molecule called a *monomer*. When two molecules of the same kind are linked together, the result is known as a *dimer*. When many molecules are linked in this manner, the result is called a *polymer*. For example, if acetylene (C_2H_2) is heated, it will polymerize to its *trimer,* benzene (C_6H_6). However, the result of such polymerization is not always as simple as the preceding example indicates. For example, vinyl chloride (CH_2:$CHCl$) polymerizes in the presence of light to form a complex vinyl resin, one of the resins used for denture construction, but little is known about the chemical structure of the final product.

In chemistry, the term "condensation" connotes reactions in which two molecules unite to form a new compound with the liberation of simple atomic groups, such as hydrogen, hydroxyl, hydrochloric acid, and so forth. However, in the case of the resins, the reactions are anything but simple; in fact, reactions which proceed simply and with uniformity do not form resinous materials of practical interest. Very likely, condensation resins (or "condensites" as they are sometimes called) may be formed by condensation to a primary resin, and then by polymerization to the final product.

For molding purposes, the dental synthetic resinous materials may be classified as thermocure and thermoplastic. As defined in a previous chapter, thermocure products are molded by heat and pressure, and a chemical reaction occurs during the curing process, whereas thermoplastic materials are softened under heat and pressure, the result being a change in shape without chemical reaction.

The optimum cure for synthetic resins is very critical. Unlike the reactions between sulphur and rubber to form vulcanite, polymerization reactions are reversible, and depolymerization may take place under too great heat, thus markedly reducing the strength and destroying the color. Undercure also results in a lack of strength and color. In both undercured and overcured dentures, the material loses its color and will disintegrate in the mouth.

Celluloid.—The celluloid material used in dentures is manufactured from wood or cotton fiber. The cellulose is treated with concentrated nitric and sulphuric acids to produce cellulose nitrate, which is impregnated with camphor and tinted. The camphor is a plasticizer and gives the material strength. However, it acts objectionably so far as the use of the material in the mouth is concerned, because of its taste. At the present date, no satisfactory substitute for camphor has been found for this particular material, nor can its objectionable odor and taste be removed.

A celluloid can be made from cellulose acetate with the use of vegetable oils as plasticizers. The latter type of celluloid is noninflammable. It also exhibits a short life when used in the mouth.

The celluloid denture materials offer certain advantages over vulcanite, in that they exhibit a translucence and color very similar to that of the natural gum tissue when they are first placed in the mouth. However, celluloid is probably the poorest nonmetallic denture material available. Aside from the camphor odor and taste of the cellulose nitrate materials, celluloid offers other disadvantages.

Because of its cellular structure, it absorbs the mouth fluids to a considerable extent, and this results in a slight swelling. The plasticizers wash out in the mouth, and the color gradually changes to a dirty brown, which is often accompanied by disintegration of the material and a halitosis on the part of the patient.

Another disadvantage, fully as serious as any of the preceding, is the tendency of the denture to warp. The celluloid materials are all thermoplastic, since no chemical change occurs during the molding process. The material is supplied to the dentist in the form of flat plates or else in a partially molded form. The blanks are molded on the flasked cast under pressure and heat. The result is a change in form only, a result which introduces permanent stresses and strains. The stresses are gradually removed during use in the mouth, with the result that the denture tends to assume the original shape of the blank, with a complete loss of fit and adaptation.

Phenol-formaldehyde Resins.—It is estimated that 90 per cent of the artificial resin products in industry are fabricated from some form or modification of the phenol-formaldehyde type of resin, known to the trade as "bakelite," so named from the inventor of the material, Dr. L. H. Baekeland. It is little wonder, then, that a material of such wide and diverse uses should be employed as a denture material.

Phenol, or carbolic acid, is formed by replacing a hydrogen atom in benzene (C_6H_6) with a hydroxyl group, thus giving the formula C_6H_5OH. Although this formula represents the compound usually designated as phenol, the organic chemist recognizes many compounds of a similar nature which belong to a general group called the *phenols*.

Formaldehyde has a structural formula of $H-\overset{\displaystyle H}{\underset{\displaystyle |}{C}}=O$ usually written: HCHO. The condensation reaction, which is typical of aldehydes and phenols in general, is as follows:

$$2C_6H_5OH + HCHO \rightarrow H_2C(O.C_6H_5)_2 + H_2O \tag{1}$$

The nature of the complete reaction is not known; although several theories have been advanced, their complexity prevents their presentation at this time. In the presence of heat and pressure, a partially cured product forms as a result of a basic condensation, and is called a *resole*. This is the material usually supplied to the dentist, and he merely completes the reaction to a *resite*, which is the final product. The resite is very inert chemically, light in weight, translucent, and completely stable. On the other hand resoles are not stable, and have a shelf life, due to the conversion of the resole to the resite at room temperature. Hence, the manufacturer should always date these materials for the information of the dentist. If aged material is used, the dentist will overcure the denture, thus destroying its color and weakening it considerably.

Attempts have been made to perfect a phenol-formaldehyde resin for filling teeth. Ellis[2] describes such a material as follows: "In preparing a filling for teeth, Albrecht uses a solution of phenol in formaldehyde diluted with a viscous retarding agent (glycerol), and mixed with a condensing agent, to obtain a preparation which will readily penetrate into the smallest cavities of the teeth, and slowly harden there, at the temperature of the body." To the author's knowledge, the material has not been perfected as yet for general dental use; however, the idea is not at all impracticable.

The denture base material is supplied to the dentist in a variety of forms. Some brands are supplied in sheets, which are cut up, warmed, and packed in much the same manner as rubber. One of the disadvantages of this process is the formation of air bubbles. One company has attempted to overcome this disadvantage by supplying the material in the form of a coarse powder, which seems to weaken the product,[3] as the latter material does not exhibit as high an ultimate strength in laboratory tests as do some of the commercial condensites of a similar nature. Nevertheless, the strength is probably sufficient for dental purposes.

Vinyl Resins.—Any organic group with a structural formula $CH_2{=}CH$ is called a *vinyl* group. Vinyl chloride ($CH_2{=}CHCl$) has already been mentioned in this connection. *Styrene* or *styrol* ($C_6H_5.CH{=}CH_2$) is another example of a vinyl compound, as is vinyl acetate ($CH_2{=}CHCO_2CH_3$). Any one of these monomers may be made to polymerize to form a vinyl resin. The resins made from styrol sometimes are called *styrol resins*, to differentiate them from the polymerization product of the other vinyl monomers.

The vinyl resins are, then, polymerization resins. They are supplied to the dentist in the form of fully polymerized blanks, which are molded under heat and pressure; they are, therefore, thermoplastic. The molding temperature is very critical; overheating causes depolymerization with loss of color and other properties.

Although stresses and strains are undoubtedly introduced during the molding process, yet, so far as is known, the stresses are not relieved over a period of time with a resulting change in shape, as is the case with the celluloid materials. From an esthetic standpoint, they are as satisfactory as any denture material known, with the possible exception of porcelain. They are insoluble in the mouth fluids, and are compatible with the soft tissues, with the possible exception of a low thermal conductivity, which is approximately the same as vulcanite and other synthetic resins.

Glyptal Resins.—The glyptal resins are condensation products obtained by the reactions between glycerol and certain organic acids. They are not used very widely for denture purposes. However, Moore[4] states: "In many respects this material has the nearest to the ideal properties: its color, color life, and translucency are practically perfect. It has a strength about the same as the cellulose compounds, and its absorptive properties are very good, if the material is properly cured. But the great difficulty encountered is that

TABLE X

Comparison of the Physical Properties of Four Denture Materials

Material.	Proportional limit (lbs./sq. in.).	Modulus of elasticity (lbs./sq. in.).	Modulus of resilience* (in. lbs./cu. in.).	Tensile strength (lbs./sq. in.).	Percentage elongation (per cent).	Surface hardness (Vickers number).
Olive base rubber..................	3900	280,000	27	7100	1.6	15.6
Maroon rubber....................	3500	410,000	15	6100	0.4	17.5
Vinyl resin (pressed at normal heat)......	3700	330,000	21	7300	2.0	15.1
Vinyl resin (pressed at low heat........	4100	330,000	26	8100	11.0	
Vinyl resin (pressed at high heat).......	3800	330,000	22	7300	3.5	
Phenol-formaldehyde resin.............	3800	320,000	23	5600	0.3	24.5

* Computed by the author.

the process of construction of a glyptal resin denture is extremely slow, requiring three to four days."

Comparison of the Physical and Chemical Properties of the Various Nonmetallic Denture Materials.—It may be stated at the outset that the celluloid materials have the lowest ultimate strength[8] in

TABLE XI
IMPACT PROPERTIES OF FOUR DENTURE MATERIALS

Material.	Impact.		
	Range.		Average. (cm. Kg.).
	From (cm. Kg.).	To (cm. Kg.).	
Olive base rubber...	14.0	over 40.0	not all broken
Maroon rubber.....	3.9	15.8	7.6
Vinyl resin.........	12.7	over 40.0	not all broken
Phenol-formaldehyde resin.......	1.6	4.8	3.3

TABLE XII
THERMAL EXPANSION OF THREE DENTURE MATERIALS

Material.	Temperature range (° C.).	Average linear coefficient of thermal expansion (per ° C.).	Remarks.
Maroon rubber.....	25–55	0.000056	Specimen started to bend or shrink at 58° C.
Vinyl resin.........	25–60	0.000071	Specimen started to bend or shrink at about 61° C.
Phenol-formaldehyde resin.......	25–43	0.000079	Specimen started to bend or shrink at 45° C.

comparison with the other nonmetallic denture base materials. However, their various other properties, as already outlined, also preclude their general use as satisfactory denture material.

Four denture materials have been studied by Barber, working at the National Bureau of Standards. Tables X to XII are taken from his data.[5] Although the research is only preliminary to more extensive work along this line, certain tentative conclusions may be drawn.* Two varieties of vulcanite base material (maroon and olive base), a vinyl resin, and a phenol-formaldehyde resin were investigated. The materials were all purchased directly from the manufacturers. The compositions of the rubbers as furnished by the manufacturers are as follows:

Maroon rubber

Rubber (crepe).....................................	35.0 per cent
Sulphur...	16.6 " "
Pigment and filler................................	47.9 " "
Magnesia (accelerator)............................	0.5 " "
	100.0 per cent

Olive base rubber

Raw rubber..	62 per cent
Sulphur...	29 " "
Inert material....................................	9 " "
	100 per cent

Whenever such data are presented, the question is always asked: "Which one is the best for use as a denture base material?" Such a question is very difficult to answer, since quantitative standards of desirable physical properties for a denture material have never been established. For example, the data in Table X demonstrate clearly that the phenol-formaldehyde resin is the weakest of the four materials, yet it cannot be stated that the material is not strong enough to be used for the construction of artificial dentures. Clinical evidence seems to indicate that it has sufficient strength. If it may be assumed that the hardness number is an indication of resistance to scratching of these materials, the phenol-formaldehyde resins are clearly in a class by themselves in this respect.

As may be noted from Table X, in general, the physical properties of the underheated and overheated vinyl resin specimens are better than those of the specimens molded at normal heat. However, the color is unsatisfactory in the first mentioned cases. This would seem to indicate a possible avenue of improvement in this material.

For reasons given in Chapter III, the modulus of resilience may be used as a basis for comparison of the probable life value of the material in the mouth under normal usage. In this respect, the olive base rubber is most outstanding. The phenol-formaldehyde ranks second, with the vinyl resin (pressed at normal temperature) a close third. Probably because of the larger amount of filler used, maroon rubber ranks fourth. By "life value," rated in this manner, is meant the time elapsing before the denture will fracture from use *in the mouth,* and does not take into account any breakage resulting from careless handling, such as dropping the denture on the floor

* It is to be understood that the interpretations of these data are those of the author, and they do not appear in the paper by Barber.

or lavatory. Breakage which occurs from the latter causes possibly may be rated on the basis of the impact test; the data for this test are given in Table XI. The olive base rubber and vinyl resin will evidently stand the most abuse in this respect, with the phenol-formaldehyde resin showing the most fragility.

Table XII shows the thermal expansions of three of the materials.[5] It is interesting to note that both the phenol-formaldehyde and vinyl resins have a greater thermal expansion than vulcanite. It should be further noted that the phenol-formaldehyde resin started "to bend or shrink" at 45° C. (113° F.). This is rather alarming since the soft tissues can tolerate hot liquids at a temperature of 50° C. (122° F.) and higher.

A general survey of the data seems to indicate that the olive base rubber is the most satisfactory material from the standpoint of durability and permanence, both of which are sacrificed to some extent in the resinous materials for the purpose of obtaining better esthetic properties.

Slazinski[6] has investigated the surface hardness of denture materials at various temperatures; his data are given in Table XIII. The phenol-formaldehyde resin is very outstanding in this regard, while the celluloid material is quite unsatisfactory.

TABLE XIII

BRINELL HARDNESS OF FIVE DENTURE MATERIALS AT VARIOUS TEMPERATURES

Vulcanite (Veneer)

Temperature (° C.)	(° F.)	B. H. N.
57	134.5	3.7
47	116.5	7.3
38	100.4	9.0
23.5	74.3	13.95
0	32.0	14.1

Vulcanite (Base)

Temperature (° C.)	(° F.)	B. H. N.
57	134.5	9.8
47	116.5	11.0
36.5	97.7	12.8
23.5	74.3	13.8
0	32.0	14.0

Vinyl Resin

Temperature (° C.)	(° F.)	B. H. N.
56	132.8	9.2
45	113.0	10.9
38	100.4	11.4
25	77.0	12.7
0	32.0	14.5

Phenol-formaldehyde Resin

Temperature (° C.)	(° F.)	B. H. N.
50	132.8	21.0
45	113.0	25.0
38	100.4	26.1
25	77.0	28.0
0	32.0	35.6

Celluloid

Temperature (° C.)	(° F.)	B. H. N.
56	132.8	4.0
45	113.0	4.6
38	100.4	4.9
25	77.0	5.8
0	32.0	8.3

All of these materials exhibit flow under a static load. Slazinski studied this effect by using a modified Brinell hardness test. His results, obtained by allowing the weighted ball to rest on the surface of each specimen for three hours at room temperature, are shown in Table XIV. The phenol-formaldehyde resin appears to be the most rigid, with the celluloid again exhibiting very poor qualities.

TABLE XIV

COMPARATIVE FLOW AND SPECIFIC GRAVITY OF FIVE DENTURE MATERIALS

Material	Flow (Per Cent)	Specific Gravity
Vulcanite (Veneer)	0.54	2.6234
Vulcanite (Base)	0.52	1.2032
Vinyl Resin	0.57	1.3640
Phenol-formaldehyde Resin	0.37	1.3283
Celluloid	1.70	1.8519

As also shown in Table XIV, there appears to be little choice as to lightness in weight between the various materials, provided the amount of rubber veneer used with base vulcanite is kept at a minimum. This is in contradiction to the opinion of many authorities, who believe that the dentures constructed from synthetic resins are considerably lighter in weight than a vulcanite denture.

Obviously there are many properties of these materials which have not been discussed. Some of them have never been quantitatively measured. In order to summarize the properties in tabular form, Table XV has been prepared by the combination of a rating given by Moore[4] with one by Owen[7] and brought up to date by the author. The various properties are rated for the various materials as: A = good, B = fair, C = poor. The criteria of judgment in rating are based upon both clinical and laboratory data.

Metallic Denture Base Materials.—Metals and alloys used in the construction of dentures, both complete and partial, will be discussed in detail in later chapters.

Gold and its alloys are probably the most widely used materials in this regard. The dentures may be made by casting in one piece, or by swaging the wrought metal, the latter probably being superior from the standpoint of strength and lack of porosity.

Stainless steel dentures are used widely in Europe and England, and to some extent in this country. They are always swaged, a process which offers considerable difficulty. In the United States, at least, the making of stainless steel dentures is restricted largely to certain licensed commercial dental laboratories. The material is extremely strong, and resistant to corrosion if treated properly. As outlined in a later chapter, the soldering of stainless steel offers certain difficulties.

Cast aluminum has been used successfully for complete denture construction. There are several tungsten alloys on the market at the

TABLE XV

RELATIVE MERITS OF VARIOUS NONMETALLIC DENTURE MATERIALS

Properties.	Phenol-formaldehyde resin.	Vinyl resin.	Celluloids.	Glyptal resin.	Vulcanite.
1. Strength...........	B	A	C	A	A
2. Permanence of form.	A	A	C	A	A
3. Absence of liquid absorption..........	A	A	C	A	B
4. Tissue tolerance....	A	A	B	A	B
5. Length of life.......	A	A	C	—	A
6. Lack of objectionable taste and odor	A	A	C	B	B
7. Pleasing color......	A	A	B	B	C
8. Permanence of color.	B	A	C	A	B
9. Volume changes during curing........	A	A	A	C	B
10. Ease of repair......	A	A	C	C	B
11. Time of cure.......	A	A	A	C	A
12. Retention by porcelain and metals..	A	B	C	A	C
13. Accuracy of reproduction..........	A	A	C	C	B
14. Hardness and density	A	B	A	B	B
15. Sanitary value......	A	A	C	B	C
16. Modulus of resilience.............	B	B	—	—	A

A = Good   B = Fair   C = Poor

present time for cast denture bases which are quite satisfactory, but because of their high fusing point, denture bases of this material can be constructed only in the commercial dental laboratory.

Various metals may be deposited electrolytically directly to the surface of a cast or model, thus giving an excellent adaptation.

The metallic bases have the great advantage of high thermal conductivity and strength, and are very sanitary. They may be rendered satisfactory from an esthetic standpoint by overlaying the buccal and labial surfaces with a translucent material, such as a synthetic resin, or a porcelain or baked enamel. Their chief and probably only disadvantage over the nonmetallic bases is their comparatively high specific gravity, which tends to increase their weight.

Porcelain.—From the standpoint of esthetics, porcelain is most ideal for a denture material. It is also very compatible with the soft tissues, and can be kept spotlessly clean. However, porcelain dentures are very difficult to construct; in fact, their construction is almost a lost art. Obviously, any accident to them outside or inside the mouth is extremely disastrous, since repair is impossible.

LITERATURE

1. Scheiber, Johannes, and Sändig, Kurt, *Artificial Resins,* pp. 302–364, Pitman.

2. Ellis, Carleton, *Synthetic Resins and Their Plastics,* p. 186.   Chemical Catalog Company.

3. Scheiber and Sändig, *Artificial Resins,* p. 336.

4. Moore, T. E., *Present Day Denture Materials,* Ohio State Dent. Soc. Jour., 8: 158–167 (Nov.) 1934.

5. Barber, Ronald, *Preliminary Tests of Some of the Newer Denture Materials,* J. A. D. A., 21: 1969–1985 (Nov.) 1934.

6. Slazinski, P. J., *Physical Properties of Plastic Base Plate Materials,* Thesis, N. U. D. S., 1934.

7. Owen, E. B., *Vulcanite vs. Substitutes,* J. A. D. A., 20: 1643–1648 (Sept.) 1933.

8. Sweeney, W. T., and Schoonover, I. C., *A Progress Report on Denture Base Material (1935),* J. A. D. A., 23: 1498–1512 (Aug.) 1936.

CHAPTER XV

ABRASIVES AND POLISHING AGENTS

ALL restorations placed in the mouth must be highly polished, not only for esthetic reasons and comfort, but also in order to prevent the accumulation of débris from foods, saliva, etc., in the surface abrasions of either the teeth or restorations. It is necessary, therefore, to keep the tooth enamel itself highly polished, and for this purpose toothpastes and toothbrushes are extensively used.

The distinction between an abrasive and polishing agent is not critical, as the difference is often one of particle size rather than difference in material. Most certainly an abrasive agent must be harder than the material to be abraded. Consider the process of polishing a vulcanite denture. Coarse scratches are made at the start with the vulcanite file or bur. These scratches are removed with a finer abrasive, the scratches of the latter being removed with a still finer abrasive, etc., until scratches scarcely visible to the eye occur, then the polishing agent is used. It was formerly thought that the polishing agent produced submicroscopic scratches, but modern theories of polishing are considerably different. A surface may be said to be polished when it reflects light in a regular manner at any angle. Often surfaces exhibit a high polish when viewed at a small angle of incidence and reflection; but if the light is allowed to reflect to the eye at an angle close to the surface, many scratches may become visible. This is particularly true when the polishing agents are used in cake form, where the binding agent is of a material which smears over the surface, filling up the scratches, instead of actually closing them.

Before consideration is given to these most interesting facts in detail, a brief description of the various agents will be given.

Emery.—Emery is a mixture of alumina (Al_2O_3) and iron. In general, the more alumina there is present, the better will be the grade of emery. It may be impregnated on paper or cloth for abrasive purposes, or used on a wheel. It may also be compressed with a binder to form grinding wheels. In its powdered form (emery flour), it makes an excellent polishing agent. *Emery cake* is a compressed composition of fine emery with a suitable binder, and may be used for buffing.

Garnet.—This is the name given to a certain group of minerals possessing similar physical properties and crystalline form. There are seven different species belonging to the garnet group, which are the silicates of any or several of the following metals: aluminum,

8   113

cobalt, magnesium, iron, and manganese. Garnet is usually coated on paper or cloth with glue or a similar binder. It is one of the common dental abrasives used in operative abrasive disks employed with the dental engine.

Pumice.—Pumice is a highly silicious material of volcanic origin, which is suitable for use either as an abrasive or polishing agent. It is used quite extensively in dentistry, many different grades of powder, "stone," or cake being employed. It is used for smoothing and polishing surfaces of dental restorations both inside and outside the mouth, as well as in prophylactic work.

Corundum is a pure form of emery.

Alumina.—Alumina is a very excellent polishing agent, used extensively in the levigated form for metallographic work.

Kieselguhr.—Kieselguhr is composed of the silicious remains of minute aquatic plants known as *diatoms*. It is excellent as a mild abrasive and polishing agent.

Tripoli.—Although superficially similar to and often confused with kieselguhr, this material originates from certain porous rocks, and was first found in northern Africa near Tripoli; hence its name. It is a mild abrasive and polishing agent.

Rouge is a very fine red powder composed of iron oxide (Fe_2O_3); it is usually employed in cake form. It is often impregnated on paper or cloth and sold as "crocus cloth." It is an excellent polishing agent, but it has the disadvantage of being extremely dirty to handle.

Putty powder, or tin oxide, is used extensively as a polishing agent in polishing teeth and metallic restorations in the mouth. It is a pure white powder, made by heating the product of reaction between tin and concentrated nitric acid to a high temperature.

Chalk is calcium carbonate ($CaCO_3$), prepared by a precipitation method. It is a polishing agent often used in toothpastes. Other dental polishing agents employed particularly in toothpastes are *magnesia, calcium phosphates* (several varieties), and *calcium sulphate*.

Chromium oxide is used for polishing purposes, particularly steel.

Sand (SiO_2) is, of course, a very common abrasive material, as used in ordinary sandpaper. It is also used in sand-blasting.

Carborundum (silicon carbide, SiC) is a very hard abrasive material, approaching the diamond in hardness. It is a manufactured material and does not occur naturally. It has an extremely high melting point (1800° C.) and is chemically very stable. It is usually formed into grinding wheels of various shapes and sizes. Most of the stone burs used in connection with the dental engine for cutting tooth structure, etc., are made of carborundum.

Abrasive Action.—The function of an abrasive is to cut away a surface in order to render it smooth. The action of the abrasive particle as it moves over the surface is exactly the same, on a smaller scale, as that of the edge of a cutting tool, such as a plane.

A shaving is formed which immediately crushes to a powder, and fills up the paper, cloth, or wheel, necessitating frequent cleaning.

The rate of cutting by the abrasive will depend upon many factors:

1. *Size of Particle.*—As in the case of any other cutting tool, the larger the cutting edge, the more surface will be removed; hence the larger the particle, the faster will be the action of the abrasive. However, the larger the particles, the deeper and wider will be the surface scratches. If a polished surface is the ultimate aim of the process, the degree of coarseness of the abrasive is a factor to be considered. The coarser the abrasive, the less will be the time involved in removing large surface nodules and grains. On the other hand, the coarser the abrasive, the more grades of increasing fineness of other abrasives used in turn will be needed to produce scratches sufficiently fine for polishing. Hence the selection of particle size is a matter of judgment as to the best economy of time and material.

2. *Shape and Hardness.*—Obviously the edge of the particle presented to the surface of the object to be abraded must be sharp. Hence round particles of abrasive are never indicated for use, nor are square particles, particularly if impregnated on paper or cloth.

Obviously, hardness of the material is very essential, in order that it may not wear away. Further, its hardness must be greater than that of the surface upon which it is to act, otherwise the surface will not be scratched. In addition to hardness, toughness is essential, but considerable plasticity is obviously undesirable. In the event of abuse, the particle should break cleanly in order to give a new sharp edge instead of becoming distorted and rounded off at the corners.

3. *Speed of Particle Movement.*—Whether the abrasive is applied by means of a wheel of some sort, or by rubbing with a paper or cloth, the speed of movement of the abrasive across the surface is most important.

It is a fact generally recognized by all users of abrasives, that the more slowly a grinding wheel turns, the deeper is the scratch per particle moving across the surface. When the speed of the wheel is increased, the scratches become less deep, but there are more particles passing over the surface per unit of time than before, hence the aggregate amount of material removed remains fairly constant, regardless of any reasonable speed of the wheel. However, there is another complicating factor when the speed of the wheel is slow, and that is the effect upon the abrasive itself. The wheel is made up of abrasive particles, varying somewhat in fineness, cemented together by a binding medium. Obviously, the adhesive forces between the binder and the particle must not be exceeded during use if the wheel is not to be worn down. It should be remembered that the operation of abrasion requires the movement of the particle across the surface of the structure, and not the imbedding or clinging of the particle to the latter. Hence the wearing away of an abrasive tool is uneconomical from the standpoint of both material and time.

A little thought will show that the deeper the scratch, the greater is the force tending to dislodge the particle from the binder. Hence, in general, the more slowly the wheel moves, the more it wears away. Since, in wearing away, it does not efficiently abrade the working surface, the worker tends to increase the pressure between the work and the wheel, which again increases the abrasion of the latter. A wheel which wears in this manner is said to have become "soft." If the speed of the same wheel is increased, it will be found to have become "hard." Obviously, the speed of the wheel should be increased in such cases. In fact the faster the wheel is traveling, the longer it will last, the magnitude of the speed being limited by the heat evolved. This principle is valid for any type of abrasive tool, whether it be a wheel, paper, or cloth.

By speed of the wheel is meant the linear speed with which the abrasive particle is traveling across the work. Hence, when the speed is measured in revolutions per minute, the linear velocity of the periphery will vary with the size of the wheel. In such cases the linear velocity is usually measured in terms of feet per minute. For example, suppose that a wheel 6 inches in diameter is traveling at the rate of 1700 revolutions per minute (abbreviated r. p. m.). The circumference of the wheel will be:

$$\pi \tfrac{1}{2} = 1.57+ \text{ ft.}$$

Since the wheel turns at the rate of 1700 r. p. m., the linear velocity will be:

$$1700 \times 1.57 = 2670 \text{ ft. per min.}$$

Although different abrasives require different speeds, the average linear speed of a grinding wheel should be probably in the neighborhood of 5000 feet per minute.[1] The 6-inch wheel mentioned above should, therefore, turn at a shaft speed of $5000 \div 1.57 = 3200$ r. p. m. The curve in Fig. 26 shows the motor speeds necessary to obtain a linear speed of 5000 feet per minute for varying wheel diameters. The horizontal dotted lines represent the two motor speeds which are usually employed on dental lathe motors, i. e., 3400 and 1750 r. p. m. Using the higher motor speed the wheel should be 5 or 6 inches in diameter. It is very evident that the lower speed has little use in abrasive work, if the wheel is to be used at its highest efficiency, unless the diameter of the wheel is made excessively large for dental purposes.

Such considerations apply to all types of grinding tools, whether they be emery or carborundum wheels, sand or garnet paper disks, emery arbors, burs, or stones. For example, consider the speed of an inverted cone carborundum stone such as is used for work in cavity preparation. Assume that the largest diameter of the stone is $\tfrac{3}{16}$

inch. Computing as above, the shaft of the bur would have to turn at the enormous speed of 120,000 r. p. m. in order that the abrasive might act at its greatest efficiency at its largest diameter. Obviously the dental engine cannot even begin to approach such a speed. The contrast between the optimum speeds of rotation and those usually used in dental practice is emphasized solely in order that the dentist

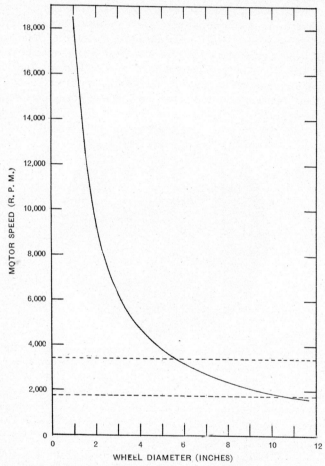

Fig. 26.—Abrasive wheel diameters necessary to obtain a linear speed of 5000 feet per minute, in terms of motor speed.

may understand why his burs and disks wear out so rapidly while cutting tooth structure; the sharp edges are torn from metal burs, and the abrasive particles of stones and disks are rapidly dislodged from their binders, and deposited on the tooth structure at the speeds of rotation necessarily employed. This obviously renders the abrasive action very inefficient indeed.

The speed at which abrasive tools may be used on tooth structure is governed somewhat by the heat of friction evolved. Although the heat evolved may be greater at higher speeds, yet a decreasing speed of revolution in sensitive areas is not always indicated. As mentioned above, the temptation is for the operator to press the abrasive more tightly against the work at lower speeds, and this will often be more painful to the patient than touching the sensitive surface lightly, with short duration of contact at a higher shaft speed.

Polishing.—Polishing or buffing,* as it is sometimes called, involves a different conception than simply abrading a surface. Modern theory indicates that a polished surface results from a disturbance of surface atoms, actually rendering them fluid and distributing them over the surface in an amorphous layer. The amorphous layer thus formed is extremely thin; hence only very fine scratches of microscopic size

Fig. 27.—Scratches on copper produced by grinding with emery. × 200. (From Desch, *The Chemistry of Solids*, Cornell University Press.)

must be present when the surface is polished, since the scratches are merely burnished over, as shown in Figs. 27 and 28. That such is the case is shown by the fact that if the surface layer is removed by chemical means, the scratches reappear when the work is examined under the microscope.

The first requisite in polishing is a very fine abrasive or polishing agent. A soft buff or flannel wheel must be used at a linear speed of approximately 7500 to 10,500 feet per minute. Higher speeds than this are likely to scorch the wheel, whereas lower speeds wear out the wheel, as previously described.

In the mouth, a soft rubber cup disk, or a wood point, is usually used with tin oxide (putty stone) as the polishing agent. In such cases, the dental engine should be run at full speed, and the rubber

* "Buffing" is a term resulting from the use of a wheel made from buff.

cup is dipped into the tin oxide, which is mixed with water or glycerin, and then carried over the surface to be polished. Excessive pressure on the polishing tool is never indicated, since the pressure generates excessive heat, wears out the tool and wastes the polishing material, which will fly off the cup under such a condition.

In gross polishing, the buff wheel is usually impregnated with a cake material, such as stick rouge. The cake binder in many cases is an oily material, and care must be taken not to streak the work. "Streaking" is invariably caused by using too much pressure in impregnating the wheel with the polishing agent, which causes the polishing material to be thrown off, leaving an excessive amount of grease.

Grading of Abrasive and Polishing Agents.—Abrasive materials are usually graded according to the fineness of a standard sieve

Fig. 28.—Scratches on copper partly removed by polishing, showing flow. × 200.
(From Desch, *The Chemistry of Solids*, Cornell University Press.)

through which they will pass. For example, an abrasive graded as number 8 will pass through a sieve which has 8 meshes to the inch but will not pass through any finer sieve than this. The standard grades of abrasive materials on this basis are as follows: 6, 8, 10, 12, 14, 16, 20, 30, 36, 46, 51, 60, 70, 80, 90, 100, 120, 150, 180, 220. Grains which will pass through a sieve of 220 meshes per inch, are designated as powders, or flours, and are graded in increasing fineness as F, FF, FFF, etc., or, in the case of abrasive impregnated papers, as 0, 00, 000, etc.

Method of Polishing.—The first smoothing of the work may be done with a file, or a coarse bur, which leaves large scratches. These scratches are removed with a finer abrasive material, but the degree of fineness must not be too great. The use of a very fine abrasive after a relatively coarse one is a waste of time, and almost impossible in many cases.   In polishing a denture, for example, at least two grades of abrasives are necessary, three grades being preferable.

Each time in changing from a coarse abrasive to a finer one, the direction of abrasion may well be changed, so that the new scratches occur at an angle to the coarser scratches.   In this manner the removal of the coarser scratches may be more accurately observed.   The first polishing is usually carried out with pumice.

In dental work, pumice is usually employed in powder form, moistened with water.   When dentures and similar large pieces are polished outside the mouth, a sewed canvas or felt wheel is generally used. It is very nearly impossible to impregnate such a wheel with pumice, using water as the binding agent, because of the fact that the water is thrown from the wheel in a manner analogous to the centrifugal drier. The dry wheel thus soon loses the pumice powder as well.   Hence, the work itself must be impregnated with the pumice paste.

It is extremely necessary that the pumice be kept wet at all times; enough water is mixed with it to give a pasty consistency.

The operator should place himself in a comfortable position before the wheel.   A linear speed of approximately 5000 feet per minute should be used, with the wheel turning toward the operator from the top.   The work is grasped *firmly* in one hand, while some of the pumice paste is placed over the portion of the work to be polished. The work is then carried quickly into the lower part of the wheel, moved slightly upward and then quickly pulled away, thus describing an approximately circular motion.   The work is again impregnated with paste, and the process repeated until the surface becomes *smooth*.

In polishing of any sort, when the buff wheel is in a vertical position, as previously noted it should turn toward the observer from the top, and the work applied near the bottom, so as to make the wheel brush over the work in a direction away from the operator. Observing this rule is most important.   Since the operator is grasping one end, the wheel is thus constantly brushing from a surface to an edge.   If the wheel is reversed, it will brush from an edge to the smooth surface, with the result that the cloth fibers will tend to wrap themselves around the edge, jerking the work from the hands of the operator, and sending it caroming from wall to ceiling.   The pumice may be used over a great many times or at least until it begins to show a metal impregnation, when it should be renewed.   If gold has been polished, the used pumice should be carefully saved and sent to a refinery.

Another precaution which should always be observed in polishing is to maintain the position of the work at all times so that the motion of the wheel is, as nearly as possible, parallel to angles and contours which must be preserved.   Brushing across them will always tend to obliterate such landmarks.

The pumice powder supplied for gross polishing is usually too coarse to give the highly polished surface desired.   After obtaining a surface free from scratches visible to the eye, the work should be carefully scrubbed with soap and water. The canvas wheel is removed and the bench cleaned free of pumice. Every precaution must be taken so that the polishing wheel does not become impregnated with pumice, even one grain of which will scratch the surface while buffing.

The cotton flannel or buff wheel is adjusted on the lathe, care being taken that it rotates in the same direction as before. The buffing agent is usually supplied in cake form, which is simply held against the wheel lightly until the latter is thoroughly impregnated. The work is held lightly against the wheel, the speed of which is somewhat greater than previously mentioned. When the final polish has been obtained, the work should be carefully washed free of the polishing agent and dried.

Burnishing.—Burnishing is simply polishing, or spreading the amorphous surface layer by means of a rounded metal point, which is worked smoothly but with some pressure over the surface of the material. Obviously the burnishing instrument must be of a material of greater hardness, and without chemical affinity for the material which is to be burnished. A reverse of such conditions is interesting. For example, a rapidly rotating gold wire brush may be used to spread a thin coating of gold over a surface of brass or silver.

Toothpastes.—Toothpastes may contain mild abrasives to aid in polishing the teeth. Naturally the abrasives must not be too coarse, or they may scratch the enamel sufficiently to roughen the surfaces of the teeth, thus giving additional sources of retention of plaques, bacteria, etc. The abrasives commonly used in toothpastes have been previously listed.

That various brands of toothpastes abrade in varying degrees has been shown by various investigators. Ray[2] demonstrated the abrasiveness of 15 popular brands of toothpastes by determining the loss of weight resulting from prolonged rubbing of the toothpastes over antimony under a paraffin disk. The minimum loss was 0.7 mg. for one toothpaste, and varied progressively with others to a maximum of 17 mg. Similar tests[3] have been made where the loss in weight of electrodeposited copper was obtained with a toothbrush used as the polishing tool. Fifteen commercial toothpastes were tested in this case also, and their abrasiveness, as measured in terms of loss in weight of the copper after 100,000 strokes of the toothbrush, varied from a minimum of 0.65 mg. to 10.18 mg. for different brands. The latter test is of interest, since the authors state: "One hundred thousand strokes represent the approximate amount of brushing that an individual will make brushing the teeth twice a day over a period of fifteen to twenty years." If the moist toothpaste abraded copper, such that the loss was only 10.18 mg., the brushing being spread over a time equivalent to a fifteen-year period, it is difficult to understand how it could be inferred that such a toothpaste could seriously harm the tooth enamel, which is much harder than copper, when used over the same period. However, *all* brands of toothpastes are not necessarily harmless in this regard.

LITERATURE

1. Jacobs, Fred B., *The Abrasive Handbook,* p. 364, The Penton Publishing Company (1928).

2. Ray, K. W., and Chaden, H. C., *The Abrasive Power of Toothpastes,* Dent. Cos., 75: 1070–1077 (Nov.) 1933.

3. *The Abrasiveness of Dentrifices.* The Pepsodent Company (1934).

CHAPTER XVI

DENTAL PORCELAINS: COMPOSITION AND CONDENSATION

In spite of the fact that ceramic chemists have thrown considerable light upon the chemical and physical reactions of porcelain during firing, there are many gaps in the knowledge of these phenomena. This is particularly true of dental porcelain manipulation where rule of thumb methods still largely prevail. As more scientific research is accomplished, considerable improvement in methods of manipulation and efficiency of dental porcelain restorations may be expected.

There can be no doubt that dental porcelain is the best restorative material available at the present time when both esthetics and service are considered. Although it is not as translucent as the silicate cements, it is probably stronger and, so far as is known, it is insoluble in the mouth fluids.

Its possible uses in dentistry are many; it has been employed for almost every type of restoration from complete dentures to small inlays. The following discussion applies principally to porcelain jacket crowns and inlays.

A general technic for the construction of a porcelain jacket crown or inlay is as follows: an impression is taken of the tooth preparation, from which a model is prepared. A thin sheet of platinum (called the matrix) is burnished over the preparation as reproduced by the model. The porcelain of the desired shade is mixed with water and condensed into the matrix-lined cavity. The porcelain is then fired in the electric furnace. During firing, the porcelain shrinks noticeably, sometimes as much or more than 40 per cent in volume. This shrinkage is one of the disadvantages of the porcelain inlay, which is likely to be too small and show a "cement line" around its margins, which is due to the solubility of the cement with which it is luted. Since these inlays are generally used only in the anterior teeth, the cement line is likely to be quite objectionable esthetically. Such a condition is not so serious in the case of a porcelain jacket crown, where the margins are beneath the gum line.

The main thesis of this discussion will be the control of shrinkage, translucence, color, and strength of porcelain.

Composition.—Many formulae for dental porcelains were published in the first half of the nineteenth century, when the dentist was forced to compound his own material. They are all very similar to a formula[1] accredited to Dr. Wildman for tooth body:

Kaolin .... 1 ounce
Silex .... 3 ounces
Feldspar .... 18 ounces
Titanium oxide .... 65 grains

The following formula for a high fusing porcelain body is given by Felcher:[2]

Kaolin .... 4½ parts
Flint .... 15 parts
Orthoclase Feldspar .... 85½ parts

Three other formulae are given by Searle.[3] Table XVI shows their chemical composition by analysis, and Table XVII the materials used in compounding them.

TABLE XVI

COMPOSITION OF DENTAL PORCELAIN

Porce-lain.	Silica.	Alu-mina.	Ferric oxide.	Pot-ash.	Soda.	Lime.	Tita-nium oxide.	Borax.	Loss.
A	68.2	16.7	trace	10.1	2.3	...	0.23	...	2.5
B	68.1	2.2	...	6.9	10.1	0.8	trace	10.6	1.2
C	69.6	11.3	0.3	11.8	1.7	2.4	0.2	0.3	...

Kaolin is not a primary mineral but rather a secondary product formed by the chemical deposition of igneous rocks which contain alumina. Its approximate composition is $Al_2O_3.2SiO_3.2H_2O$. It fuses at a very high temperature.

TABLE XVII

MIXTURES USED
(Per cent)

Porce-lain.	Kaolin.	Feldspar.	Flint.	Na_2CO_3	Borax.	$CaCO_3$	K_2CO_3.
A	4	81	15	...	...	...	...
B	...	61	29	2	1	5	2
C	...	12	60	8	11	1	8

Feldspar is one of the most important constituents of rocks, and has an empirical formula of either $K_2O.Al_2O_3.6SiO_2$ or $KAlSi_3O_8$. The latter is probably the formula for orthoclase or potash feldspar, which is the variety generally used in dental porcelains. It has no sharp melting point, but becomes a viscous and somewhat opaque liquid around 1300° C. (2372° F.). It is a eutectiferous mixture (see footnote, page 126), the components being *lucite* ($KAlSi_2O_6$) and silica (SiO_2). X-ray data indicate that it begins to melt at 1100° C. (2012° F.); 1300° C. should be designated, therefore, as its softening temperature rather than its melting point.

Its opacity is caused by its high alumina (Al_2O_3) content, and by the development of fine included bubbles. Clark[4] has identified such bubbles as those which occur in dental porcelain, although they may be due to occluded air as well as the feldspar. Although the material is crystalline in its natural state, it becomes amorphous after firing.

Feldspar is the lowest in softening temperature of any of the main ingredients, and acts as a flux* during firing. In spite of its relative opacity when fused in the "pure" condition, it aids in imparting translucence to the porcelain. It imparts strength in the cold mass after firing because of the glassy bond formed between it and the kaolin and quartz, but at higher temperatures it definitely weakens the mass. During firing it is capable of taking into chemical combination all of the kaolin and quartz ordinarily used in a dental porcelain.

Quartz or flint (SiO_2) will be discussed at length in a subsequent chapter (see pages 254–256). It gives body to the mass during firing.

Contrary to the opinion of some dental writers, there are but few fundamental differences between the best grades of industrial porcelains and the dental variety. They differ chiefly in that translucence is emphasized in dental porcelains. Mellor[5] gives the following formula as typical of industrial porcelain body:

Feldspar .... 1 part
Quartz .... 1 part
Kaolin .... 2 parts

If this formula is compared with those given for dental porcelain (Tables XVI and XVII), it may be noted that the feldspar is the largest constituent in the latter, with quartz and kaolin in a considerable minority. In fact "B" and "C" contain no kaolin at all. The fundamental differences between dental porcelains and ordinary porcelains is, then, the feldspar content of the former. The high feldspar content of the dental variety, causes them to have a narrow maturing temperature, as compared with ordinary porcelain. It also imparts the surface glaze or gloss so necessary to the reproduction of tooth characteristics, as well as enhancing the strength and translucence.

In the production of dental porcelains, it must not be thought that any materials going under the names of feldspar, quartz, and kaolin can be thrown together in the correct proportions, with a high grade

* As used in ceramics, a *flux* is the part of a mixture which fuses *at the lowest temperature.*

of dental porcelain resulting. Since these materials are mined from the earth, their properties vary in different parts of the world and even in one locality. The ingredients must be selected with care and conscientiously refined before use.

Pyrochemical Reactions.—However, chemical composition is by no means the most important factor. The firing of the material is the prime element which determines the final nature of the product. For example, in the ceramic industry, two identical formulae may be used for either earthenware or fine porcelain, the difference depending upon the firing procedure. The firing process is a matter of control of the pyrochemical reactions. In other words, the reactions are arrested at certain stages to give the desired product.

The so-called pyrochemical reactions probably consist of the feldspar and other fluxes which act on the kaolin and quartz, and form a eutectiferous mixture* somewhat comparable with that of metals. The action begins at approximately 1000° C. (1832° F.), and its speed increases as the temperature is raised.

Manufacture of Dental Porcelain.—The dentist usually classifies dental porcelains according to their fusing temperatures as follows:

High fusing .... 2400–2500° F. (1315–1370° C.)
Medium fusing .... 2000–2300° F. (1092–1259° C.)
Low fusing .... 1600–1950° F. (870–1065° C.)

However, from the standpoint of manufacture, only two general types need be discussed, viz., high and low fusing porcelains. In general, the principal difference between the two, aside from possible differences in composition, is the pyrochemical treatment given them in the manufacturing process. Contrary to the methods which prevail in the manufacture of porcelain ware, for example, the manufacturer usually partially fuses or entirely fuses the dental porcelains before placing them on the market. In the manufacture of the high fusing type, the pyrochemical reactions are not completed, because of certain manufacturing difficulties encountered at the high temperatures involved in producing such reactions. This heat treatment as given to the low fusing porcelains may proceed until the pyrochemical reactions are nearly completed. After firing, the mass is finely ground, and, in some instances, modifiers are added. However, those porcelains whose ingredients are not sintered or fired in one mass before they are ground are apt to segregate in the container, with the result that the dentist has considerable trouble in obtaining uniform results. The material is now ready to be given the desired shade or color.

The pigments are usually metallic oxides of various sorts, which are baked into a porcelain body in a separate firing. After such a

_____

* A eutectiferous mixture is a mixture of two or more substances, which produces a material whose melting temperature is lower than that of the constituent substances. See pages 196–198.

body is ground, it is introduced into the original white powder in sufficient amount to give the desired shade.

The powder received by the dentist is, then, a partially fused or fully fused body. In the case of the high fusing porcelains at least, the dentist continues the pyrochemical changes, and arrests them at the proper stages. In the case of a low fusing porcelain, the material may be merely softened by the heat, in order to establish cohesion.

There are at least two advantages to the dentist in this prefusing process:

1. A homogeneous mass is more readily assured.

2. The firing temperature is more critical and a shorter firing time is required.

Some manufacturers introduce a binder into the powder, such as starch or sugar, in order to give the material a molding plasticity when mixed with water. In some products, however, the water added during manipulation is the only binding agent.

So far as the composition of the two types is concerned, the fusion temperatures are controlled by the fluxes. When the feldspar alone is the fluxing agent, the porcelain is generally of a high fusing variety, but when sodium and potassium carbonates, borax, etc., are baked into the material, the softening temperatures are decreased.

There is an opinion prevalent in the dental profession that the low fusing porcelains are less resistant to the corrosive action of the mouth fluids, in comparison to the higher fusing varieties. However, such a statement is not borne out by ceramic products in general. There are many ceramic products which mature at lower temperatures than any of the dental porcelains available at the present time, yet they are highly resistant to both acids and alkalis. The physical properties of the high and low fusing porcelains will be compared in the next chapter.

Under the microscope, a glazed dental porcelain body appears to consist of a vesicular structure. Often the center shows more porosity than the region nearer the periphery. The entire mass is amorphous in character, and appears to be made up of amorphous aggregates suspended in a glassy matrix.

If the surface is properly glazed, it is absolutely impervious to fluids. The pores cannot be burnished over by polishing, as is the case with metals; this fact is shown by the "red ink test," borrowed from the ceramic industry: a drop of red ink is placed on the surface to be tested; if it can be rubbed off, the surface is said to be impervious.

Shrinkage of Porcelain.—As previously stated, a dental porcelain always shrinks while firing. The shrinkage may be controlled to some extent by the method of condensation, but its control by this means is often overestimated.

The first shrinkage which takes place is the "air shrinkage," or simply the shrinkage that takes place in air due to the evaporation or the drawing off of the water during condensation. The size and shape of the particles govern this shrinkage, as well as the degree of condensation. Clark[4] states that the major portion of the shrinkage is due to lack of condensation. He found the shrinkage to be negligible when dry porcelain was condensed under a 150-ton load.

Other shrinkages are due to ignition loss of binders and other organic material, and the effect of surface tension by the fluxes during firing. Clark places the average minimum linear shrinkage, which is not under control of the operator by the methods of condensation available to him, at 10 per cent.

Condensation of Porcelain.—The porcelain should be kept wet at all times. The powder is mixed with water until it is of such a consistency that when a portion is picked up with the spatula, it may be smoothed back into the main mass easily and smoothly. The air bubbles must be completely removed, and the work must be kept spotlessly clean.

There are five general methods which are used at present for condensing the porcelain. It should be noted that the aim of any technic is to get the mass of porcelain powder as closely packed as possible.

The *brush application method* consists of applying the wet mix to the platinum matrix with a brush, and then dry powder is added to bring out the excess water by capillary action, thus condensing the powder.

Tylman[7] gives a modification of this method for inlays, which results in better condensation. In brief, two or more small holes are drilled in the bottom (pulpal wall) of the platinum matrix, which is then seated* in investment. The wet porcelain is then applied with a brush, but no dry powder is added. The condensation is accomplished by the investment which removes the water from the porcelain by capillary action, through the holes in the matrix.

The *gravitation method* consists of adding water to the wet porcelain after it has been placed in the matrix. The sudden addition of water is supposed to disturb the particles and then allow them to settle, after which the water is drawn off by means of a linen cloth or blotting paper.

The *spatulation method* is simply smoothing the wet porcelain with some pressure into place with a spatula, which brings the water to the surface.

In the *whipping method* the porcelain is applied as usual, and the water is brought to the surface by whipping with a brush.

The *vibration method* consists of placing the wet porcelain in the matrix, after which it is vibrated with the idea that the porcelain particles will be disturbed, turned, and twisted so that they will fall into a closely packed mass. The excess water comes to the surface and is removed as before.

Theory of Condensation.—Although some technics appear to give

* The platinum is not burnished to an investment model, but rather to a previously constructed cast gold inlay.

less shrinkage of the porcelain than others, it should be noted that all of them have one factor in common—the removal of as much excess water as possible. The powder particles may be porous, and thus absorb water. Furthermore, the water obviously fills all interstices between the particles, and when it is suddenly removed, the resulting condensation may be due to two phenomena:

1. It is a principle of physics that when two bodies are in close proximity in a current of fluid, they will be forced together. For example, imagine two boats tied in the middle of a stream in which a strong current is flowing. Because of the fact that the boats are close together, the water between them is flowing more rapidly than the water about them (a well-known hydraulic principle). Bernoulli's theorem[6] states that when the speed of a liquid is increased, its pressure diminishes; hence, because of the difference 'in pressure caused by the difference in speed of the water on the two sides of each boat, they will come together. Aeroplanes collide in the air for the same reason, under similar circumstances.

Another example of such a phenomenon is the packing of the sands at the seashore when the water rushes up over them and recedes. However, there is another effect which is very important and even more effective.

2. The effect of surface tension is a very decided factor in the condensation. Because of its surface tension, a drop of water when free always takes up a position such that it occupies the greatest volume for the least exposed surface. Geometrically such a volume is a sphere. Although the water in the porcelain powder does not hold the wet mix in the position of a sphere, yet it does tend to contract it. The less water that is present, the greater this action becomes, provided that *the mass is completely wet with water*.

A simple experiment will illustrate this principle. If a camel's-hair brush is immersed in water, the hairs will separate. If the brush is withdrawn from the water, the hairs will come together because of the surface tension of the water film. If the brush is now wiped with a cloth, the bristles will be tightly compressed together, and will not separate until the brush becomes dry, or else is replaced in the water.

Theoretically the vibration method is probably the best method of condensation, due to the re-orientation of the particles during vibration in addition to the other phenomena described. However, the method is not always practical, particularly when the porcelain is not confined within the walls of a matrix. Hence a combination of the spatulation and vibration methods is largely employed.

LITERATURE

1. Prothero, J. H., *Prosthetic Dentistry* (4th Ed.) p. 273. Medico-Dental Publishing Company.

2. Felcher, F. R., *The Art of Porcelain in Dentistry*, p. 36. The C. V. Mosby Company.

9

3. Searle, A. B., *The Chemistry and Physics of Clays and Other Ceramic Materials* (2nd Ed.) p. 420.   D. Van Nostrand Company.

4. Clark, E. B., *Manipulation of Dental Porcelain*, J. A. D. A., 22: 33–40 (Jan.) 1935.

5. Mellor, J. W., *A Comprehensive Treatise on Inorganic and Theoretical Chemistry*, 6: 147.

6. Stewart, O. M., *Physics* (Rev. Ed.) pp. 179–185.   Ginn and Company.

7. Tylman, S. D., *Porcelain Inlay: Indications, Preparations and Construction*.   Trans. Ill. State Dent. Soc. p. 122 (1927).

CHAPTER XVII

DENTAL PORCELAIN (Continued): FIRING AND PHYSICAL PROPERTIES

The Porcelain Furnace.—One type of porcelain furnace is shown in Fig. 29. It consists of three parts, a muffle which contains the electric heating unit, a pyrometer with a platinum, platinum-rhodium thermocouple, and a rheostat.

The heating element consists of approximately 13 feet of No. 28 Brown and Sharpe gauge platinum wire, imbedded in a refractory. The heat is due to the electrical resistance of the platinum wire. Any conductor of electricity generates heat when an electric current passes

Fig. 29.—A dental porcelain furnace. (Courtesy of The S. S. White Dental Maufacturing Co.)

through it, the amount of heat generated being directly proportional to the product of its electrical resistance and the square of the current. The current is controlled by the external resistor or rheostat. When the furnace is new, its muffle resistance will be constant for some time, but gradually the resistance will increase because of the volatilization of platinum at the high temperatures, which gradually reduces the size of the wire.

The thermocouple,* as supplied with some dental units, is entirely too short in length. The cold junction should always be kept at

* The electrical theory of the thermocouple is discussed on pages 166, 167, 200.

131

room temperature, which is a factor too often overlooked by the manufacturers in the design of such furnaces. In cases where the cold junction is made directly behind the muffle, it absorbs heat from the latter and by thermal conduction along the thermocouple wires. Such a condition causes the pyrometer to read too low. Experimental tests show that such an error may vary from 15° F. (8.3° C.) with a cold furnace, to 30°–100° F. (17°–55° C.) upon consecutive firings.

Under no circumstances should carbon or silica be allowed to come in contact with the wires of the heating element while they are hot, since either element will alloy with the platinum at the high temperatures involved, thus rendering the wire brittle. A brittle heating element may result in breakage when the wire contracts during cooling. The work is always placed in the muffle on fire clay forms or slides.

Firing of Dental Porcelain.—In the firing of dental porcelains, it must be kept constantly in mind that the porcelain body is a very poor thermal conductor, and therefore too rapid heating is to be avoided. Failure to observe this precaution will result in case hardening, i. e., a fusion on the outside, with a less fused mass in the center portions. Also stresses may be introduced which will show up as cracks after firing.

Furthermore, when successive bakes are made with the same porcelain, each bake carries the pyrochemical reactions further in the portion already baked, which seems to lower its softening temperature, possibly because of a eutectic action (see footnote on page 126).*

A measurement of time must be combined with one of temperature in order to provide the best control of the firing process. As with many other reactions, the higher the temperature, the more rapid is the rate of reaction. Also, the higher the temperature, the less is the viscosity of the molten material. Even before any devitrification stage which might set in, a tendency toward spheroiding may be observed; hence, modern technics employ a soaking period at a lower temperature than was formerly used, a procedure which allows the action to go on more slowly with less tendency for the formation of rounded margins and angles.

Gill[1] recognizes two stages in the firing of porcelain, *the physical stage* and *the chemical stage*. The physical stage, in the case of a high fusing porcelain, begins at 200° F. (94° C.), and continues to 900° F. (480° C.). This is called the dehydration period, since the free water is removed. Between 900° and 1200° F. (480°–650° C.), any water of crystallization present is driven off. The oxidation period occurs between 900° and 1600° F. (480°–870° C.), when the organic material (principally the binder) is driven off in the form of carbon dioxide gas and free carbon. This is also known as the smoking period, and until this period is past, the door of the muffle must be kept ajar so

---

* Another factor, probably of equal importance, is that the porcelain is less porous after the first bake, and hence, transmits heat more rapidly.

that the products of combustion will not injure the platinum wire. Above 1400° F. (760° C.) the porcelain loses no more perceptible weight. The fluxes go into solution between 1400° and 2300° F. (760°–1260° C.), and begin a reaction with the other ingredients, thus lowering the softening temperature. This is accompanied by a slight contraction and a definite decrease in porosity, due to the fact that the fluxes fill the interstices and exhibit a surface tension action similar to that described for the water during condensation.

There is no marked division between the physical and chemical stages; in fact the two overlap somewhat. The chemical stage consists of the continuation of the pyrochemical reactions of the flux with the kaolin and quartz, already started during the prefusing process. The bonds formed by the glassy matrix between the particles are completed, and the surface glaze is formed. In general these reactions occur around 1900° F. (1040° C.) and above, provided that low fusing fluxes are present to start them, whereas if feldspar is the only flux present, the action starts 300° to 400° F. (150°–200° C.) higher. Generally in practice, the firing is not done in one bake; usually at least two bakes are necessary. Theoretically, the glaze bake should always be done separately, and at a somewhat faster rate of heating, as it is primarily concerned with melting only the portions near the surface, in order to cause the molten material to flow over the outside. The glaze should be nonporous and uniform.

The temperature must be under control at all times, particularly during the pyrochemical reactions, and it must be raised at a constant rate determined largely by experiment. Failure to do this will likely result in overfusion and even devitrification, which is characterized by spheroiding, loss of color, and a glassy mass.

Gill[1] is most extreme in the firing time advocated. For example, using a popular high fusing porcelain, he advocates ten minutes to bring the work up to 1400° F. (760° C.) with the oven door open to allow ample time for the gases to be expelled; then five minutes to raise the temperature to 2250° F. (1230° C.), at which temperature the work is held for five minutes in order to allow a slow diffusion of the molten mass through the interstices; then fifteen minutes more is allowed to bring the work to a temperature of 2400° F. (1310° C.), where the case is soaked for five minutes, thus making a total time of forty minutes necessary for the bake. Other writers advocate a shorter fusing time. For example, Clark[2] advocates that the work should be brought up to the beginning of the chemical stage in a short time, and then the timing is begun. He states that a rise in temperature of 50° F. (28° C.) per minute to the final temperature is sufficiently slow.

The lower fusing porcelains are fired in an analogous manner, the main difference being their lower fusing temperatures due to the low fusing fluxes. All authorities advocate slow cooling to avoid crazing (cracking).

PHYSICAL PROPERTIES

Each advocate of a certain condensation technic claims superiority in strength, density, translucency, etc., for his particular method. It is very difficult to evalute these properties, and much of the research along these lines has been subject to error and questionable procedure.

Porosity.—Comparison of methods of condensation by radiographs and photomicrographic sections of baked specimens as a test for pores and blebs has not been conclusive. Gill[3] claims to have found a correlation, but Sayre[4] failed completely in this regard; he found no correlation in the radiographs of two samples made by the same technic, or between the various technics themselves. Felcher[5] reports absolutely no difference in condensation methods when the fired specimens were observed under the microscope. Undoubtedly the amount of observable air spaces depends almost entirely upon the success in removing air from the mix before and during condensation.

Shrinkage.—Table XVII shows Sayre's results on baked specimens, condensed by various technics. It is very evident that the vibration method is the best from the standpoint of volume shrinkage. As may be noted, the difference between shrinkages by the various methods is surprisingly small. This is in distinct contradiction to various reported linear shrinkage values for different condensation technics. Such data are obtained by the measurement of a specimen with a micrometer caliper before and after firing, a method which is subject to considerable error.

For example, let it be assumed that a 5-mm. cube is condensed and measured between two sides. Assume that it shrinks 10 per cent at the high biscuit temperature.* This means that the cube should measure 4.5 mm. between faces at this stage. However, the porcelain always spheroids or warps to a slight extent because of the high flux content, even under the most controlled conditions. Such spheroiding will cause a curvature of the sides of the cube, not discernible to the eye, yet of such magnitude as to register considerable error when it is measured with the micrometer caliper. For example, assume that the distance between the faces of the cube was found to be 4.6 mm. after firing, instead of 4.5 mm. This would involve an unnoticeable error of 0.05 mm. on each face, yet the investigator would conclude that the shrinkage was 8 per cent linear, instead of the actual value

---

* The dental ceramist recognizes four stages in the firing of porcelain: the *low biscuit* bake is the stage in which the changes have barely begun, the mass being chalky in appearance, with little cohesion of the particles. In the *medium biscuit* bake, the reactions are more advanced; the chalky appearance has disappeared, but no surface glaze is apparent. The bulk of the shrinkage takes place during this stage. The *high biscuit* bake is the period when all of the shrinkage is thought to have been realized, and a slight surface glaze is visible. The fourth stage is known as the *final fuse* or glaze bake, in which a smooth surface glaze is given to the mass.

of 10 per cent. Sayre determined the volume shrinkage* by determining the volume of water displaced by weighing in water and air,† and comparing with the original volume. Such a method is not subject to differences in surface irregularity.

Density.—When the density or specific gravity of porcelain is discussed, a distinction must be made between *apparent specific gravity* or density and *true specific gravity* or density. The former is determined upon an entire specimen, and includes all the air spaces, blebs, etc., whereas the latter represents the density of the material only, when pulverized to a fine powder. For the particular dental porcelain upon which he worked, Sayre found the true specific gravity to be 2.418, which value was *constant for and independent of the method of condensation*. This indicates that the values for the apparent density in Table XVIII are low, for the simple reason that the

TABLE XVIII

INFLUENCE OF CONDENSATION IN A MATRIX ON PHYSICAL PROPERTIES

Method of condensation.	Volume shrinkage (%).	Apparent density (g./cc.).	Mod. of rupture (lb./sq. in.).
Vibration..........	38.1	2.350	7000
Spatulation........	38.4	2.338	7200
Brush application...	40.5	2.363	5300
No condensation ...	41.5	2.386	4900

specimens include blebs (small bubbles) which cannot be removed by any method now used by the dental ceramist. Furthermore, the apparent densities shown in the table are, from a practical standpoint, constant for all three methods of condensation employed; the slight differences which occur are only of academic interest.

Strength.—The *strength* of dental porcelains may be measured most conveniently by a cross bend test. Sayre adapted the cross bend test as specified by the American Society of Testing Materials[6] for testing brick. The specimen is placed between two knife edge supports, one at each end, and the breaking load is applied at the center. The modulus of rupture or transverse strength is computed from the following formula:

* For all practical purposes, the linear shrinkage may be considered to be one-third of the volume shrinkage.

† This method is based upon the principle of Archimedes, which states that a body immersed in water is buoyed up by a force equal to the weight of the water displaced. Hence, the difference between the weight of the porcelain in air and in water will give the weight of the water displaced. Since the specimen is entirely immersed, it must displace its own volume of water; the volume of the water thus displaced is easily calculated from the weight of the water displaced.

$$R = \frac{3\,W\,l}{2\,b\,d^2}$$

where R = modulus of rupture in pounds per square inch.

W = the total load in pounds at which the specimen failed.

l = the distance between the supports in inches.

b = the width of the specimen in inches.

d = the depth of the specimen in inches.

As may be noted from Table XVIII, the strength (modulus of rupture) varies, within the limits of experimental error, with the degree of condensation as judged by the volume shrinkage.

Texture.—The strength of a dental porcelain varies with the size and shape of the powder particles. Small angular grains of varying sizes are probably best, since a more closely packed mass will be obtained during condensation; the small grains of various sizes will pack into the interstices between the larger grains.

Comparison of the Physical Properties of Various Dental Porcelains.—Fitzgerald[8] has studied the physical properties of eight popular dental porcelains under controlled methods of condensation and firing. His results are shown in Table XIX.

TABLE XIX

PHYSICAL PROPERTIES OF VARIOUS DENTAL PORCELAINS

Porcelain.	Specific gravity.	Volume shrinkage (per cent).	Modulus of rupture (lb./sq. in.).
High fusing			
A	2.32	32.2	7800
B	2.33	31.7	7900
C	2.32	32.2	8200
Medium fusing			
D	2.30	32.6	7100
E	2.32	34.6	8300
Low fusing			
F	2.29	39.5	3700
G	2.32	33.3	7700
H	2.50	37.4	7000

As may be noted, there is little difference in the properties of the three brands of high fusing porcelain. As to the lower fusing varieties, the success or failure of these materials is very largely due to their process of manufacture. For example, medium fusing porcelain E compares very favorably with the high fusing materials in regard to apparent specific gravity and strength. Especial attention should be directed to the low fusing porcelain G, whose properties are very good indeed. This particular material is becoming very popular at the present time for porcelain jacket crown work, and its popularity is very evidently justified. Porcelain F is obviously rather unsatisfactory.

It may be concluded from these data, that a dental porcelain does not necessarily need to fuse at a high temperature in order to exhibit satisfactory physical properties.

OPTICAL PROPERTIES AND COLOR OF DENTAL PORCELAIN

Light Phenomena.—In order to appreciate adequately the phenomena of light as applied to dental porcelains and tooth structure, a considerable knowledge of applied geometrical and physical optics is required. Only a rudimentary idea can be given here.

When a ray of light strikes a reflecting surface, the reflected beam always passes away from the body at an angle exactly equal to that of the incident ray, both angles being measured from the normal to the surface at the point of incidence. The law is, then, that the angle of incidence is always equal to the angle of reflection. If the surface is smooth in comparison with the wave length of the light, as in the case of a mirror, the reflection will be *regular*, that is, an image may be seen. If the surface is rough in comparison with the wave length of the light, as is this sheet of paper, for example, the light will be diffused or scattered after reflection, and no image will be seen.

Another phenomenon of interest is refraction. Whenever a light ray enters a body which is denser than the medium from which it comes (air for example), the ray will be bent toward the normal to the surface at that point, and, *vice versa*, when it leaves the denser body into the air or less dense medium, it will be bent away from the normal to the surface. According to the wave theory, the velocity of light is less in the denser medium than it is in the less dense medium, hence, it is bent in passing from the latter to the former. The amount that the light is bent toward the normal depends upon, and is inversely proportional to, its velocity in the denser body. The constant of proportionality, when its speed in the denser body is compared with that in air, is called the *index of refraction*, and may be expressed as follows:

$$\frac{\text{Speed in air}}{\text{Speed in any other substance}} = \text{Index of refraction.}$$

If the body is opaque, the light waves will not penetrate it, but will be reflected or absorbed or both, depending on the nature of the body.

If the body is transparent, as window glass, for example, the light will be regularly transmitted, although it will be bent in accordance with the above law. However, if regular transmission occurs, so that the objects on the other side can be observed undistorted, the material must be homogeneous as to density and surface throughout

If the body transmits light diffusely so that the objects cannot be seen through it, the material is said to be *translucent*. Translucence may be caused by a number of factors, such as the constituents in the material with different indices of refraction, different orientations, etc.

When a light ray passes from a more dense to a less dense medium, there is a certain angle of incidence which must not be exceeded, which is called the *critical angle*. If this angle is exceeded, a total *internal* reflection occurs.

Whenever light is transmitted through a body, the transmitted ray is never as intense as the incident ray, due to the fact that part of the energy is reflected at each point of change in media. For example, when light strikes a window pane, part of it is reflected on the outside surface of the glass, and the remainder is refracted toward the normal inside of the pane. As it strikes the inside surface nearest the observer, just before it enters the air, another portion will be reflected, and the remainder will be refracted away from the normal to the eye. If these fundamental points have been mastered, a discussion will be given concerning the optical properties of the tooth in comparison with the porcelain inlay.

Optics of Tooth Structure and Dental Porcelain.—The dentin of the tooth may be regarded as an opaque material for all practical purposes, but the enamel is very likely quite complicated in its optical properties. Leaving out of consideration any anisotropy, the enamel may be optically considered as a coating formed by a bundle of translucent prisms (enamel rods) with their outer ends on the surface of the tooth, and their inner ends adjacent to an opaque medium which forms the interior body (dentin). This opaque body has a reflecting surface. Moreover, the prisms are shaped something like truncated pyramids.

Between the prisms is a material (interprismatic substance and organic sheath) which has a greater index of refraction than the prisms themselves. Consider the enormous number of internal and external surface reflections of light possible, together with the many possible refractions and total reflections. The problem becomes extremely complicated indeed, and a translucent quality is exhibited which defies accurate imitation.

As has already been noted, dental porcelain is amorphous in character, and not crystalline, as is the enamel. The optical properties then resolve themselves into a scattering of light due to different indices of refraction and transmission coefficients, caused by different "aggregates," bonds, blebs, etc. It may be seen at once that the optical structure does not resemble that of the enamel. The porcelain inlay may match the tooth structure from the front, yet a side view will show it to have a different texture and color due to a difference in optical property in this direction. It will diffuse light differently than will the enamel under different illuminants. Fortunately the difference is not great and is apparent only to a discerning eye. It is the best material available at the present time for this purpose and beautiful effects can be obtained from its use.

Obviously, the cement used in the luting of the porcelain inlay or crown will have an effect. A silicate cement is best because of its translucence. However, if the cement washes out at the margin, the familiar "cement line" appears, not because of the cement, but rather because of its absence which changes the optical property in this region.

Color.—Although the tooth structure cannot be faithfully reproduced, its color values can be copied, if care is exerted by the dentist in matching the tooth with his porcelain.

The porcelains may be had in a wide variety of colors. Also surface stains may be used.

The physicist recognizes color phenomena as due to *selective absorption* and *selective reflection*. As an example of the former, if "white light" from an arc or the sun is transmitted to a screen, and if a red glass is interposed at the source, only red light will appear on the screen. The white light is made up of six different physical primary colors, as noted in a spectrum, such as a rainbow. Each color has a definite wave length, but they shade into one another in the rainbow, and produce different hues, such as dark red, yellowish green, etc. In the experiment cited, the red glass absorbs all wave lengths except the red, a green glass will absorb all colors but the green; a blue, all but the blue, etc., all of which are examples of selective absorption.

If the entire color spectrum is projected upon the screen, and if a piece of red cloth is held progressively in the different colored lights, starting with the violet, it will appear black or brown in all light except red, where it will reflect its own color, red; this is an example of the phenomenon of selective reflection.

Selective reflection may be used in the mixing of pigments, which are never spectrally pure. Take, for example, the mixing of blue and yellow pigments: the ordinary blue pigment absorbs all the colors of white light, and reflects blue and some green; the yellow absorbs all colors except yellow, some red, and also some green. When they are mixed, the green color is the only one reflected. Furthermore, the green may be "bluish" or "yellowish," the shade of which depends upon the proportions of the pigments used in mixing. In this way, mixed colors such as purple, magenta, cerise, etc., may be made. Such principles of color mixing must be strictly adhered to by the dental ceramist.

Another color phenomenon which is of interest is the mixing of colored lights. If blue and yellow *lights* are superimposed, *white* light results. These two colors are therefore said to be *complementary,* as is true with any other two colors which give white light when superimposed. Because of certain phenomena of color vision, many color illusions may be created by the use of complementary colors. For example, if one looks steadily at a bright red light for some time, and then looks toward a white background, the source of light persists on the retina as its complementary color of bluish green, the effect being wholly physiological. Another example which has a more direct application to dental ceramics is the influence of environment on color. For example, if a small white disk is inserted in a blue background, it will appear to the eye to have the complementary color of blue—a pinkish hue. Similarly, the white teeth are influenced by the environment of the lips and facial color. Cosmetics are especially deceiving in this connection, when the dentist is attempting to determine true tooth color.

The final physical phenomenon to be considered in color matching is the type of illumination. Different types of illumination give different color effects. For example, an ordinary incandescent lamp is strong in the red-orange-yellow portion of the spectrum; hence, the reds and yellows may be enhanced at the expense of the blues, because of a selective reflection. The blue from the sky is caused by a scattering of blue color from sunlight, and light from this source will cause the yellows to become grayish, and the blues to stand out. Selective reflections from buildings, trees and office walls will contribute similar effects.

The problem of matching tooth structure as to color, then, becomes fully as difficult as that of matching its optical properties. The color of the tooth is due largely, although by no means entirely, to its optical properties, but the color of the porcelain is the result of pigments. It follows that the pigments must change in hue under different illuminants and environments, in a different manner than the tooth structure itself. It is very necessary, then, that color selection be carried out under average lighting conditions, that is, a source of light whose color intensities approach that of sunlight.

Diffused daylight through a north window is the best light for color selection. Unfortunately such light is available only on a light cloudy day, when the clouds can diffuse the light equally. However, there are lamps supplied with proper color filters which are quite satisfactory. It must be remembered that diffused light is an absolute necessity, in order to avoid glare and abnormal reflection.

In matching the tooth color, then, the dentist must consider environment, illumination, angle of observation, and eye fatigue. Needless to say, any form of color blindness on his part entirely precludes his working in this field.

Inasmuch as the ideal can only be approached in this work, all possible precautions should be observed so that all conditions are as nearly *average* as possible. The patient should be in an upright position when the color selection is made, and the operator should observe the tooth coloring both from the front and the side. The lips of the patient should be drawn back excessively from the teeth. The dentist should note carefully the color contrasts in different portions of the tooth. Normally the tooth is a yellowish white in the gingival third, due to the selective reflection of the dentin being diffused through the enamel. The yellowish color usually shades to a gray as the incisal edge is approached. Careful comparison with a shade guide will give the correct color. Correct shading, condensation, and firing will produce an effect worthy of the highest artistry in dentistry. However, the fact remains that the color and texture cannot be identical with that of the enamel under all lights and conditions, but nevertheless the conscientious operator can be sure that it is the best that can be done.

LITERATURE

1. Gill, J. R., *Pyrochemical Reactions in the Firing of Porcelain.* J. A. D. A., 18: 280–290 (Feb.) 1931.

2. Clark, E. B., *Manipulation of Dental Porcelain.* J. A. D. A., 22: 33–40 (Jan.) 1935.

3. Gill, J. R., *Methods and Results in Condensation of Dental Porcelains.* J. A. D. A., 19: 1147–1154 (July) 1932.

4. Sayre, L. D., Thesis. N. U. D. S., 1936.

5. Felcher, F. R., *The Dental Porcelain Subject as Seen from the Experimental Laboratory.* Dent. Cos., 76: 1266–1270 (Dec.) 1934.

6. *Standard Methods of Testing Brick.* A. S. T. M. Designation C67–31.

7. Searle, A. B., *The Chemistry and Physics of Clays and Other Materials* (2nd Ed.) p. 171. D. Van Nostrand Co., Inc.

8. Fitzgerald, P. A., Thesis. N. U. D. S., 1936.

CHAPTER XVIII

DENTAL CEMENTS: COMPOSITION AND SETTING REACTIONS

CEMENTS are used in dentistry both as a lute for inlays, crowns, etc., and for restorative purposes. The materials may be classified as zinc phosphate cements, copper cements, and silicate cements. All types have much in common as to content, chemical reaction, and manipulation. They all consist of a powder which is mixed with liquid which contains mainly orthophosphoric acid; the two react to form a hard mass.

An ideal cement, whether it is used as a cementing medium or restoration, should have the following properties:

1. It should be strong and hard, yet not excessively brittle. Its hardness should be comparable with that of the tooth structure.

2. It should be cohesive and adhesive. It should show adhesion to any substance in the mouth with which it is brought in contact while soft, both before and after setting.

3. It should be insoluble, particularly in the mouth fluids.

4. At no time should it have any detrimental corrosive, or other harmful pathological action upon the mouth tissues with which it comes in contact.

5. It should not contract during set, and subsequently, during use, it should never contract under any normal conditions, nor should it expand sufficiently to harm the restoration in any way.

6. It should have a coefficient of thermal expansion similar to that of the tooth structure, and should exhibit a low thermal conductivity.

7. It should be easy to manipulate, both in and out of the mouth.

8. It should be able to take and retain a high polish.

9. It should be absolutely nonporous in nature, and should be free from bubbles of any sort.

10. Its physical and chemical form should not be impaired by moderate changes in temperature and humidity.

11. Its color and general appearance should harmonize with that of the tooth structure, if the cement is to be used in a position where it will be exposed to view.

There is no cement at the present time which even approximately meets these requirements. Some of the properties noted are under control of the dentist, and the others must be met by the manufacturer. Considerable improvement is needed from both quarters, which can be gained only by diligent research and study.

THE ZINC PHOSPHATE CEMENTS

Composition.—The composition of the powders of 16 zinc phosphate cements as analyzed at the National Bureau of Standards[1] is shown in Table XX. These are all commercial dental brands bought in the open market by the American Dental Association Research Commission.

It will be noted that the cements are of 3 types as to composition.

The first 4 cements, with the exception of the coloring material, may be said to be pure zinc oxide (ZnO) powders, the rest of the ingredients probably being accidental.

The next 7, again if coloring matter and impurities are excluded, may be called zinc oxide-magnesium oxide cements, the powder having been modified by the addition of magnesium oxide in the approximate ratio of 10 parts of ZnO to 1 of MgO.

The following 5 powders, although mainly zinc oxide, have been modified further by the addition of silica and bismuth trioxide in addition to the magnesium oxide. The last material, Q, is a silicate cement powder.

TABLE XX

COMPOSITION OF ZINC PHOSPHATE CEMENT POWDERS
(Percentage by Weight)

Sample.	ZnO.	MgO.	SiO_2.	R_2O_3.	Bi_2O_3.	Miscellaneous.
A	100.0	....	0.05	0.05	....	
B	99.7	....	0.1	0.1	....	CaO, 0.1
C	98.0	....	....	....	1.9	
D	99.4	....	0.6	0.1	0.04	
E	92.4	7.5	0.1	0.06	....	CuO, 0.1
F	90.3	8.2	1.4	0.1	....	
G	90.2	9.4	0.4	0.07	....	
H	89.9	9.1	0.4	0.5	....	
I	89.5	9.4	0.3	....	....	$BaCrO_4$, 0.8
J	89.3	9.4	0.3	0.1	....	CuO, 0.02; $BaCrO_4$, 1.0
K	88.0	9.4	0.8	....	1.8	
L	89.1	4.0	1.8	0.5	4.5	
M	82.2	9.0	3.0	0.9	4.1	CuO, 0.8
N	83.1	7.2	0.1	0.04	....	$BaSO_4$, 8.2; CaO, 1.3
O	84.0	7.2	4.9	1.0	....	CaF_2, 2.7
P	74.9	13.0	1.3	2.6	....	BaO, 2.2; B_2O_3, 5.1
Q	9.4	....	36.5	26.3	....	F, 12.0; Ca, 5.9; Mg, 0.5; Na, 4.6; P_2O_5, 3.2; ignition loss 6.9.

It is very difficult to penetrate the trade secrecy which surrounds these materials, in order to determine just what part the modifiers play in the cements. In consideration of the meager information available, the modifiers are supposed to make the cement stronger and more insoluble. The results of one investigation[2] seem to indicate that the bismuth trioxide contributes to the smoothness of working properties while mixing.

In the manufacturing of the powder, the ingredients are sintered into a cake at temperatures between 1000° and 1400° C. (1832°-2552° F.),[3] which is ground and sifted to the powder form.

The chemical analyses of the liquids supplied for use with the powders given in Table XX, are shown in Table XXI. The letters

TABLE XXI

COMPOSITION OF ZINC PHOSPHATE CEMENT LIQUIDS

(Percentage by Weight)

Sample.	Analysis.				Calculations.			
	PO_4.	Al.	Zn.	Mg.	Free H_3PO_4.	Combined H_3PO_4.	Total H_3PO_4.	Phosphate.
A	57.4	1.8	10.0	...	42.8	16.6	59.4	27.8
B	55.2	3.4	3.1	...	41.6	15.5	57.1	21.5
C	64.3	2.7	....	...	56.8	9.8	66.6	12.2
D	57.3	2.1	10.0	...	41.7	17.6	59.3	29.2
E	64.6	2.7	1.6	...	55.5	11.4	66.9	15.4
F	52.6	2.5	7.1	...	38.2	16.2	54.4	25.3
G	59.9	2.9	2.0	...	49.4	12.6	62.0	17.0
H	59.7	2.1	4.1	...	50.1	11.7	61.8	17.6
I	57.9	2.8	....	0.3	48.9	11.0	59.9	13.7
J	61.1	2.8	....	...	53.1	10.2	63.3	12.7
K	64.0	3.2	....	...	54.7	11.6	66.3	14.5
L	64.2	2.7	0.9	...	55.8	10.7	66.5	14.0
M	67.2	3.0	....	...	58.7	10.9	69.6	13.6
N	64.9	2.9	....	...	56.6	10.6	67.2	13.1
O	54.6	2.3	10.3	...	37.8	18.7	56.5	30.7
P	53.4	2.7	....	...	45.5	9.8	55.3	12.2
Q	47.9	1.9	4.4	...	38.3	11.3	49.6	17.3

designate the same brands of cement as before. It may be noted that the principal constituent is orthophosphoric acid (H_3PO_4), the principal modifiers being presumably aluminum and zinc hydroxide. In the table, the first four columns after the identifying letters give the chemical analyses, whereas the last four give the calculated compositions. It was assumed that all of the neutralizing elements, or basic modifiers, combined to form a neutral salt whose amount is given in the eighth column. The total amount of orthophosphoric acid in the liquid is shown in the seventh column. The original liquid undoubtedly contained water in addition. The calculated free H_3PO_4, and combined H_3PO_4, are shown in the sixth and seventh columns respectively. The seventh column is obviously the sum of the fifth and sixth columns.

Chemistry of Setting.—When zinc oxide powder is mixed with orthophosphoric acid to form a solid as a result of their chemical combination, two solid phases may be present in the set cement,[3] *i. e.*, secondary and tertiary hydrated zinc orthophosphate [$ZnHPO_4$. $3H_2O$; $Zn_3(PO_4)_2 4H_2O$]. However, the formation of the tertiary salt, to any noticeable extent, is questionable. Hence the set cement probably consists of the acid phosphate salt. Ray[4] gives the following chemical reaction:

$$ZnO + H_3PO_4 + 2H_2O \longrightarrow ZnHPO_4.3H_2O$$

Note that water is essential to the reaction.

The hydrated acid phosphate is relatively insoluble in water, and the tertiary salt is even less soluble.

The reactions must be pictured as being first a chemical reaction which results in the formation of the zinc acid phosphate; this then deposits as crystals only as it becomes supersaturated in solution; although interdependent, there are thus two distinct phenomena involved. The formation of the crystalline phase must not be interfered with by prolonged manipulation, if a strong cement is to be obtained.

Not all of the powder combines with the liquid, and the final hardened mass consists of uncombined particles in suspension in a matrix of hydrated zinc acid phosphate crystals. Considerable heat evolution accompanies the reaction and in general the materials shrink while setting.

If ordinary commercial zinc oxide is used with an unmodified orthophosphoric acid solution, the reaction is very rapid with considerable heat evolution. The setting time is altogether too rapid for dental use, and the resulting product is likely to be porous and friable. Hence, the time of set must be retarded.

There are various methods of bringing this about, such as:

a. Decreasing the surface of the powder in contact with the liquid.

b. Varying the concentration of the liquid.

c. Adding retarders to the powder.

d. Buffering, or partially neutralizing, the acid liquid with a base.

e. Reducing the temperature of the mixing slab.

f. Reducing the rate of addition of the powder to the liquid.

g. Reducing the amount of powder used in ratio to the liquid.

The time of set is obviously very important to the dentist since he must have ample time for manipulation, yet the cement must harden quickly after it has been applied.

Items *a*, *b*, *c* and *d* are obviously under the control of the manufacturer. The surface of the powder is controlled by sintering and grinding as described.

10

The manufacturer gives the correct concentration to the liquid. The maintaining of this concentration is the task of the dentist, and is accomplished by keeping the container tightly stoppered at all times. Failure to do this will usually result in loss of water from the liquid, which prolongs the set. If water is added to the mix by the use of a damp mixing slab, for example, the set will be hastened. This latter point will be treated more fully later.

Perhaps some of the modifiers in the powder may act as retarders, but the simplest method is to partially neutralize the liquid. As may be noted from Table XXI, the base probably used for this purpose is aluminum hydroxide. An effect often observed when a bottle of liquid is left unstoppered, is the deposition of crystals on the walls of the bottle, due to an increased concentration of the liquid by the loss of water.

THE COPPER CEMENTS

The copper cements are generally zinc phosphate cements with a salt of copper added to the powder, although in exceptional cases the powders may contain 100 per cent CuO.[5]

The salt of copper used may be identified by the color of the powder. Cupric oxide (CuO) gives a black colored powder, cuprous oxide (Cu_2O)—red, cuprous iodide (Cu_2I_2)—white, and the silicate ($CuSiO_3$)—green. The main object in the addition of the copper is to render the cements germicidal in the mouth. Silver salts have also been used for this purpose.

In all probability, the chemistry for these cements is similar to that of the zinc phosphate cements, since the liquids used are very similar. However, few data are available. They gradually wash out in the mouth as do the other cements, but in general they maintain a polished surface which enhances their value and popularity in cases where the cement is indicated for restorations in the posterior teeth.

SILICATE CEMENTS

Composition.—Regarding the compositions of the powder and liquid, Crowell[3] states as follows:

"Silicate cements differ from zinc phosphate cements chiefly in the composition of the powder. The liquids are solutions of phosphoric acid partially neutralized with zinc oxide and alumina, differing from zinc cement liquids only in the amount of water contained. . . .

"The powders are made by melting together silica, alumina, and fluxes, and heating until fusion is complete. A high temperature, about 1400° C.,* is required. The resulting glass is crushed and ground to a fine powder.

"Several compounds have been used as fluxes. The earlier cements,

* 2552° F.

made in Germany, used beryllium silicate. Most of the cements manufactured in the United States use calcium fluoride. Calcium silicate, calcium borate, and soda-lime glass have also been used, but the resulting cements have been deficient in translucence."

Setting Reactions.—In contrast with the zinc phosphate cements, the problem involved in the control of the setting time is one of acceleration rather than retardation. The aluminum oxide (Al_2O_3) speeds up the reaction, but at the same time it tends to reduce the translucence if the content is unduly increased. Otherwise the speed of reaction may be controlled by taking advantage of the variables noted (see page 145) for the control of the setting time of zinc phosphate cements.

The powder is usually ground very fine. The set may be delayed by the use of a cool mixing slab, but it is speeded up when the cement comes in contact with the warm tooth. The activity of the liquid is controlled much in the same way as for the zinc phosphate cements.

The process of setting is rather complicated. The water present seems to hasten the reaction. The liquid reacts with the powder to produce certain bases and silicic acid. When the acidity drops to a certain value, silicic acid gel forms in a network of phosphate crystals, together with portions of powder particles which are not attacked. The reaction probably continues slowly for some days, the final product being hard and translucent.

At no time must the gel be disturbed, once it starts to form. Once it is broken it will not rejoin.[3] This is very important, and is undoubtedly the cause of many failures when this material is used as a filling material.

The silicic acid gel is an irreversible colloid, and it must be kept moist at all times. Failure to do this causes dehydration of the gel, which is accompanied by a serious contraction.[6] A chalky layer results which is lacking in translucence. Rehydration occurs to some extent, but the surface layer is permanently ruined. It is for this reason that silicate restorations are never indicated for mouth breathers. The effect is particularly bad if the water is removed during set. For this reason, the prepared cavity should not be drastically dehydrated before the insertion of the cement. As with all cements, water must not be allowed to come in contact with it while it is gaining its initial set. In order to prevent the silicate cement from losing water while this occurs, the surface must be coated with an impervious material.

Solubility.—The solubility of these cements is generally conceded to be less than the zinc phosphate cements, although any dentist who has used them can testify to the fact that they "wash out." When he tested their solubility in 1 per cent lactic acid solution, Voelker[7] found it to be approximately twice as great as for distilled water only. He considers this to be very important as an explanation for the solubility of the cement in the mouth.

Probably their chief advantage over other filling materials for use in the mouth is their esthetics. They may be matched very closely in color and translucence with tooth structure. They are superior even to porcelain in this respect when first placed.

Their thermal properties are excellent. All of the cements have a low thermal conductivity and the silicate cements have a coefficient of thermal expansion more nearly equal to that of the tooth structure itself than any other filling material[8] (see Table II, page 36).

LITERATURE

1. Paffenbarger, G. C., Sweeney, W. T., and Isaacs, Aaron, *A Preliminary Report on the Zinc Phosphate Cements*. J. A. D. A., 20: 1960–1982 (Nov.) 1933.

2. Ward, M. I., and McCormick, R. M., *The First Report of a Study of the Composition and Properties of the Cements Now in Use in Dentistry*. J. N. D. A., 2: 354–370 (Nov.) 1915.

3. Crowell, W. S., *Physical Chemistry of Dental Cements*, J. A. D. A., 14: 1030–1048 (June) 1927.

4. Ray, K. W., *Metallurgy for Dental Students*, p. 265. P. Blakiston's Son and Company.

5. Ward, M. L., *Our Present Cements with Special Reference to Those Containing Copper*. Dent. Rev., 30: 691–704 (Aug.) 1916.

6. Ray, K. W., *The Behavior of Silicious Cements*. J. A. D. A., 21: 237–251 (Feb.) 1934.

7. Voelker, C. C., *Dental Silicate Cements in Theory and Practice*. Dent. Cos., 58: 1098–1111 (Oct.) 1916.

8. Souder, W. H., and Peters, C. G., *An Investigation of the Physical Properties of Dental Materials*. Bureau of Standards Technological Paper No. 157 (1920). Dent. Cos., 62: 305–335 (March) 1920.

CHAPTER XIX

DENTAL CEMENTS (Continued): BIOLOGIC ASPECTS. PHYSICAL PROPERTIES. MANIPULATION

SOME BIOLOGIC ASPECTS OF CEMENTS

Germicidal Properties.—All cements are undoubtedly germicidal when first mixed, due to the excess of acid. Only in the case of the silver and copper cements does the germicidal property persist for any length of time. Copper and silver are both bacteriostatic,* but any germicidal property of the cement after setting must depend upon the formation of a soluble salt. It is interesting to note that all germicidal properties mentioned in the literature depend upon a *solution* of some of the constituents in the set cement.

The work of Hill and Boester[1] indicates that the copper and silver cements show a satisfactory germicidal property when tested by adding the thoroughly set cement to broth inoculated with *Staphylococcus aureus*. One of the specimens, which showed a germicidal property comparable to any of the commercial copper and silver cements, was a nongermicidal zinc phosphate cement, to which phenylmercuric nitrate was added—1 part to 5000 parts of the powder. It would be of interest to treat a silicate cement in the same manner.

They also determined the solubility of the cements as measured by their diffusibility in agar, but found no general correlation in this respect with the previous test. Using a similar method, Fraser[2] at certain intervals transferred the cements from one inoculated agar plate to another. She found, with the exception of one silver cement, that they all lost their germicidal property, so far as diffusibility in agar was concerned, after two to five successive platings. The clinical application of her data is still open to question.

If the cavity has been properly sterilized before the cement is applied, and if a tight cement filling is possible, it is difficult to understand why a germicidal cement is needed.

Pulp Death.—Another biologic factor which has been widely discussed is the injurious action of the cements on the pulp. According to Crowell:[3] "The dental literature of thirty years ago contains frequent references to pulp irritation and pulp death following the use of zinc phosphate cements. Because of the widespread use of silicate cements in the past fifteen years, zinc phosphate cements have ceased to be suspected."

In spite of the diligent research that has been carried on, and the many papers which have been written, the cause for this alarming

* *i. e.,* the preventing or arresting of the growth of bacteria.

pulp action has not been disclosed. It is difficult to understand, in the light of the voluminous clinical evidence for the solubility of the silicate cements in the mouth fluids and their possible physiological action on the pulp, why these cements have been and are being used so persistently.

Various theories have been advanced as to the cause of pulp death. One of the most prevalent is that it is caused by the residual ortho-phosphoric acid or phosphates in the cement.

Undoubtedly all cements are acid while setting, yet the copper and zinc cements are generally conceded not to have an injurious action. Eberly[4] reports the pH* of the cements as follows:

	Silicate cement pH.	Zinc cement pH.	Copper cement pH.
pH of liquid	0.8	0.6	0.6
30 days after mixing	5.5	7.3	4.8

Since the saliva itself is a buffered solution with an average pH of 6.6 in the resting state,[5] it would seem that this latter figure should be an indication as to an allowable acidity. It may be noted that the zinc cements are not likely to be a disturbing factor. As noted before, their reaction is very rapid, quite in contrast to that of the silicate cements. The interesting fact to be noted from the data is that the copper cements show a greater acidity than the silicate cements at the end of the thirty-day period. Copper cements, as restorative materials, are not generally credited as being pathologic-ally injurious. On this basis, it is difficult to understand why acidity should be a factor in the case of the silicates. Others have confirmed this viewpoint.[3]

Crowell[3] is of the opinion that the pulp irritation is due to resid-ual infection in deep-seated cavities. He reasons that the germicidal action of the copper cements prevents or destroys bacterial action, whereas a silicate filling placed in a cavity which has not been properly sterilized, will allow a deep bacterial invasion, since the cement is not germicidal.

The presence of fluorine in the cements has been mentioned as a possible source of pulp injury.[7] However, it is present in an extremely insoluble form. Two months' soaking of a silicate cement specimen in distilled water (11 grams in 70 cc.) showed fluorine to be present only to an extent of 1.007 per cent,[3] which would seem to be a negligible amount in consideration of the rigor of the test as com-pared to practical conditions.

The presence of arsenic as an impurity has been advanced as a possible cause of pulp irritation, but in modern cements the prob-ability of its presence is very small.

* pH is an abbreviation for hydrogen ion concentration; pH $= 7$ is neutral, anything higher is progressively more alkaline, and a pH of less than 7 is progres-sively more acid in action.

All cements are impermeable to bacteria,[2] but some of the silicates are permeable to water.[2, 6] Peripheral leakage, due to volume shrinkage, is very commonly accepted. However, for some reason the suggestion of recurrent caries due to this leakage, as being the cause of pulp death, is not found in the literature; yet it is commonly accepted that this is one of the dangers which result from a similar condition in amalgam restorations.

Other theories have been advanced, such as the poisonous action of colloidal silicic acid on the soft tissue,[8] and the possible surface development of aluminum phosphate and acid aluminum phosphate crystals, due to tooth moisture, which may be dissolved and carried to the pulp by capillary action.[9] Both of these theories are rather speculative, although worthy of note.

PHYSICAL PROPERTIES OF CEMENTS

Hydraulicity.—There appears to be no cement at the present time which is "hydraulic,"[10] notwithstanding much advertising propaganda to the contrary. The term hydraulic infers that the product will harden under water, and remain impervious to water. All cements must be kept dry until the initial set occurs, otherwise the orthophosphoric acid and other products will be leached out.

Adhesion.—It is generally conceded that zinc phosphate cements are adhesive, whereas the silicate cements are not. This opinion is probably due to the fact that the former are extremely "sticky" while mixing, whereas the latter are only moderately so. If the physical definition of adhesion, as being the attraction between unlike molecules, is strictly adhered to, there is no adhesion between the set cements and the structures involved.[10]

If the term "adhesion" is used in a broader sense, i. e., the interlocking of surfaces due to surface irregularities, there may be some basis for such an opinion. This is brought out in the discussion of a paper by Dr. Vogt.[11] The point is made that even glue is not adhesive when hard, as it may easily be stripped from the surface of smooth glass in this condition. However, if there are small surface irregularities or pores into which it may be forced while plastic, its retention is very great. In a similar manner, cements hold inlays in place. They are difficult to remove because of the shearing stresses involved. In other words, their degree of retention depends upon the nature of the surface irregularities in the inlay and cavity walls. This is verified by the excellent experiments of Dr. Head.[17]

Tests have shown that the thinner the layer of cementing medium, the stronger will be the union of substances cemented together, hence the importance of the film thickness test as given in the American Dental Association Specification for zinc phosphate cements (see appendix, page 392). Obviously, the film thickness depends primarily upon the size of the powder particles.

Another reason for paying attention to film thickness is to allow the correct seating of carefully made inlays. In the past, some dentists have objected to accurately fitting inlays because "there was no room left for the cement." This objection is not valid if a good quality cement is used. No inlay can be cast with sufficient accuracy so that a cement film cannot form between the inlay and the walls of the prepared cavity. Assuming that the wax pattern can reproduce all the microscopic undercuts and scratches in the cavity preparation from the burs and cutting instruments (very likely an impossible assumption), the markings would be smoothed out when the pattern was removed; otherwise removal would be impossible. Therefore, assuming an accuracy of 100 per cent in reproducing the pattern for a casting, there should remain ample room for the cement film, if the cement meets the specified requirements.

Setting Time.—The factors influencing the setting time, which are under the control of the manufacturer, have already been mentioned. The factors under control of the dentist are the following (unless otherwise stated, it may be assumed that the statements apply to all types of cements, so far as can be determined from the literature):

1. Powder:liquid ratio. Thick mixes set faster than thin ones.

2. The faster the powder is added to the liquid, the quicker is the set.

3. Within limits, prolonged mixing lengthens the setting time.

4. In general, the higher the temperature of the mixing slab, the quicker is the set, provided the cement is allowed to set on the slab, but if transferred to the mouth, the slab temperature seems to be of little importance in this respect. However, a cool slab gives a smoother mix because of its retardation of set while mixing. The relative humidity appears to have little effect upon the setting time.[13]

5. Dilution of the liquid with water hastens the set, whereas evaporation of water retards it. Evidently the degree of dissociation of the acid is the explanation for this factor.

Crushing Strength.—The crushing strength of cements is important, both in their use for luting inlays and for restorative purposes. Studies[13] on the zinc phosphate cements as to crushing strength demonstrate some interesting facts as shown in Tables XXII to XXV.

The samples were prepared from 16 different brands of zinc phosphate cements (compositions given in Tables XX and XXI, pages 143 and 144) and 1 silicate cement. Seven samples of each were stored in distilled water for twenty-four hours and crushed. The lowest crushing strength observed was 3500 pounds per square inch, and the highest, 12,000 pounds per square inch. Twenty more specimens of each brand were prepared. Ten were immersed in distilled water for six months at 99° F. (37.2° C.). The other 10 were placed in liquid petrolatum for a like period of time. The latter liquid was assumed to be inert so far as the cements were concerned, and served

TABLE XXII
COMPRESSIVE STRENGTH OF ZINC PHOSPHATE CEMENTS
Compressive Strength (lb./sq. in.)

Cement.	Distilled water.		Liquid petrolatum (U.S.P.) 6 months.
	24 hours.	6 months.	
A...............	3,500	5,000	6,500
B...............	4,500	3,500	3,500
C...............	6,500	3,500	7,000
D...............	5,500	8,000	13,500
E...............	12,000	8,000	14,000
F...............	9,000	11,500	13,000
G...............	11,000	14,000	13,500
H...............	13,000	12,000	14,000
I...............	12,000	11,500	14,000
J...............	11,500	13,000	14,500
K...............	10,500	11,500	11,000
L...............	11,500	8,000	9,500
M...............	11,000	9,500	12,500
N...............	9,000	6,000	7,000
O...............	7,500	6,000	7,000
P...............	8,500	12,000	14,000
Q...............	16,500	19,000	16,000

TABLE XXIII
EFFECT OF POWDER : LIQUID RATIO ON COMPRESSIVE STRENGTH OF CEMENTS

Powder (grams).	Liquid (cc.)	Compressive strength (lb./sq. in.)	
		Cement F.*	Cement I.†
0.50	0.50	5,500	
0.75	0.50	8,000	
1.00	0.50	9,000	12,000
1.25	0.50	13,000	13,500
1.50	0.50	14,500	18,000
1.75	0.50	14,000	17,500
2.00	0.50	15,000	19,000
2.50	0.50	16,000	19,500
3.00	0.50	16,500	19,000

* Specimens immersed in distilled water for twenty-four hours.
† Specimens immersed in distilled water for two weeks.

as a control to compare the action of the water as regards crushing strength. It may be noted from Table XXII that many of the cements showed an alarming decrease in crushing strength in the distilled water in comparison to the specimens kept in the liquid petrolatum.

As may be noted from Table XXIII, the crushing strength of the zinc phosphate cements increases as the powder:liquid ratio is increased up to a certain value, stiffer mixes do not alter it appreciably.

TABLE XXIV

CHANGE IN COMPRESSIVE STRENGTH WITH TIME AFTER MIXING

Cement.	Compressive strength (lb./sq. in.)				
	1 hour.	3 hours.	1 day.	1 week.	4 weeks.
F*........	10,000	11,500	13,000	16,000	17,500
F†........	11,000	13,000	14,500	15,000	15,000
K*........	10,000	10,000	16,500	17,000	16,500
K†........	10,500	10,000	15,500	16,000	16,500

* Specimens were immersed in liquid petrolatum.
† Specimens were immersed in distilled water.

TABLE XXV

COMPRESSIVE STRENGTH WITH COLOR

Cement.	Color.	Compressive strength (lb./sq. in.)
C............................	Cream white	6,500
C............................	Yellow white	3,000
C............................	Yellow	4,000
C............................	Light gray	7,000
C............................	Pearl gray	4,500
C............................	Grayish brown	3,500
C............................	No. 1 white*	10,000
C............................	No. 6 dark brown†	8,500
I............................	Snow white	13,000
I............................	Light yellow	12,000
I............................	Golden yellow	12,000
I............................	Pearl gray	13,000
I............................	Grayish brown	13,000
I............................	Golden brown	10,500
K............................	Light	10,500
K............................	Light yellow	11,000
K............................	Light gray	10,000
K............................	Pearl gray	10,500
K............................	Golden yellow	9,500
K............................	Golden brown	9,500

* Specimens immersed in distilled water for twenty-four hours.
† Special inlay cement of the same brand.

For a given mixing consistency, the crushing strength reaches its maximum in approximately twenty-four hours after mixing (see Table XXIV). Table XXV shows the effect of color of the cement upon its crushing strength. It has been thought that the dark colored cements were stronger than the lighter colored cements, an opinion which these data prove to be erroneous.

According to Ray[14] the crushing strengths of silicate cements vary from 5650 to 8450 pounds per square inch in the specimens tested. He found that the crushing strengths were nearly independent of the temperature of the mixing slab, and of the consistency of the mix; in the latter case the very thin mixes showed slightly greater strengths than the excessively thick mixes, the medium consistency being the strongest. Furthermore, the crushing strength was independent of the liquid concentration, when 10 per cent of its water was evaporated.

Dimensional Changes.—Provided the change is not excessively great, the dimensional changes for zinc phosphate cements used pri-

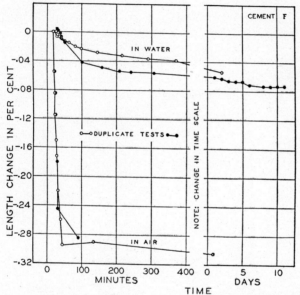

Fig. 30.—Dimensional change of zinc phosphate cement on setting. (Paffenbarger, Sweeney, Isaacs, Jour. Amer. Dent. Assoc., Nov., 1933.)

marily for cementing inlays are perhaps not as important as for those of copper and silicate cements which are employed for restorations. There are no quantitative data available for the copper cements, but very likely their dimensional changes are similar to those of the zinc phosphate cements described below.

Using the dental interferometer,* the setting changes have been measured for both the zinc phosphate cements[13] and the silicate cements.[14]

The zinc phosphate cements shrank under water 0.05 to 2 per cent. In no case was a permanent expansion noted. The shrinkage takes

* Described on page 320.

place within two to three hours, after which the specimens usually remain fairly constant in dimension. As may be noted from Fig. 30, one specimen, which was allowed to stand in air, showed an enormous shrinkage. In water its total shrinkage was approximately 0.05 per

TABLE XXVI

DIMENSIONAL CHANGES OCCURRING DURING THE SETTING OF SILICATE CEMENTS

Cement	Contraction (per cent)	
	6 hr.	24 hr.
I	0.025	0.035
II	0.085	0.115
III	0.060	0.085
IV	0.030	0.040
V	0.045	0.070
VI	0.070	0.085

cent, whereas in air the shrinkage was in the neighborhood of 0.3 per cent. Obviously, the cements must not be allowed to dry out.

The magnitude of the shrinkage of the silicate cements when tested under water is quite comparable with that found for the zinc phosphate cements. Ray's results[14] in this connection are summarized in Table XXVI. Ray further found the water content of the liquid to be

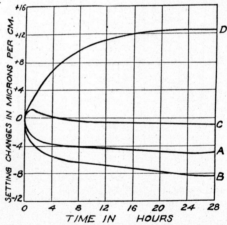

Fig. 31.—Effects of water content on setting changes of cement VI, Table VI. Curve A, cement mixed in usual manner. Curve B, cement mixed with a liquid diluted with water 5 per cent of its weight. Curve C, cement mixed on slab heated to 95° F. to cause evaporation of water during mixing process. Curve D, cement with liquid from which 10 per cent of its weight of water had been evaporated. (Ray, Jour. Amer. Dent. Assoc., Feb., 1934.)

a large factor in the dimensional change values. Figs. 31 and 32 show that the more water present in the liquid the greater is the shrinkage, whereas decreasing the water content apparently causes an expansion. Such facts are undoubtedly accounted for by dehydration and hydration of the colloids present while the material is setting. From a practical viewpoint this means that the water content of the liquid must be governed not only to control the setting time, but also the apparent dimensional changes. If the cement is mixed upon a cold slab below the dew point of the surrounding atmosphere, the setting time will be hastened and the contraction increased by the absorption of the droplets of water thus formed on the mixing slab. On the other hand, if a warm slab is used, water is evaporated while mixing, the setting time is increased, but the contraction is apparently less, as is illustrated by Fig. 31, curve C, and Fig. 32, curve B. Obviously equilibrium conditions of the slab temperature must be different from those occurring after the cement is placed in the mouth, unless the slab temperature is identical with mouth temperature; these facts are beautifully illustrated in the curves mentioned.

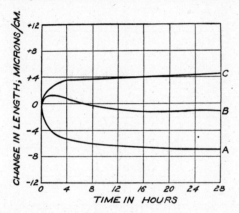

Fig. 32.—Effects of water content on setting changes of cement V. Curve A, cement mixed in usual way. Curve B, cement mixed on slab heated to 95° F. to cause evaporation of water during mixing process. Curve C, cement with liquid from which 10 per cent of its weight of water had been evaporated. (Ray, Jour. Amer. Dent. Assoc., Feb., 1934.)

On the basis of such data, an expanding silicate cement should be possible of attainment.* However, the setting reactions will be slower in such a case, and will have to be increased by chemical or other means. A slight expansion in these cements would be desirable, provided that it takes place before the cement becomes hard enough to introduce strains within the restoration which might shorten its life.

* As this book goes to press, certain evidence is at hand which indicates that such setting expansions are only surface phenomena, and are not to be relied upon as providing a permanently sealed silicate restoration. This evidence was presented by Dr. George C. Paffenbarger at the Louisville Meeting (1936) of the International Association of Dental Research, as a result of some preliminary tests carried out at the National Bureau of Standards. In all probability, all silicate cements shrink in varying amounts under all clinical conditions of manipulation. The data in Figs. 31 and 32 were obtained by means of the dental interferometer, which is possibly not adaptable for the observation of this particular phenomenon.

Fig. 33 shows what happens to a silicate cement which is allowed to dry in air, and is then immersed in water. The colloid shrank upon dehydration, and reexpanded when hydrated,* as might be expected; however, it should be noted that the original dimensions were not completely attained. Furthermore, such a partial recovery of volume after dehydration might be accompanied by a certain amount of warpage and surface friability. This demonstrates very clearly that the silicate restoration must be kept moist at all times, a precaution which is sometimes neglected by dentists while they are operating with the rubber dam over a tooth which contains such a restoration. For the same reason, silicate restorations are never indicated for use in the teeth of chronic mouth breathers.

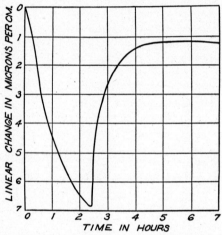

Fig. 33.—Changes occurring in fully set silicate cement during exposure to air for two and one-half hours followed by submergence in water. (Ray, Jour. Amer. Dent. Assoc., Feb., 1934.)

Density of the Powder.—In the case of the zinc phosphate cements, at least, the density of the powder has just the opposite effect upon the physical properties than one would be apt to predict. It has been thought that a dense powder would produce a stronger cement, with greater resistance to disintegration in the saliva. According to the data of Paffenbarger, Sweeney, and Isaacs,[10] the cements having the denser powders were distinctly inferior. They exhibited low crushing strengths, and were slow in setting. This may be due to the fact that smaller amounts of powder must be used in order to give a standard consistency comparable with the other cements.

Effect of Particle Size.—Swanson[16] has investigated the effect of particle size of the powder upon the physical properties of silicate cements. He selected three different sizes of particles and determined the effect of each upon crushing strength, setting time, perme-

* This also may be only a surface effect.

ability, shrinkage, and translucence, in comparison with the original powder which contained all three sizes, as supplied by the manufacturer.

As might be expected from the chemical theory of setting given in the previous chapter, the smaller the particle size, the shorter is the setting time of the cement. Swanson also found that the smaller particles increased the crushing strength of the hardened cement; if it is assumed that the silicic acid gel and phosphate network act as a binding agent, obviously, the smaller the particle size, within limits, the stronger the cement should be, because of the greater amount of binding surface between the particles and the matrix.

His data also indicate that the use of large particle sizes results in more contraction of the cement while setting. However, when the large, medium, and small particles were mixed, as in the original powder from which he separated them, more shrinkage resulted than when the small particles were used alone, but the specimens did not contract to the extent exhibited by a cement mixed with the large size alone. Also, the permeability of the set cement to a water soluble dye was greatest for the large particles, and progressively smaller as the size was decreased, yet the original cement showed very little permeability. As to translucence, the original was the best in this respect, and the effect became progressively less as the particle size was decreased.

It may therefore be concluded that the cements may be improved in many respects, if more attention is given to the grading of particle size. However, further work is necessary along this line, before drawing more definite conclusions.

MANIPULATION OF CEMENTS

Any discussion of manipulation of cements with the view of improvement of their properties is handicapped at the outset. The greatest disadvantage of the cements is their solubility in the mouth fluids, a factor which is probably not within the control of the dentist, and which will not be improved greatly by any reasonable method of manipulation. All of the cements shrink in spite of anything the operator can do to prevent it. None of the restorative cements can be called permanent in any sense; they should be either improved radically or else discarded. The above detailed discussion has been given in order that their present state of uncertainty may be understood, in the hope that the dentist will be more critical and demand better products, if such can be produced.

However, in order to get the most out of the present day cements, there are certain details of manipulation to which the dentist must strictly adhere. In the selection of cements, the dentist should demand products which are guaranteed to meet the specifications of the American Dental Association. This, of course, applies to all dental materials as well as cements. When the brand of cement has been selected, it is necessary to adhere strictly to the directions given by the manufacturer.

One of the precautionary measures to be observed in handling cements is to keep the bottle of liquid tightly closed at all times. The dropper should be either kept in the liquid, or thoroughly cleaned and dried after use. Under no circumstances should the smallest drop of water or other impurity be allowed to get into the liquid. The liquid has been carefully made and buffered by the manufacturer, and its concentration or purity must not be changed.

The powder must be carefully protected from dust or other contamination. The slab and other utensils must be kept spotlessly clean. Such precautions must be diligently observed, if the color and other properties are to be preserved.

In the mixing of the cement, it should be remembered that the aim in the mixing of the zinc phosphate cements is to prolong the setting time, hence, the powder is incorporated in small portions and the spatulation carried on longer than is the case with the silicate cements. In the mixing of the latter, the general tendency should be to shorten the setting time, hence, more powder should be incorporated at one time than in the previous case.

Under no conditions should the mixing be prolonged until the reaction products begin to form, thus breaking them up. This is particularly true of the silicate cements, which are somewhat critical in manipulation. In any case, a uniform mass must result with no voids of unmixed powder or liquid, since such a condition will cause a weakness in structure. The mix must be plastic and not too stiff. As noted previously, a very stiff mix shows no superiority in strength over a thinner one of medium consistency.

The mixing of the zinc phosphate cements is preferably done on a cool slab (65°–75° F.), provided the temperature is not below the dew point of the air in the room. This provides a smooth mix which will not set too quickly before insertion in the cavity. The slab temperatures for mixing silicates may be somewhat higher without impairing the cement.

The cement should be used immediately after it has been mixed and remain undisturbed until set. Particularly silicate cements should be inserted promptly and held in place with a celluloid strip. They must not be disturbed until the first set has taken place; the silicic acid gel, once broken, does not grow together again. The finishing of the latter should be delayed for at least twenty-four hours.

All of the cements must be kept absolutely dry until they have hardened. In the case of the silicates, a varnish or a coat of cocoa butter should be applied to their exposed surfaces. After they have hardened, the cements should be kept moist.

The color of the silicate cements should be selected to match the natural tooth. Their color is always lighter when first mixed, but as the cement hardens it increases in translucence and the color deepens. For this reason the color should be selected from a shade guide, and not from the mixed cement. The phenomena of color are discussed in connection with dental porcelains (see pages 139–141), and many of the fundamentals apply here.

Specifications.—American Dental Association Tentative Specification No. 8. See Appendix, page 392.

LITERATURE

1. Hill, T. J., and Boester, K. W., *Relative Efficiency of Germicidal Cements.* J. A. D. A., 21: 1565–1571 (Sept.) 1934.

2. Fraser, C. Jane, *A Study of the Efficiency of Dental Fillings.* Jour. of Dent. Res., 9: 507–517, 1929.

3. Crowell, W. S., *Physical Chemistry of Dental Cements.* J. A. D. A., 14: 1030–1048 (June) 1927.

4. Eberly, J. A., Jr., *Development of a Silicate Cement Tending to Eliminate Pulp Irritation.* Dent. Cos., 76: 419–424 (April) 1934.

5. Starr, D. E., J. Biol. Chem., 54: 43 (Sept.) 1922.

6. Matthews, Ernest, *Some Observations on Silicate Cements.* Brit. Dent. Jour., 56: 431–439 (May 1) 1934.

7. Council of Dental Therapeutics: *Report on Plastic Materials.* J. A. D. A., 18: 2012, 2013 (Oct.) 1931.

8. Doubleday, F. N., *The Silicate Cement Filling.* Brit. Dent. Jour., 47: 493–497 (May 1) 1926.

9. Tompkins, H. E., *Silicate Cements and "Neutropism."* Dent. It. of Int., 44: 881–887 (Dec.) 1922.

10. Paffenbarger, G. C., Sweeney, W. T., and Isaacs, Aaron, *Zinc Phosphate Cements: Physical Properties and a Specification.* J. A. D. A., 21: 1907–1924 (Nov.) 1934.

11. Vogt, C. C., *The Chemistry of Silicates and Their Application in Dentistry.* J. N. D. A., 5: 354–373 (April) 1918.

12. U. S. Patent No. 1, 760, 388.

13. Paffenbarger, G. C., Sweeney, W. T., and Isaacs, Aaron, *A Preliminary Report on the Zinc Phosphate Cements.* J. A. D. A., 20: 1960–1982 (Nov.) 1933.

14. Ray, K. W., *The Behavior of Silicious Cements.* J. A. D. A., 21: 237–251 (Feb.) 1934.

15. Poetschke, Paul, J. Ind. Eng. Chem., 8: 303 (April) 1916.

16. Swanson, E. W., Thesis, N. U. D. S. (1936).

17. Head, Joseph, *Modern Dentistry,* pp. 317, 318. W. B. Saunders Company.

11

CHAPTER XX

INTRODUCTION TO THE SCIENCE OF METALS. PYROMETRY

Metals.—Although metals are very common in human experience, they are extremely difficult to define accurately. Certainly a metal is a chemical element, yet not all the chemical elements can be classified as metals. A metal always has a characteristic "metallic luster" in the gross solid state. Possibly the ultimate criterion which determines whether or not a chemical element is a metal is its behavior in electrolytes. If it is attracted to and deposited at the cathode during electrolysis, it may be defined as a metal. Generally speaking, all metals are good electrical and thermal conductors, and have high density, strength, ductility, and malleability in comparison to the nonmetals. They are crystalline under all conditions when solid, and they exhibit definite melting and boiling points characteristic of each metallic element.

This rather lengthy definition may be recognized as being extremely broad in scope, and it applies mainly to the solid state. By no means do all the metals included in the definition exist as solids at ordinary room temperatures; mercury and gallium (m.p. 29.7° C.) are outstanding exceptions. So far as the definition is concerned, hydrogen, which is ordinarily a gas, is also a metal, yet if it is solidified, it shows a definite metallic luster.

Metalloids.—At least three elements—carbon, silicon and boron— are on the borderline between metals and nonmetals. They have many of the properties of metals, such as fairly high electrical and thermal conductive properties, but they are almost totally lacking in plasticity at ordinary temperatures. Elements of this type are called *metalloids*.

Alloys.—The term "metal" when used in a wider sense may also include alloys; strictly speaking, this usage is incorrect. An alloy* is a metallic substance composed of two or more metals, which are mutually soluble in the molten or liquid state.† An *amalgam* is an alloy one of the constituents of which is mercury. The properties of alloys will be discussed in Chapters XXIII and XXIV. Table XXVII gives a few of the common physical properties of the alloy-forming elements.

* According to the Standard and Webster Dictionaries, both the verb and noun are pronounced: al-loy′ (accent on the last syllable).

† Although this definition is not all inclusive, it is sufficiently accurate for the purpose of this book. It should be noted that the so-called "two-layer alloys" are excluded from consideration as alloys.

TABLE XXVII*

PHYSICAL CONSTANTS OF THE ALLOY-FORMING ELEMENTS

Element.	Symbol.	At. Wt.	Melting point (° C.).	Boiling point (° C.).	Density (g./cc.).	Linear coefficient of thermal expansion (per ° C. × 10⁴).
Aluminum....	Al	26.97	659.7	1800.0	2.70	0.224
Antimony....	Sb	121.76	630.5	1380.0	6.618	0.136
Arsenic.......	As	74.93	(820)	615†	5.730	0.05
Bismuth......	Bi	209.00	271.3	1450.0	9.747	0.014
Boron........	B	10.82	2300.0	......	2.535	
Cadmium.....	Cd	112.41	320.9	766.0	8.37	0.54
Carbon.......	C	12.00	>3500.0	(4200)	2.25	0.06
Chromium....	Cr	52.01	1615.0	2200.0	6.93	0.068
Cobalt.......	Co	58.94	1480.0	3000.0	8.71	0.123
Copper.......	Cu	63.57	1083.0	2300.0	8.89	0.162
Gold.........	Au	197.20	1063.0	2600.0	19.3	0.140
Indium......	In	114.8	155.0	>1450.0	7.28	0.417
Iridium......	Ir	193.1	2350.0	>4800.0	22.42	0.065
Iron.........	Fe	55.84	1535.0	3000.0	7.86	0.118
Lead.........	Pb	207.22	327.4	1620.0	11.342	0.312
Magnesium...	Mg	24.32	651.0	1100.0	1.741	0.254
Mercury.....	Hg	200.61	38.87	356.9	13.546	1.8182‡
Molybdenum.	Mo	96.00	2620.0	3700.0	10.2	0.053
Nickel.......	Ni	58.69	1455.00	2900.0	8.8	0.126
Osmium......	Os	190.8	2700.00	>5300.0	22.5	0.066
Palladium....	Pd	106.7	1553.00	2200.0	11.5	0.1173
Platinum....	Pt	195.23	1773.5	4300.0	21.37	0.0887
Rhodium.....	Rh	102.91	1985.00	>2500.0	12.44	0.0850
Silicon.......	Si	28.06	1420.00	2600.0	2.42	0.0763
Silver........	Ag	107.88	960.5	1950.0	10.47	0.1846
Tantalum....	Ta	181.84	2850.0	4100.0	16.6	0.065
Tellurium....	Te	127.5	452.0	1390.0	6.25	0.016
Tin..........	Sn	118.70	231.89	2260.0	7.29	0.214
Tungsten.....	W	184.0	3370.0	5900.0	18.8	0.0444
Zinc.........	Zn	65.38	419.47	907.0	7.1	0.305

* Compiled from the Smithsonian Physical Tables.
† Sublimation temperature.
‡ Volume coefficient of thermal expansion.

Solidification of Metals.—Generally speaking, metals are crystalline in form, belonging mainly to the cubic system. One of the general characteristics of pure crystalline materials is their constant solidification or fusion points. If the temperature is recorded over a period of time until the metal has changed from the molten to the solid state, and if the temperature data are plotted as a function of the time, a curve similar to the one in Fig. 34 will result. From A to B, the molten mass is gradually cooling, but it should be noted that the temperature between B and C remains constant for a time, before it drops to D. This is most interesting since the system is receiving no heat from its surroundings, but rather giving it up. As a matter of fact BC represents the point of solidification of the metal, and the heat results from the energy exchange during change in state. The liquid state has more internal energy than does the solid state; hence, when the metal changes from the liquid to the solid state, the excess energy appears as heat, thus preventing the fall in temperature during such a transition. The number of calories of heat liberated by 1 gram of a substance when it is changing from the liquid to the solid state is known as the *latent heat of fusion.*

In the light of such a theory, the interpretation of the time-temperature cooling curve in Fig. 34 is that above the temperature cor-

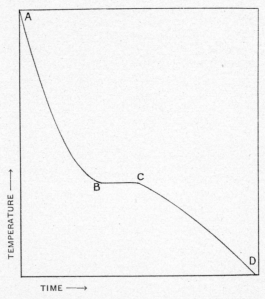

Fig. 34.—A typical time-temperature cooling curve for pure metal.

responding to BC, the metal is a liquid, and below BC, it is a solid, regardless of whether it is heated or cooled through this temperature. This phenomenon is not at all outside of ordinary human experience. For example, ice in a refrigerator cools the latter by *melting,* not simply because the ice is "cold"; for every gram of ice melted, 80 calories of heat are required for the process. Conversely, winter weather will be several degrees warmer, in general, near the shore of a large body of fresh water, such as Lake Michigan, than it will be even a few miles inland, since for every gram of water changed to ice, 80 calories of heat will be liberated.

This property of fusion is of considerable importance in casting, since the higher the heat of fusion value, the more heat will be required to melt the metal. For example the heat of fusion of gold is 15.9 calories per gram, whereas that of aluminum is 94 calories per gram; hence, more heat will be required to change aluminum from the solid to liquid state than gold, if equal weights of both are used, in spite of the fact that the aluminum melts at a lower temperature than the gold (see Table XXVII).

High Temperature Measurement.—Many metals melt at a high temperature, and the method for the measurement of such temperatures is of interest. The glass mercury thermometer may be employed for temperatures as high as 525° C. (977° F.), or if the thermometer is made of fused quartz, temperatures as high as 800° C. (1472° F.) may be measured.* However, in general, such thermometers do not register the higher temperatures as accurately as do certain other temperature indicators.

When a body is heated to a temperature greater than its immediate environment, modern physical theory teaches that it radiates energy in the form of electromagnetic waves. At lower temperatures, the wave length of the radiation will be comparatively great, but as the temperature is increased the wave length shortens and finally becomes visible to the eye. Experienced men can determine the temperature of a hot body with surprising accuracy by observation of its color. Table XXVIII shows the relation between temperature and

TABLE XXVIII
Howe's Color Scale

Color.	Temperature. (° C.)	(° F.)
Lowest visible red	475	887
Dull red	550–625	1022–1154
Cherry red	700	1292
Light red	850	1562
Orange	900	1652
Full yellow	950–1000	1742–1832
Light yellow	1050	1922
White	1150 or above	2100 or above

color. It is to be assumed that such color observations are made with the object out of line with a direct source of light, or the effect will be masked.

Certain instruments, known as *radiation pyrometers*, may be used which will measure the radiation directly in terms of temperature with considerable accuracy. Still another means of measuring radiation is by the use of the *optical pyrometer*. The latter consists of an electrical filament which is calibrated for its temperature, when incandescent, in terms of the electrical current which flows through it. The equipment is so arranged that when it is held to the eyes, one

* In such high-temperature thermometers, an inert gas such as nitrogen is introduced under pressure in order to raise the boiling point of the mercury.

eye looks directly toward the hot body whose temperature is to be measured, whereas the filament is in the range of vision of the other eye. The current through the filament is then adjusted until the color of the filament exactly matches the color of the furnace or hot body. The current indicating instrument, which is calibrated in degrees, gives the temperature directly.

The above methods are of use only for comparatively high temperatures. For lower temperatures, and in certain cases the higher temperatures as well, resistance pyrometers may be used. It is a physical law that the electrical resistance of platinum, for example, increases with increase in temperature. Hence, if a platinum wire, previously calibrated for its relation between change in electrical resistance and temperature, is placed in the molten metal or furnace,

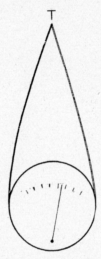

Fig. 35.—A thermocouple with indicator.

the temperatures may be determined by the changes in electrical resistance in the wire.

The most common equipment employed in dentistry for the measurement of high temperatures is the *thermocouple*. The thermocouple consists of two wires of dissimilar metals or alloys, the ends of which are welded together. If one of the junctions is held at a higher temperature than the other, a difference in electrical potential will exist between them, thus causing an electrical current to flow. The junction at the higher temperature is usually designated as the *hot junction*, and the other union, the *cold junction*. If the cold junction is held at a constant temperature, the difference in electrical potential between the two junctions will be, for all practical purposes, directly proportional to the difference in temperature between them.

In practice, the thermocouple is usually attached directly to a millivoltmeter, as shown in Fig. 35; the point **T** is the hot junction, and the cold junction is made through the instrument. At first thought it might seem possible that the contacts of the thermocouple wires at the terminals of the instrument might introduce extraneous effects, since the metal of which the terminals are made is usually different from the thermocouple wires themselves. However, a little thought will show that such is not the case, inasmuch as a differenece in temperature between the contacts is essential for the production of thermoelectricity; this condition is not satisfied since presumably the binding posts and all other parts of the instrument are at the same temperature. It should be further noted that the temperature of the

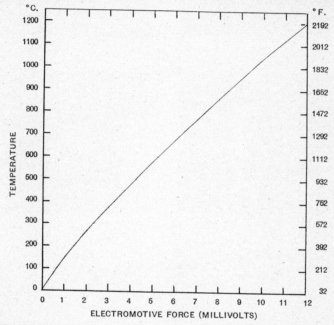

Fig. 36.—Calibration curve for a platinum, platinum-rhodium thermocouple.

cold junction in the figure will always be room temperature; hence any variation in the latter will necessitate that a correction be applied to the millivoltmeter reading, unless compensation is made in the instrument itself.

In dental work, the millivoltmeter is usually calibrated so as to read directly in degrees of temperature, otherwise it must be calibrated by the operator. Fig. 36 shows a calibration curve for a millivoltmeter with a platinum, platinum-rhodium thermocouple. Instead of a millivoltmeter, a potentiometer may be used with greater accuracy.

In dental work, the materials used for the thermocouple are usually either chromel and alumel, or platinum and an alloy of platinum (90 per cent) and rhodium (10 per cent). Chromel is an alloy of nickel and chromium, whereas alumel is an alloy of nickel and aluminum. The chromel-alumel thermocouple may be used to a temperature not higher than 1000° C. (1832° F.), and develops a max-

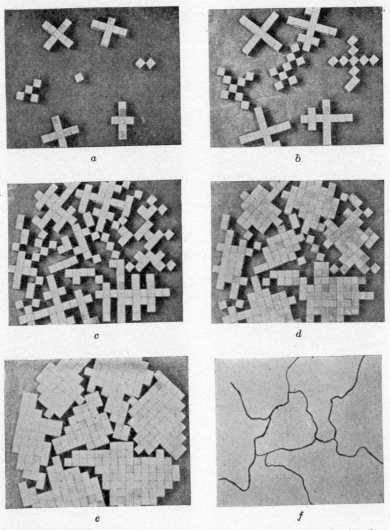

Fig. 37.—Stages in the formation of metallic crystal grains by the freezing of a molten mass. (Rosenhain, *Introduction to Physical Metallurgy*, Constable and Company, Ltd.)

imum potential difference of 40 millivolts at this temperature. The platinum, platinum-rhodium thermocouple develops much less difference in potiential than this, as may be observed from Fig. 36, but it has the advantage of being able to measure temperatures as high as 1500° C. (2732° F.). The latter type is used extensively in dental porcelain furnaces such as have been described in Chapter XVII.

Mechanism of Solidification.—The manner in which a metal or alloy solidifies may have considerable influence upon its physical properties in the solid state. When a metal crystallizes from the liquid state, the method of crystallization is not unlike that of gypsum as described in Chapter VI. First a nucleus of crystallization must be present upon which the space lattice may form. This nucleus may be an unmelted crystallite (minute crystal) of the metal, or else the atoms in the molten state may form in exact proximity for the formation of a nucleus. That nuclei formations are sometimes difficult to

Fig. 38.—Microstructure of an ingot of 24 carat gold. × 100. (Photomicrograph by S. D. Tylman.)

obtain is shown by the phenomenon of *supercooling*. For example, water may be cooled a considerable number of degrees below its solidification temperature without freezing, but if the container is jarred, or a microscopic ice crystal is introduced, the crystallization will take place very rapidly.

Once the nucleus is present, the crystals begin to grow, branching out in all directions with the nucleus as a center. Normally the growth produces tree-like formations called *dendrites*, as may be observed in the beautiful formations of frost on the inside of a window during the winter. Fig. 37 gives a schematic reproduction of such crystallization of a metal in two dimensions, but it must be remembered that the process actually occurs in three dimensions. In Fig. 37a, several nuclei may be observed, and others upon which the growth has already started. The subsequent pictures demonstrate the continued growth, until the final crystallization shown in Fig. 37*f* is reached. The grain structure of a cast ingot of pure gold is shown in Fig. 38, thus demonstrating the microstructure diagrammed in Fig. 37*f*.

The significance of such growth is extremely important. It should be noted that a space lattice is formed upon each nucleus, and grows until it meets the space lattices formed on adjacent nuclei, when growth stops. Although the space lattices formed on various nuclei in a pure metal are the same, *the orientation of the various lattices with respect to one another will not be the same.* Hence, the solid metal is not made up of a continuous space lattice, but rather it

Fig. 39.—Crystal grains formed by the freezing of a metal in a square mold. (Williams and Homerberg: *Principles of Metallography*, McGraw-Hill Book Co., Publishers.)

consists of small crystals, all of the same space lattice but differently oriented one with another. These small crystals are called *grains*. The type of grains illustrated in Fig. 37*f* are known as *equiaxed grains* because of their tendency to be spherical in shape. However, it should be emphasized that the grains are never spherical, but irregular, as shown in Fig. 38. This lack of symmetry is due to unfavorable conditions of growth. As noted previously, the growth takes place in all directions simultaneously from a large number of nuclei, until further progress is stopped by adjacent crystals crowding against one another, thus forming irregular boundaries. Certain polycrystalline aggregates, such as brass and chromium steel, have been treated so as to separate the grains, in order that they may be studied individually in three dimensions. The predominant forms were pentagonal dodecahedra, *i. e.*, twelve-faced cells, with each face five-sided.[1]

Equiaxed grains do not always form during solidification. For example, if a metal freezes in a square mold which is at room temperature when the metal is cast, the crystal growth will be from the sides of the mold inward toward the center, and this results in *columnar grains*, as shown in Fig. 39. The diagonals are definite planes of weakness, and are to be avoided. If the mold were cylindrical, the grains would radiate from the center, and would be called *radial grains*. In general, casting into a cold mold is contraindicated.

Under specially controlled laboratory conditions, a metal can be solidified in such a manner that it forms a single crystal throughout, with no grain formation whatever. The study of such *single crystals* brings to light considerable information concerning the various properties of crystals, but the discussion of this most interesting subject is not within the scope of this book.

Grain Boundaries.—There can be no doubt but that a metal composed of many grains is completely solid and, in general, homogeneous throughout. Since the grains are closely packed crystals with varying orientations with one another, the question at once arises as to what is the structure between the grains at their boundaries.

Due to the fact that the space lattices of the grains are oriented differently from one grain to the next, it is difficult to imagine a crystalline formation of any sort at such a discontinuity. One theory postulates that the grain boundary material, or *intergranular cement*, is amorphous in character; that is, when two or more grains meet during crystallization growth, the last atoms to solidify are crowded together between the grains in a random arrangement. Such a theory is rather difficult to prove experimentally, as all attempts to produce a metal or alloy in a completely amorphous condition have so far failed. Nevertheless the theory accounts for many phenomena to be discussed in succeeding chapters.

As mentioned in Chapter XV, a polished surface consists of an amorphous layer spread over the surface of a material by the action of the buffing wheel. Such a statement follows directly from the amorphous metal hypothesis outlined above. If a carefully polished surface is subjected to chemical action, such that the "polish" is removed (called *etching*), the grains may be observed under a microscope, yet they are not visible before etching. All photomicrographs of grain structures appearing in this book were made from specimens prepared in this manner.

LITERATURE

1. Desch, C. H., *The Chemistry of Solids,* p. 60 Cornell University Press 1934.

CHAPTER XXI

PHYSICAL PHENOMENA OF GRAIN STRUCTURE

Shaping of Metals.—Metals and alloys may be fabricated or shaped into useful articles, either by casting or by working. The two operations require different principles of manipulation. The physical properties of a finished structure will depend considerably, in many instances, upon the shape and size of the resulting grains. In general, the smaller the grain size, the greater will be the strength, hardness, and ductility. The grain size of castings may be regulated by the rate of cooling from the solid state; within limits, the faster the castings are cooled, the smaller their grain size. However, after a metal has been mechanically worked, as in rolling, drawing, swaging, etc., the control of grain size is not so simple.

Physical Properties of a Metal.—The physical properties of various materials were discussed in Chapters II to IV. In the case of metals and alloys, the degree to which the metallic materials may or may not be elastic, strong, resilient, ductile, etc., depends considerably upon the space lattice and grain structure involved. Let the typical stress-strain curve, Fig. 2, on page 25 be considered in the light of the metallic space lattice and grain structure.

Along the straight portion of the curve, elastic deformation took place. This is interpreted as an elastic distortion of the space lattice; the atoms exert *atomic forces* about each other, which are very large, and these forces act to bind the atoms rigidly in a lattice structure;* that is, if the atoms are forced apart slightly, the atomic forces† will cause them to spring back when released, provided that the disturbance of the atomic distance is not too great. Such an atomic phenomenon is readily recognized as a pure elastic tensile stress, as defined on page 22. However, the elastic phenomena introduced into the wire, whose stress-strain curve is given in Fig. 2, are not so simple as this.

For purposes of simplification, let it be assumed that the space lattice involved is of the simple cubic type, as illustrated in Fig. 5, page 43. As noted on page 22, the wire elongates under the tensile load, but its cross section area decreases simultaneously with the increase in elastic tensile strain. Hence, it follows that the atoms of

---

* For purposes of simplification, atomic vibrations are being neglected, since they contribute nothing directly to the theory.

† An elementary conception might be that the atoms are joined by springs, which are capable of both compression and tension. Hence, if any two of the atoms are moved apart slightly, the "interatomic spring" will bring them back to their original positions, when the load is released; similar arguments are true for compression.

172

the space lattice must move apart in the direction of the tensile load, but are forced closer together in directions perpendicular to the tensile stresses; the latter movement is obviously a compressive strain, and the combination of the two strains produces a certain amount of shear.

Similar atomic interpretations may be given for stresses and strains which appear under compressive and shearing loads, thus theoretically substantiating the discussion of complex stresses given on page 22, i. e., pure tensile, compressive, and shearing stresses do not exist individually under ordinary methods of loading; one type may be predominant, but the other two types will be present nevertheless. It should be emphasized that this theory applies in its entirety only to

Fig. 40.—A photomicrograph of 68:32 brass showing slip bands. ×100. (Courtesy of S. D. Tylman.)

elastic stresses and strains; from the standpoint of atomic phenomena, the elastic stresses are the forces which act interatomically, and the strains refer to the increase or decrease of the interatomic distances or spacings. It should be further evident that stresses are *internal* forces, and not external loads.

Theory of Slip.—As soon as the elastic limit is exceeded, something within the lattice must give way, since the structure does not return to its original size when the load is released.

It should be noted that the atoms in Fig. 5, page 43, lie in planes; in fact the positions of the atoms in a space lattice might be defined as the points located by the intersection of three or more planes in space, the number depending upon the type of space lattice. These are called *crystal planes*, or, in some instances, *cleavage planes;* the latter term denotes those planes through which a brittle crystal fractures when broken.

When the crystal is loaded beyond its elastic limit, modern theory indicates that the atoms in one plane are displaced or slide over those on the plane below; this action is called *slip*, the plane in which the slip occurs being known as a *slip plane*. After slip, the adjacent atoms may or may not adhere, as will be discussed later. The intragranular lines, shown in the grain structure of the metal in Fig. 40, are a direct result of the formation of slip planes in the metal, and are known as *slip bands*. They are steps on the polished surface of the metal "produced by the elevation or depression of blocks or fragments of the grains." [1]

Fig. 41.—Dendritic grain structure of a cast ingot of a gold alloy. (Courtesy of the J. M. Ney Co.)

Once a slip occurs, the metal exhibits permanent deformation. The general direction of slip will be that of the applied force, but since the orientations of the individual grains differ, the orientations of the planes along which slip occurs must also differ in direction.

Ductility, and, to a lesser extent, malleability will depend upon the number of slips possible in the material. If little or no slip is possible, the material is said to be brittle; otherwise it is ductile.

The number of slips possible in a ductile material such as gold is enormous, particularly when the metal is fine grained. Each grain contains many potential slip planes, and, according to modern theory, each plane is capable of repeated slip. When the limit of slip is reached, the interatomic bonds are of course broken and the structure is fractured. Although a testing machine registers a certain strength value upon fracture, it must not be thought that the datum actually represents the collective forces of cohesion between the atoms, for the latter are many times greater than the force observed.

In the light of this discussion it should be evident why no simple law has been devised connecting stress and strain in permanent deformation, similar to the stress-strain relationship given by Hooke's law for elastic deformation.

Cold Work.—When a metal or alloy is bent, swaged, drawn, rolled, contoured, or worked in any manner at room temperature, it is said to be *cold worked.* Severe cold work produces a change in the physical properties of the metal. For example, suppose that one attempts to

Fig. 42.—Grain structure of a wire drawn from the cast ingot shown in Fig. 41. ×500. (Courtesy of the J. M. Ney Co.)

flatten a nail by hammering at room temperature. The first few blows are quite effective, but as the process is continued, the metal becomes harder. Finally, instead of becoming thinner under the hammer, it cracks, a result which indicates an overworked condition. Such a phenomenon is known as *strain hardening,* and it is the direct result of grain distortion.

Whenever a metallic structure is deformed by cold work, the grains are deformed in the general direction of working. Fig. 41 shows the microstructure of a gold alloy as it solidified from the molten state, and in Fig. 42 may be seen the grain structure of a wire drawn from the same alloy. The fibrous structure is very evident. The result of strain hardening is an increase in elasticity, hardness, and strength, the latter often being increased from two to three times when tested under tension.[2] The thermal conductivity, density, resistance to corrosion,[4] and ductility are all decreased, the last mentioned property often being decreased alarmingly. The increase in physical properties is usually directional, that is, a wire will be stronger longitudinally than across its diameter.

When a metal is drastically deformed at room temperature, slip, of course, will take place, but it is stopped by various means along certain planes. According to the *slip interference theory*, certain grains may be broken up, and this causes the atoms to lie no longer in absolutely parallel layers, thus disregistering the slip. Furthermore, slip may be stopped by an intersection with an adjacent grain boundary; on further cold work, the surface atoms of such a "lapped over" fragment may be used to increase the amount of amorphous cement, thus producing a wedging effect. Since the amorphous material is thought to be of a vitreous nature, this, together with the first mentioned phenomenon, causes the metal to become brittle, and hence, the structure fractures upon further cold work. If it is not carried too far, such strain hardening may be relieved by a proper heat treatment, and at the same time a uniformity and reduction or *refinement* of grain size is effected, as will be outlined in the next section.

Recrystallization.—This change in size and form of the grains which is brought about by heat treatment after cold work is known as *recrystallization*. No change in space lattice type occurs; merely an atomic diffusion takes place, the parent lattice persisting in the recrystallized grain, a process which is definitely allied with its prototype, the crystallization of the metal or alloy from its molten condition. After a cast metal or alloy has been worked, it is no longer a cast structure, but rather a *wrought* structure. The phenomena under discussion deal only with the recrystallization of a cold worked structure.*

For example, if a cast clasp is swaged and contoured to shape on a model, it becomes a wrought clasp, since it has been strain hardened. Obviously, too much cold work may impair its life value considerably. However, if the clasp is heated to a certain temperature known as the *recrystallization temperature* for a definite length of time, the strain hardening will be removed, and its desirable properties may be enhanced even over its original cast condition in many cases. This phenomenon is known as recrystallization, and the process of bringing it about is *annealing*.

During the process of annealing, the grain structure changes from the distorted cold worked structure to a refined equiaxed structure, and the size of the latter grains depends upon the annealing temperature and time. The recrystallization temperature may be defined as

---

* It must not be inferred that a cast structure cannot be recrystallized; the recrystallization of castings and the differences between the various types of recrystallization will be discussed later.

the lowest temperature which will produce new grains from a strain-hardened structure, which are visible under a high-powered microscope. The exact temperature of recrystallization will depend upon the previous history of the metal. The more the material has been strain hardened, the lower this temperature will be. It will also be lower if the grains were small before working.

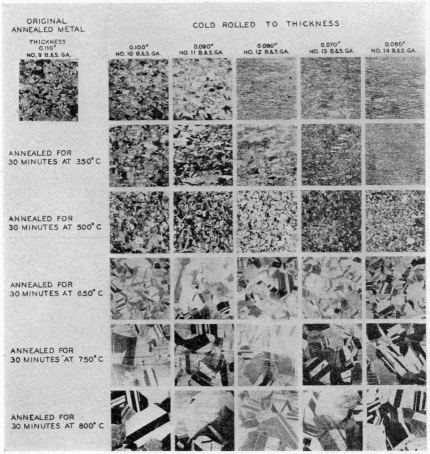

Fig. 43.—Grain size after working and annealing brass (copper 66 per cent; zinc 34 per cent). ×40. (Prepared by L. H. DeWald.)

While discussing the magnitude of the recrystallization temperature, it should be remembered that a period of time must be specified also; in general, the higher the annealing temperature, the shorter is the time required for recrystallization. As previously noted, a small grain size is most desirable, and the overstepping of the recrystallization temperature will produce *grain growth* as discussed in the next section.

12

These phenomena may be studied by means of an illustration. Fig. 43 shows the effect of cold work and annealing upon the grain size of brass.* The grain structure of the brass, before starting the experiment, is shown in the upper left hand corner of the figure. Specimens of this material were rolled to various thicknesses, as shown in the top row. The increased distortion of the grains in the direction of rolling is easily discernible by noting each photomicrograph in the top row progressively from left to right.

Specimens from each cold worked specimen, shown in the top row, were then heated at temperatures of 350° C. (662° F.), 500° C. (932° F.), 650° C. (1203° F.), 750° C. (1382° F.), and 800° C. (1473° F.), and were held at each temperature for thirty minutes. The change in grain structure at the various temperatures is shown in the columns below each cold worked specimen.

Consider, specifically, the extreme right column. When the specimen, rolled to a thickness of 0.06 inch (No. 14, Brown and Sharpe gauge), was heated at a temperature of 350° C. (662° F.) for thirty minutes, a distinct change in grain structure resulted as is shown in the picture immediately below. Minute examination demonstrates a tendency toward the formation of very small equiaxed grains, but striations, indicating strain, are still present, hence, the metal has not entirely recrystallized.

The grain structure of the specimen in the same column, treated at 500° C. (932° F.) for thirty minutes, shows a distinct equiaxed structure, thus indicating that recrystallization has taken place. The brass is now annealed, and its ductility has been restored, but its strength, hardness, and elastic properties are undoubtedly less than they were in the strain-hardened condition.

Now consider the third row, starting with the specimen discussed in the preceding paragraph—the third photomicrograph from the top in the column on the extreme right. As the photomicrographs are examined successively from right to left, a general tendency toward different grain form may be observed in each succeeding picture. If it is noted that the corresponding specimens at the head of each column have been strain hardened in different degrees, the fact that the less the strain hardening involved, the higher is the recrystallization temperature becomes evident at once; for example, the grain size of the extreme left specimen in the third row is of such a nature that it must be concluded that the metal has not been heated to its recrystallization temperature.

A few metals, such as tin, zinc, and lead, will not strain harden readily, because of the fact that their recrystallization temperatures are close to or below normal room temperature. However, if they are worked at lower temperatures, they exhibit a strain-hardened condition similar to that of any other metal.

---

* Although brass is used as an illustration, most wrought dental alloys are subject to similar phenomena.

Grain Growth.—In order to maintain a wrought metal with its desirable physical properties intact, it is absolutely essential that it be annealed at the correct temperature so as to produce a minimum yet uniform grain size. As the recrystallization temperature is exceeded, the grains become progressively larger, as may be noted in the specimens in Fig. 43, when the annealing temperatures are increased. Such a phenomenon is thought to be the result of a coalescing of the smaller grains into larger grains at the higher temperatures, in order to reduce their surface energy, in a manner similar to the coalescing of two drops of mercury when they come in contact. This phenomenon is known as *grain growth*.

For reasons aforestated, a large grain size is undesirable and is to be avoided. In dentistry, such phenomena play a vital part in soldering as will be discussed in detail in a subsequent chapter. For example, in soldering a wire clasp or orthodontic appliance, prolonged application of heat will cause grain growth of the wire at the soldered joint which is usually the position of greatest stress when the structure is in use; this abuse is probably the greatest single factor causing breakage at this point. After grain growth has once occurred, it can be refined only by reworking at room temperature and annealing, or by recasting, both of which are usually impractical in the case of a finished dental restoration.

Grain growth can be controlled by alloying with some substance which obstructs it. For example, wrought dental gold alloys can be made to withstand considerable abuse while they are heated, if they contain a sizable amount of platinum, which tends to obstruct grain growth. However, this does not mean that the wire or plate is absolutely foolproof in this respect.

Aside from worked metals and alloys, grain growth may also occur in compressed metal powders and electrodeposited metals,[5] but in practice it seldom occurs in solid castings except as a result of a change in allotropic form (*e. g.*, iron) or a change in phase.

Hot Work.—Hot work, as distinguished from cold work, may be defined as the mechanical working of a structure above its recrystallization temperature. Generally, under such conditions, the grains may be somewhat refined, but the room temperature physical properties remain unchanged, provided that the working temperature is not sufficient to cause grain growth. If it is properly carried out, hot working usually will produce the same effect as cold working followed by proper annealing.

It is interesting to note, in this connection, that fractures which occur at a temperature near the melting point of a metal or alloy are different in nature from those occurring below the recrystallization temperature. For example, if a gold wire is ruptured in tension at room temperature, the fracture will occur *across* the grains. However, if the wire is ruptured at a temperature near its melting point, the fracture will take place between the grains, through the intergranular amorphous material. This is additional evidence in support of the amorphous metal hypothesis. It is a well known fact that an amorphous material, such as glass, becomes weak and plastic at high temperatures, yet the same glass will exhibit a tensile strength of the enormous magnitude of 492,000 pounds per square inch under certain conditions at normal temperatures. The amorphous metal hypothesis therefore postulates that at ordinary temperatures the amorphous metal is stronger than the grains themselves, while at high temperatures the grains are the stronger.

LITERATURE

1. Jeffries and Archer, *The Science of Metals,* p. 48.   McGraw-Hill.
2. Jeffries and Archer, *The Science of Metals,* p. 197.
3. Jeffries and Archer, *The Science of Metals,* p. 150.
4. Desch, C. H., *The Chemistry of Solids,* p. 161.   Cornell University Press
5. Jeffries and Archer, *The Sciences of Metals,* p. 117.

CHAPTER XXII

GOLD FOIL AND ITS MANIPULATION

VERY few metals are used in the pure condition for dental restorative purposes, gold being the outstanding exception. Because of its extreme softness, pure gold is not indicated for use in the mouth except in the form of *gold foil*. Since gold is the most malleable of metals, it may be rolled into extremely thin sheets, and then beaten until it is so thin that it will transmit light. Gold foil appears yellow by reflected light, but it is green by transmitted light.

Pure gold is one of the most noble of metals, and hence it neither tarnishes nor corrodes in the mouth. When used in the form of foil, it is an ideal dental restorative material from the standpoint of permanently preserving tooth structure. Its chief disadvantages are its color, high thermal conductivity, and difficulty of manipulation.

If the surface of the foil is free from adsorbed gases and other impurities, it exhibits the remarkable property of welding at room temperature, that is, complete cohesion may be established between the molecules of two different pieces of foil, a phenomenon which is usually exhibited by metals and alloys only at high temperatures. This property of the foil is taken advantage of in constructing a gold foil restoration by driving each piece of foil together in the cavity preparation, thus gradually building up a coherent mass by welding. The gold foil condenser is a rod-like instrument approximately 6 inches long, which ends in a small flat surface called the face or working point. The point is placed on the foil to be condensed, and the other end of the instrument is struck with a small mallet.

The gold foil is generally supplied in sheets 4 inches square of varying thicknesses. If the sheet weighs 4 grains, it is called "No. 4"; if it weighs 6 grains, it is called "No. 6"; etc. The sheets may be made into pellets by cutting them into eighths, sixteenths, sixty-fourths, etc., and compressing them into cubes. The foil also may be made into ropes, or perhaps corrugated by placing it between sheets of paper, which are ignited in a closed container. This latter form of gold foil is of historical interest since it was an outcome of the great Chicago fire of 1871. A dental depot had some books of gold foil in a safe. After the fire, the safe was opened, and it was found that the paper had charred, but the gold leaf itself was unharmed, except that it had become corrugated because of the shriveling of the paper while oxidizing in the air-tight safe. After removing the carbon, it was found that the gold exhibited a superior welding property.

181

Other forms in which the gold may be supplied for malleted restorations are electrodeposited crystals and "sponge gold," the latter probably resulting from a gold amalgam from which the mercury has been removed by heat.

Platinum foil may be covered with gold and used for the same purpose as the pure gold foil. Black[1] reported restorations made with such a material to be superior to those of pure gold foil in respect to both strength and abrasive resistance.

Cohesive and Noncohesive Gold Foil.—*Cohesive* gold foil will cohere or weld at room temperature, whereas *noncohesive* foil will not. The difference between the two is merely a matter of surface impurity, usually gaseous. The gases are *adsorbed* on the surface of the foil, producing a film which prevents the atoms from cohering.

G. V. Black has studied such phenomena at length, and his classic research can best be presented in his own words:*

"Gold does not attract oxygen or nitrogen to its surface, and it is for this reason that it can be welded cold. Gold does, however, attract to its surface certain gases that are often present in our atmosphere. These are often condensed upon it in such quantities as to prevent its surface from coming in contact and destroy, temporarily or permanently, its welding property. These, however, do not unite with the gold to form any compound. They do not affect its purity. Some of these gases are such as will be removed from the surface of the gold by volatilization when heat is applied (by annealing), rendering the surface again clean, with restoration of welding property. Other gases, notably those of the sulphur and phosphorus groups, condense upon the surface of gold and refuse to volatilize by heat, and thus the welding property of the gold is permanently destroyed. In these cases it seems probable that compounds in the form of fixed salts—non-evaporable—are formed on the surface of the gold. A salt that may be completely volatilized by heat may destroy the welding property temporarily. By annealing, such a salt is removed and the welding property is restored.

"These general facts with regard to gold may readily be illustrated by a few simple experiments, which any one with a reasonable familiarity with inorganic chemistry can perform. Ammonia is strongly attracted to gold. Place a small quantity of spirits of ammonia, or of aqua ammonia, in a large glass jar. The ammoniacal gas from this will fill the space above the liquid. Now take a rope of gold, which has been annealed and the welding property of which is perfect, and swing it by a cotton thread above the liquid in the jar and replace the cork. In fifteen minutes remove the gold and try its welding property. It will not weld any more than so much tissue paper. Another rope of gold is swung above strong chlorin water; the welding property will be completely destroyed in two minutes.

* Quoted from G. V. Black, Operative Dentistry (6th ed.) Vol. II, p. 229. Medico-Dental Publishing Company.

Now anneal these ropes of gold; the welding property is completely restored."

Annealing Gold Foil.—Gold foil must be annealed, not only to remove any strain hardening, but also to remove the gas film. Annealing is absolutely necessary inasmuch as the foil is usually supplied in the noncohesive condition in order to facilitate its handling before condensing. The success or failure of the finished restoration depends almost entirely upon proper condensation and adaptation.

It may be annealed in a gas flame directly, if care is taken not to allow it to melt. However, this method is perilous because of the danger of incomplete combustion of the flame with the resulting adsorption of gas on the surface of the foil. A special plate of mica, covered with a hood and placed over the flame, is much to be preferred. The pieces of foil may be laid on the plate and picked up with the foil carrier as needed. The electric annealer is superior to all other devices of this nature, as the danger of gas adsorption is completely eliminated. Each piece must be heated entirely throughout its mass. Heating it while holding it with tweezers or forceps is poor practice, as the part held in the appliance will not anneal because of the conduction of the heat away from that point. If such a procedure must be resorted to, the piece of foil should be laid down and again heated, after it has been picked up at a different place.

Condensation of Cohesive Gold Foil.—The foil is generally welded with a condensing instrument and mallet. Each piece is welded by driving it against the mass already incorporated. This procedure strain hardens the metal, making it much harder than ordinary 24-carat cast gold.

The specific gravity of pure cast gold at 68° F. (20° C.) is given as 19.3 grams per cubic centimeter.[2] If the foil is properly condensed, its density should approach this value. Black[3] reports a density of 19.4 for a gold foil hammered into a matrix. Table XXIX gives Coleman's[4] results when testing the hardness and density of gold foils in comparison with other gold restorative materials.

TABLE XXIX

PROPERTIES OF FOIL FILLINGS AND SOFT INLAY GOLD

Material.	Density (grams/cc.)	B.H.N.
Gold foil filling, sample No. 1	17.0	36*
" " " " No. 2	17.3	50
" " " ' No. 3	14.2	18†
" " " " No. 4	16.8	51
" " " " No. 5	18.2	61
" " " " No. 6	19.0	60
Cast-inlay 24-carat gold	19.3	27
" " 22-carat gold alloy (0.5 per cent copper)		32
" " 22-carat gold alloy (3.7 per cent copper)		54

* B.H.N. of different spots varied from 22 to 46.
† B.H.N. of different spots varied from 13 to 26.

The gold foil specimens were made by six representative dentists in the United States. The foil used was the product of a well-known manufacturer, the same brand being employed in all cases. The specimens were condensed in split steel molds.

It should be noted that the hardness of the better specimens surpasses that of 22-carat inlay gold, even though the density in each case was not as great as that of 24-carat gold. Also the general trend of the data indicates that the denser the filling, the greater is its hardness. If the Brinell hardness number may be taken as a measure of the resistance to scratching or abrasion, this factor is very significant. Black[5] made similar studies, determining the density, but not the hardness; instead he subjected the filling to large loads and determined the percentage of shortening. His results show also wide variance between different operators.

Density and hardness alone are insufficient to insure permanent fillings. In addition there must be a retention secured by wedging the filling between the cavity walls, so that advantage may be taken of the elasticity of the dentin. The dentinal walls of the cavity must be slightly distended by the condensation process, in order to give a tight retention under all conditions.

Forces Involved.—It may be readily recognized that these considerations involve a study of both the magnitude and direction of the force applied during condensation. The direction of the force must always be perpendicular to the surface of the foil that is being welded. The area over which the force is to be applied is so small that changing the angle of the condenser from the perpendicular will produce a shearing stress and likely ruin the work.

Inasmuch as the condensation process is done by malleting, the resulting force is an impact blow, and exists for a very short time. The magnitude of the impact force is proportional to the product of the force exerted and the square of the velocity with which it is applied. In the case of the mallet, the weight of the mallet is the exerting force and the velocity will be determined by the operator. In the study of physics it is more convenient to discuss the *mass* of a body than its weight. The mass of the mallet may be computed by dividing its weight by the acceleration of gravity, which has the approximate value of 32 feet per second per second.

The impact force cannot be computed directly, yet some very interesting facts can be discovered about it, if the energy involved is considered. The physicist recognizes two forms of energy, *kinetic* and *potential*. Kinetic energy is energy of motion, and potential energy is energy by virtue of position. It is very evident that energy of motion is being dealt with in this case. It can be shown that the kinetic energy is proportional to the product of the mass of a body and the square of its velocity. In fact, this may be expressed by a very simple mathematical equation, and the energy of the blow delivered by the mallet on the condenser may be computed:

Let W = weight of the mallet.

   32 ft./sec./sec. = Acceleration of gravity.

   v = velocity of the mallet at the instant it strikes the plugger.

Then the kinetic energy at the instant of impact $= \dfrac{W}{32} \times \dfrac{V^2}{2} = \dfrac{WV^2}{64}$

The law of conservation of energy states that energy can neither be created nor be destroyed; hence the energy of the blow must be dissipated or transferred in some manner. Undoubtedly some of it is lost (not destroyed) in the form of heat, but this will be very small and can be neglected.

The major portion of the energy will be received by the condenser, foil, tooth, and other mouth tissues. In other words the *resilience* of these structures resists or "takes up" this energy. Therefore all of the energy is not transmitted to the foil itself. If the mouth tissues are not injured, the impact is elastic, that is, the structures are elastically deformed and spring back to position after the blow has been delivered. The foil, on the other hand, is inelastically deformed, and this, so far as the operator is concerned, is the useful part of the energy.

The efficiency of the blow in welding the foil will depend upon the other structures involved in the system. If the shaft of the condenser is too thin, it will bend elastically under the blow, and this resilience will dissipate considerable of the energy before it reaches the foil. The diameter of the condenser point will also be a factor, since the larger this dimension, the greater will be the bulk of the foil inelastically deformed, and hence the energy transmitted to the mouth structures will be lessened in proportion. A thick peridental membrane will take up more energy or "shock" than will a thin membrane. Also the larger the tooth and the bony structure, the stronger the blows may be without pain. Hence the possible strength of the blow and, as a consequence, the degree of condensation, will vary with the patient, and will not always be under control of the operator. Although this elastic resilience decreases the efficiency of the operation to some extent, yet it is very necessary, otherwise the tooth and other structures might be fractured by a blow of sufficient strength for welding purposes.

The action of the mouth structures as shock absorbers, and its effect upon gold foil condensation, may be illustrated by some scientific observations of G. V. Black.[5] He discovered that much denser fillings could be condensed into his steel dies when they were placed on a steel block, than if they were placed on a cushion, the latter supposedly being comparable to the peridental membrane in its action.

By a series of ingenious experiments,[6] Black also arrived at an approximate value for the magnitude of the impact force in terms of a static force. This was accomplished by allowing a weight to fall a known distance, striking a pointed instrument, which drove a piece of cardboard into a wood block. By applying a static load so that the cardboard was pressed into the block to the same depth, employing the same instrument, such an equivalence was established. By carrying the experimentation further in a similar manner, he established the fact that an impact force, equivalent to not less than 15 pounds of static force on a circular gold foil condenser point 1 mm. in diameter, was necessary in order to condense the foil properly. For most men this is too much pressure to be exerted by the hand alone, and hence malleting is necessary. Furthermore, the suddenness of the blow may possibly be more effective in strain hardening the material, than would a static force by hand pressure of equal magnitude, even though the latter may be equally effective in welding the gold.

Size of the Condenser Point.—The diameter of the condenser point is an important factor in determining the effectiveness of the welding. As previously noted the minimum impact force necessary to weld the foil is equivalent to a static load of 15 pounds on a *1-mm.* condenser point. Assuming the condenser point to be circular, its surface area will be directly proportional to the square of its diameter. Hence, if the diameter of the point is 2 mm., the 15 pounds of impact force will be distributed over four times as great a surface, and, therefore, it will be only one fourth as effective as with the 1-mm. condenser point. Hence, the larger the surface area of the condenser point, the greater must be the magnitude of the blow. This fact was beautifully demonstrated by the experiments of Dr. Black noted above. The relation of instrument diameter to exerted pressure will be discussed more at length in Chapter XXXV.

However, there is another factor which must be considered in this case where an impact force is used. For example, consider what happens if one hammers a piece of drill rod with a broad smooth end into the surface of a block of steel. Little or no impression will be made. Yet if the drill rod is given a pointed end it will penetrate the steel block slightly, even though the magnitude of blow is as before.

If the condenser point is too small, the blow may drive it into the foil, thus chopping the latter, rather than condensing it. Considering all facts together, the diameter of the condenser point which can be used successfully is quite limited. If it is too large, the necessary force required for welding the gold will be greater than the patient can endure. If the diameter is too small, it will be driven into the foil. Dr. Black states that the desirable limits of a condenser point diameter may vary between 0.5 mm. and 1 mm. The smallest point should be used only with hand pressure in particular places, as in starting fillings in very small convenience points. The condensing points for general use should vary between 0.75 mm. and 1 mm. in diameter. In giving the dimensions of the point in diameters, it should be understood that it is the surface area which is significant—not the diameters themselves. The points may be of any shape desired provided that the surface areas are within the limits signified by the corresponding diameters.

It should be evident that the force of the blow is not the only factor in condensing the gold to a dense mass. In fact, heavy impacts may even dislodge the foil, if other factors are not considered. The foil must be condensed in small pieces, and each piece as it is condensed must be welded thoroughly over its entire surface to the foil already in place. Failure to do this results in the bridging of voids, which are likely to result in porosity and a decrease in density. Fig. 44 shows two photomicrographs of a gold foil filling, one section being ground perpendicularly and the other parallel to the direction of condensation. The voids are very apparent, and probably are present to some extent in the best foil restoration. The microstructure is very interesting as it distinctly shows the laminated structure, much of which is due to incomplete condensation. The porosity may be so extensive as to actually cause recurrence of caries, as reported by

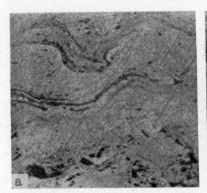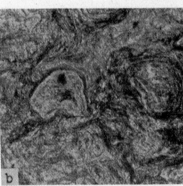

Fig. 44.—Micrographs of gold foil fillings, etched with aqua regia, × 90. *a*, Section parallel to the direction of packing; *b*, section perpendicular to the direction of packing. Note the laminated structure and voids due to incomplete condensation. (Coleman, in Research Paper No. 32, U. S. Govt. Printing Office.)

Black.[7] His studies in this connection indicate that fillings of density less than 15 grams per cubic centimeter are subject to leakage.

There are other methods of condensing the foil than by means of the mallet and ordinary condenser. There are automatic condensers of various sorts on the market. Some have adjustable spring releases, others are electrical in operation, and still others have been devised for attachment to the dental engine. However, all of them should be provided with removable points of various shapes and sizes. They are all subject to the same laws of impact as is the hand-malleting procedure.

Literature

1. Black, G. V., *Physical Characters of the Human Teeth.* Dent. Cos., 37: 756 (Sept.) 1895.
2. Smithsonian Physical Tables (8th Ed.) p. 159.
3. Black, G. V., *Operative Dentistry* (6th Ed.) Vol. 2, p. 233.

4. Coleman, R. L., *Physical Properties of Dental Materials.* Research Paper No. 32, p. 907. United States Government Printing Office.

5. Black, G. V., *Physical Characters of the Human Teeth.* Dent. Cos., 37. 744–757 (Sept.) 1895.

6. Black, G. V., *Operative Dentistry* (6th Ed.) Vol. II, p. 237–244.

7. Black, G. V., *Practical Utility of Accurate Studies of the Physical Proper ties of the Teeth and of Filling Materials.* Dent. Cos., 38: 302–310 (April), 1896

CHAPTER XXIII

TYPES OF ALLOYS AND THEIR CONSTITUTION

As already noted, in order that two or more metals may form an alloy, they must be mutually soluble in one another in the molten state. In the case of two metals which are insoluble* in the molten condition, two distinct layers will be formed upon solidification, the component with the lesser specific gravity being uppermost. Such a solid is only of academic interest, and cannot be called an alloy in a practical sense.

After solidification an apparently homogeneous structure may obtain, which gives no indication that it is composed of two or more metals. Such an alloy is called a *solid solution*. Another type of homogeneous structure which may prevail after solidification, is one in which certain constituents of the alloy may unite in definite atomic ratios to form an *intermetallic compound*. An intermetallic compound is differentiated from a solid solution, in that the constituents may combine in almost any conceivable proportion in the latter type. A third type of alloy is characterized by the fact that certain constituents or components separate out as distinct entities, the resulting alloys possessing a melting temperature which is lower than any of the constituents. These materials are known as *eutectiferous* alloys, and the entity solidifying at the lowest temperature is called the *eutectic*. A fourth type, hereafter to be designated as a *mixed type alloy*, is a combination of any of the other three types. For example, a eutectiferous alloy might be composed of two solid solutions, a metal and an intermetallic compound, etc.

Alloys may be also classified as to the number of alloying elements, which may be comparatively large. If only two metals are present, a *binary* alloy is formed; if three metals are present, it is called a *ternary* alloy; with four metals, a *quarternary* alloy results, etc. As the number of elements increases above two in number, the systems become increasingly more complex. Consequently only binary systems will be studied in detail at the present time.

In general, the physical properties of alloys cannot be accurately predicted from their composition. For example, zinc and copper will alloy in certain proportions to form brass, which is stronger and more elastic than either copper or zinc singly.

The word **system,** as used above, connotes an aggregate of two or more substances which are being considered as an entity. For ex-

---

*Very likely complete insolubility of molten metals does not exist, but the solubility may be so limited as to escape detection.

ample, the gold-silver system means that all of the possible alloys of gold and silver are being studied as a whole.

Phase.—A word which will appear frequently is the term *phase*, which may be defined as any physically distinct, homogeneous, and mechanically separable portion of a system. A nugget of gold would be a distinctly homogeneous system in the solid condition. Yet if it is heated to a sufficiently high temperature, it will change to a liquid, or even a vapor or gas at still higher temperatures. Obviously, the three states of matter, solid, liquid, and gas are mechanically separable, and hence they are three different phases.

Different phases may also be distinguished in certain types of alloys after solidification, but the term cannot be used in the same sense as in the preceding paragraph, because equilibrium conditions are not usually attained in the solid alloy. For example, it will be shown in a subsequent section that certain phases may be precipitated from a solid solution under proper temperature conditions, even though the alloy is in the solid state.

Component.—A component is any chemical element or compound which participates in the system or phase. For example, the components of a gold-silicon system are gold and silicon. Furthermore, the system is eutectiferous, and there are two phases present. On the other hand, a gold-silver system forms a series of solid solutions which are as homogeneous as a solution of sugar in water, for example. Hence there are two components present, but only one phase in the solid state.

Equilibrium.—Equilibrium connotes a state of rest, with all forces balanced, and with no property changing with time. For example, using the illustration of the molten gold described above, at a given temperature and pressure, the molten gold is in equilibrium with its vapor, and remains so as long as the variants are held constant.

In alloys, complete equilibrium is rarely or never attained in the solid state. This condition is due to several reasons, one being the rigidity of the solid, which prevents the ready diffusion of the atoms. Furthermore, at lower temperatures such internal changes may be entirely arrested, thus making an unstable structure permanent and apparently stable for all practical purposes.

Nevertheless, an equilibrium condition must be assumed in the subsequent discussions, and it must be remembered that the conditions to be described are approached as a limit under conditions of slow cooling and prolonged annealing, thus providing ample opportunity for atomic rearrangement.

Solid Solutions.—The term *solution* as applied to liquids is familiar to everyone. For example, a solution of sugar and water connotes a homogeneous system in which molecules of sugar diffuse through and intermingle with those of the water. The same is true of a molten solution of silver in palladium. However, if the sugar and water are frozen, each component will crystallize separately, but a palladium-silver alloy, low in silver content, will crystallize in such a manner that the atoms of the silver will be scattered through the space lattice of the palladium, presenting a condition analogous to that of the liquid or ordinary solution. Such an alloy is called a *solid solution.* Since the atoms of silver enter directly into the space lattice of the palladium, it is obvious that the system is not mechanically separable, and hence it has only one phase. Furthermore, if the atoms of silver are segregated for any reason, and are not scattered throughout the palladium space lattice, they may be made to *diffuse* in a manner quite analogous to that of undissolved sugar in water. Grain growth and recrystallization are both examples of atomic diffusion in the solid state.

Solute and Solvent.—When the sugar is dissolved in water, the water is known as the *solvent* and the sugar the *solute.* When two metals are soluble in one another in the solid state, the solvent is that metal whose space lattice persists, and the solute is the other metal. In the case of the palladium-silver alloys, the two metals are completely soluble in all proportions, and the same type of space lattice persists throughout the entire system. In such a case the solvent may be defined as the metal whose atoms occupy more than one-half the total number in the space lattice. Some metals exhibit a partial solid solubility. For example, the maximum solubility of copper in silver is 8.8 per cent. When more copper is introduced, a new substance appears which, in this case, is a eutectic composed of two different solid solutions of copper and silver. In other alloys, the new phase may be an intermetallic compound, or perhaps a metallic element.

The requisites for the complete solid solubility between two metals is that the two components have the same type of space lattice, similar atomic volumes,* somewhat similar melting points, and the attraction between unlike atoms being greater than that between like atoms. For example, silver and gold form a continuous series of solid solutions; they both belong to the face-centered cubic space lattice system, their atomic volumes are identical (10.2), and their melting points are 960.5° C. (1760.9° F.) and 1063° C. (1945.4° F.) respectively.

All solid solution alloys which are used in dentistry melt and freeze over a range in temperature, which is quite in contrast with the constant melting and freezing temperatures described for pure metals.

Constitution Diagrams.—In order to understand completely the phase relationships of various alloy systems, it will be necessary to introduce certain conceptions of a metallographic nature known as *constitution diagrams,* which are diagrams, or graphs representing the constitution of the alloy system for various temperatures and composition. The temperature is usually plotted on the vertical coordinate, and the composition in percentage by weight on the horizontal

* The atomic volume is computed by dividing the atomic weight by the density.

coordinate. Fig. 46 illustrates such a diagram for the palladium-silver system. In order better to appreciate the significance of the diagram, the method of obtaining it will be described.

Let Fig. 45 represent the time-temperature cooling curves for alloy combinations of 0 per cent palladium and 100 per cent silver; 10 per cent palladium, 90 per cent silver; 20 per cent palladium, 80 per cent silver, and so on, up to 100 per cent palladium and 0 per cent silver. At either end, where the pure metals occur, obviously a constant freezing temperature is found, but for all other alloys, a range of freezing temperatures occurs, which is characteristic of solid solutions. For example, consider the time-temperature cooling curve for the alloy 20 per cent palladium and 80 per cent silver. At B, the solidification commences and the alloy will be partly liquid and partly solid until the temperature falls to C, when it will be completely solidified.

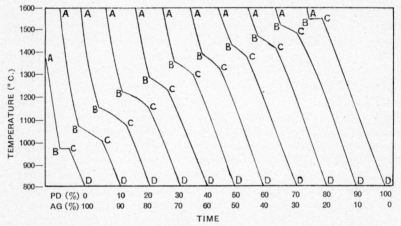

Fig. 45.—A diagrammatic representation of the time-temperature cooling curves for the palladium-silver system.

In other words, at all temperatures above B, the alloy will be wholly molten, and it will be entirely solid below C, whereas between B and C it will be partially liquid and partially solid. This is true for all the *alloys* given in the illustration.

Now if the temperatures corresponding to the points B and C of all the cases illustrated are plotted against their corresponding compositions, and if a smooth curve is drawn through the points thus plotted, Fig. 46 will result. For example, in Fig. 45, if the temperature, at which 0 per cent palladium and 100 per cent silver solidify, is plotted, only one point in Fig. 46 will result, namely 960° C. (1762° F.) which is the melting point of silver. In Fig. 45, B occurs at approximately 1060° C. (1942° F.), and C at 1000° C. (1832° F.) for the alloy of composition 10 per cent palladium and 90 per cent silver. Both of these temperatures are plotted in Fig. 46, for the composition 10 per cent palladium and 90 per cent silver.* Each alloy composition in Fig. 45 is treated similarly until the pure metal palladium is reached, when the temperatures B and C again coincide in one point in Fig. 46, at the melting point of palladium.

Considering the diagram as a whole, the line ABC in Fig. 46 is evidently a curve passing through all the points B of Fig. 45, and the lower curve ADC represents the locations of the points C in the other figure. Since in Fig. 45, the alloys are molten above all temperatures B, the alloy must be liquid at all temperatures above the line ABC in Fig. 46. For this reason, the curve ABC is called the *liquidus.* By similar reasoning, the alloy must be solid at all temperatures

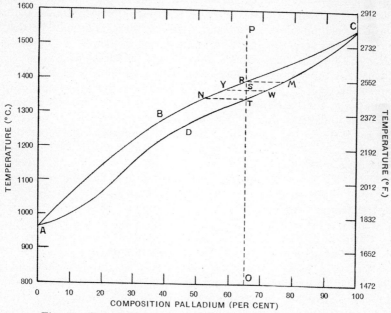

Fig. 46.—Constitution diagram of the palladium-silver alloys.

below the curve ADC, which is therefore called the *solidus.* In the area between the curves, the alloy is partially liquid and partially solid.

As an illustration of how the constitution diagram is used practically, consider an alloy of composition 65 per cent palladium and 35 per cent silver, which cools from the liquid state along the dotted line PO in Fig. 46. Obviously, at any temperature above the point of intersection R of the line PO with the liquidus, the alloy will be molten. When the temperature falls to approximately 1400° C.

* In general, the composition of only one element is given on the abscissa of the constitution diagram. In Fig. 46 the composition of palladium only is given, but the corresponding silver composition is obtained by subtracting each palladium value from one hundred.

13

(2552° F.) at R, the first solidification begins. The composition of the alloy first solidifying may be found by drawing the line RM through R parallel to the base line such that it intersects both the liquidus and solidus; the point of intersection with the solidus (M) gives the composition of the solid as determined from the base line, and the intersection with the liquidus (R) denotes the composition of the remaining liquid in the same manner. In the case just cited, the solid phase will be approximately 77 per cent palladium and 23 per cent silver, whereas the composition of the remaining liquid will be 65 per cent palladium and 35 per cent silver.

Now assume that the temperature decreases to approximately 1370° C. (2497° F.) as denoted by the point S. At this temperature, the material will be partially solid and partially liquid. As before, the composition of the solid and liquid at this stage may be determined by drawing the line YW, and locating its points of intersection with the liquidus and solidus respectively in terms of composition. Hence, the approximate composition of the liquid will be 58 per cent palladium and 42 per cent silver as given by the projection of the point Y on the base line, whereas that of the solid will be about 71 per cent palladium and 29 per cent silver, determined by projecting the point W to the base line. At the temperature corresponding to the point T on the graph (approximately 1340° C. or 2442° F.), the alloy will completely solidify, with the last portion of liquid freezing having the composition of 50 per cent palladium, and the corresponding solid phase being 65 per cent palladium. No further change occurs as the temperature falls to that of the room. In a similar manner any alloy composition of the entire system may be analyzed.

Coring.—As may be noted from the above description, solid solution alloys are not homogeneous in structure when cooled from the molten state. The solid which freezes first, is always richest in the component which tends to raise the melting point, a process which gradually depletes the remaining liquid of this component. Hence the grains will be different in chemical compositions in various portions of their volume. The first portion to freeze will begin to form the dendritic structure, which necessitates the remaining portions freezing between the dendrites already formed, such a condition results in *cored* crystals.

Since coring does not represent a condition of equilibrium, the physical properties of the alloy are not of the best. For example, its resistance to corrosion is distinctly less than when it is rendered homogeneous throughout, a condition which may be realized by recrystallization.

Homogenizing Anneal.—A homogeneous structure is produced most easily from a cored structure by cold working and then annealing as described in Chapter XXI. However, when this is impossible, the alloy may be recrystallized, or *homogenized*, by annealing at a high temperature for a considerable time in the cast condition. The latter process is slower than the first, since the strain-hardened condition generally implies a certain degree of space lattice distortion which facilitates atomic diffusion during the anneal.

This may be illustrated by a special example. Fig. 47[2] shows the microstructure of a cast ingot of a copper-silver alloy. The copper-rich dendrites are very evident. Coring is evidenced by the dark areas, which are presumably rich in silver. After thoroughly annealing the alloy, the grain structure shown in Fig. 48 resulted.[2] As may be noted, the grains are definitely equiaxed, and present a different appearance from the original. No segregation is visible, and complete grain homogeneity prevails.*

Very slow cooling of the alloy will produce a similar effect, but this is rarely attained in practice.

Fig. 47.   Fig. 48.

Fig. 47.—Copper-silver alloy (1 per cent silver), as cast. Dendritic structure. × 100. (Van Wert, *An Introduction to Physical Metallurgy*, McGraw-Hill Book Co., Publishers.)

Fig. 48.—Copper-silver alloy (1 per cent silver), after annealing. Equiaxed structure. × 100. (Van Wert, *An Introduction to Physical Metallurgy*, McGraw-Hill Book Co., Publishers.)

Physical Properties of Solid Solutions.—The densities of most dental gold alloys are very nearly the same as the values calculated from their compositions,[1] which is typical of solid solution alloys in general. However, in cases of limited solubility, the calculated density is apt to be lower than the actual density.

In general, the hardness and strength of a metallic solvent is increased by the atoms of a solute. Within limits, the more of the latter added to the former, the greater is the hardness and strength; in the case of two metals forming a continuous series of solid solutions with one another, the maximum hardness will be reached at approximately

* Asher and Comstock have demonstrated the homogenizing of a gold-copper alloy. See Jour. of Dent. Res., 13: 409 (Oct.) 1933.

50 atomic per cent* of each metal. Usually the ductility is decreased under such conditions.

Eutectiferous Alloys.—Although completely miscible in one another in the liquid state, the components of a eutectiferous alloy are insoluble in the solid state. The constitution diagram for the gold-silicon eutectiferous system is shown in Fig. 49, an examination of which will demonstrate some interesting facts concerning this type of alloy.

BEC is the solidus and AED the liquidus, which are obtained from a series of time-temperature cooling curves, exactly as in the case with the solid solution alloys. The points A and D represent the melting points of silicon and gold which are 1420° C. (2588° F.) and 1063° C. (1945.4° F.) respectively. Whereas the addition of palladium to silver raised the melting temperature of the solid solution, yet if approximately 40 per cent or less silicon is added to gold, the liquidus

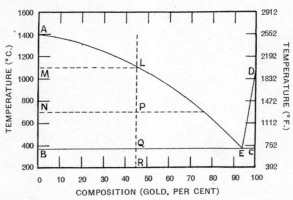

Fig. 49.—Constitution diagram of the gold-silicon alloys.

temperature of the alloy will be lowered below that of gold, in spite of the fact that the fusion temperature of silicon is much greater than that of gold. On the other hand, the addition of gold to silicon in any proportion will lower the melting temperature of the alloy below that of silicon.

In order to clarify this point, consider the cooling of an alloy composition 45 per cent gold and 55 per cent silicon, as represented by the line LR in the figure. As the alloy cools from the molten state, it starts to solidify at the temperature represented by L. As before, the composition of the first solid phase is found by drawing the line LM, which intersects the ordinate AB; hence, the composition is 100 per cent silicon. As the temperature falls to P, the silicon is still the only solid phase. Furthermore, as the temperature decreases,

*Atomic per cent is computed on the basis of atomic weight of each metal, rather than actual weight per cent.

the liquid gradually becomes richer in gold until the solidus is reached, when the entire mass freezes with the composition E, 94 per cent gold and 6 per cent silicon, which solidifies as a mechanical mixture at 370° C. (698° F.). In the case of an alloy of composition greater than 94 per cent gold, the method of freezing is similar, except that pure gold freezes out of the melt as the temperature falls, until the liquid again reaches a composition of 94 per cent gold and 6 per cent silicon, which freezes as a mechanical mixture as before. The crystals of pure metal which freeze first are called *primary crystals*, whereas the alloy formed at E is known as the *eutectic*, the term meaning "lowest melting." As may be noted from the diagram, an alloy of

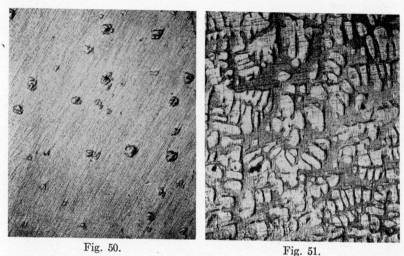

Fig. 50.   Fig. 51.

Fig. 50.—Microstructure of a eutectiferous alloy of composition 20 per cent silicon and 80 per cent gold. The nodular-like formations are the primary crystals of silicon and the remainder is the eutectic. ×100.

Fig. 51.—Microstructure of a eutectiferous alloy of composition 96 per cent gold and 4 per cent silicon. The light portions are the primary gold crystals, and the dark portion is the eutectic. ×100.

the eutectic composition (94 per cent gold and 6 per cent silicon) will freeze at a constant temperature, and will exhibit a time-temperature cooling curve similar to that of a pure metal, whereas all other alloy compositions in the system will solidify over a range in temperature, the range becoming smaller and lower in temperature, as the eutectic is approached.

When examined under the microscope, the primary crystals and eutectic are readily observed. For alloys containing less than 94 per cent gold, primary crystals of silica are present, imbedded in the eutectic. Observation of the eutectic (94 per cent gold) shows it to be made up of very fine crystals, which can be distinguished only under high magnification. The alloys of composition greater than 94 per cent gold exhibit primary crystals of gold, imbedded in a eutectic as in the first case.

Inasmuch as eutectiferous alloys are intimate mechanical mixtures, their physical properties are very nearly what might be expected from the proportions and properties of the constituents, although the hardness may be somewhat greater due to the obstruction of the grain growth of one constituent with another during solidification. The primary crystals form first, and the eutectic obviously fills up the spaces which are left.

Eutectiferous alloys do not occur in dental metals to the extent that solid solutions do. In fact, they are to be avoided, in general, because of their low resistance to corrosion. However, they are present in the low-fusing technic alloys used for the construction of dies and counterdies, which will be described in Chapter XXXIX.

Fig. 52.—A portion of Fig. 51 under high magnification showing the microstructure of the eutectic. ×500.

Intermetallic Compounds.—Metals may combine with one another to form chemical compounds, which are definitely stable in the solid state under given temperature conditions, but which do not exist in the molten state, as evidenced by the fact that they have never been successfully distilled. Nevertheless they exhibit heats of formation, though small, and combine in definite stoichiometric proportions. Furthermore they exhibit a time-temperature cooling curve similar to that of a pure metal, in that they melt and freeze at a constant temperature.

The constitution diagrams for these alloys are usually somewhat complicated, and since they occur only in special cases in dental alloys, their constitution will be discussed as the need arises.

In general, the laws of valence are not satisfied in these alloys. For example, a very important intermetallic compound, Ag_3Sn, which occurs in dental amalgam alloys, is characteristic of the failure of valence rules. The reasons for this failure are not understood at the present time.

In general, these compounds are characteristically very strong, hard, and brittle. This is thought to be due to their complex crystal lattices which do not permit easy slip as do the simpler space lattice types.

LITERATURE

1. Brumfield, R. C., *Precious Metal Alloys,* Trans. A. S. S. T., 19: 333-355 (Feb.) 1932.

2. Van Wert, L. R., *An Introduction to Physical Metallurgy,* pp. 239, 240. McGraw-Hill (1936).

CHAPTER XXIV

MIXED TYPE ALLOYS. HEAT TREATMENT

DENTAL gold alloys may contain any two or more of the following metals: gold, silver, platinum, palladium, copper, and zinc. Of these six metals, gold, silver, platinum, and palladium may be classed as *noble metals*. Hodgen[1] defines a noble metal as a metal whose compound with oxygen is decomposable by heat alone, at a temperature not exceeding redness. He gives the complete list of noble metals as follows: mercury, silver, gold, platinum, palladium, rhodium, ruthenium, osmium, and iridium. The noble metals are also strongly resistant to corrosion in comparison to the *base metals,* whose oxides are not decomposable by heat alone.

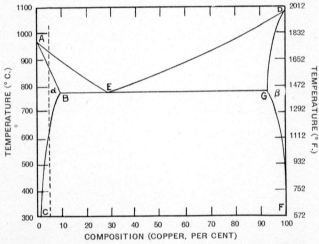

Fig. 53.—Constitution diagram of the copper-silver alloys.

In order to appreciate the significance of a discussion of the more complicated dental gold alloys, a few of the binary systems of the noble metals and copper will be described.

Copper-silver System.—Copper is a very important element in the composition of dental alloys; it forms a continuous series of solid solutions with the other noble metals usually found in dental gold alloys with the exception of silver, provided the alloys are quenched from near their solidi.

Fig. 53 shows the constitution diagram of this system, the liquidus being AED, and the solidus ABEGD. It is a mixed type alloy consisting of a eutectic composed of two solid solutions. One of the solid solutions is a solution of copper in silver and exists in the area between the left ordinate and ABC. The other is a solution of silver in copper, and exists in the area between the right ordinate and DGF. The solid solution on the left of the diagram will be hereafter designated as the α component, and that on the right as the β component. At the eutectic temperature (779.4° C. or 1444.9° F.), the copper is soluble in the silver to the extent of 8.8 per cent, the limit of solubility at other temperatures being given by the curve ABC. Similarly, the solubility of silver in copper at various temperatures is given by the curve DGF, its maximum solubility being 8 per cent, which also occurs at the temperature of the eutectic. Hence, any alloy whose composition falls between the range of 8.8 and 92 per cent copper will solidify as a eutectic, whose components will be the α and β solid solutions. The composition of the eutectic is 71.9 per cent silver and 28.1 per cent copper.

Assume that an alloy of composition 5 per cent copper and 95 per cent silver cools *slowly* from the molten state to room temperature. It will obviously begin to solidify at a temperature slightly above 900° C. (1652° F.), and will completely freeze as a solid solution (α) at approximately 860° C. (1580° F.). As the temperature falls, the solid solution phase will remain intact until an approximate temperature of 630° C. (1170° F.) is reached, when copper appears in a mixture with the α solid solution. The reason for this is very interesting. Just as the line AB represents the solubility limit of the copper in the silver at the respective solidification temperatures, so does the line BC represent the solubility limit of the two metals in the solid state. If more than 8.8 per cent copper is added to the melt, the eutectic appears upon solidification. But the solubility of the copper in the silver becomes less as the temperature decreases below the eutectic solidification temperature, as shown by the line BC; hence, when the above mentioned alloy is slowly cooled below 630° C., the solid solution becomes *supersaturated* with copper, and the excess phase is *precipitated*. The entire phenomenon is analogous to similar phenomena in supersaturated liquid solutions.

The significance of such a phenomenon is very great. For example, if the alloy had been quenched in water at a temperature above 630° C. (1170° F.), a solid solution, apparently stable at room temperature, would have resulted; the rapid cooling in this case prevents the precipitation from taking place. Similarly, the slowly cooled alloy might have been heated at a temperature above 700° C. (1292° F.), which would redissolve the precipitated phase into the solid solution. Since the two conditions have different physical properties, by correct treatment the properties of the alloy may thus be governed at will. Such a treatment of an alloy is known as *heat treatment*. The β component may be heat treated in a similar manner, but alloys of composition occurring between the two components cannot be so treated.

The copper-silver alloys are of general interest aside from their uses in dentistry, as they are the basis for the silver coinage of the principal nations of the world. In the United States, the silver coins contain 10 per cent copper, and in Great Britain, an alloy of composition 7.5 per cent copper and 92.5 per cent silver is employed for coinage. The latter alloy is known as *sterling silver* and is extensively

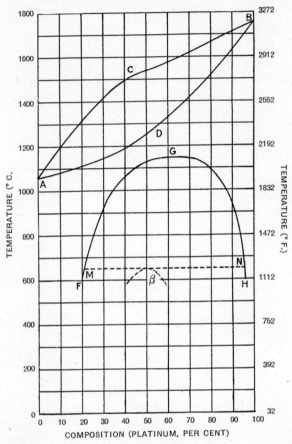

Fig. 54.—Constitution diagram of the gold-platinum alloys. (Adapted from work of Wise, Crowell, and Eash.)

used in tableware. It is of interest to note that sterling silver is susceptible to heat treatment.

Gold-platinum.—The gold-platinum system has not been investigated entirely. Fig. 54 represents the constitution diagram adapted from the work of Wise and Crowell.[2] The system is a continuous series of solid solutions near the solidus temperatures (liquidus, ACB; solidus, ADB). Upon slow cooling the alloy compositions below the area FGH break up into two components,[2] one consisting of gold saturated with platinum, and the other, platinum saturated with gold. At about 650° C. (1202° F.), a transformation occurs, which probably results in the formation of a gold-platinum intermetallic compound.

The large area between the liquidus and the solidus should be noted. Alloy compositions in the central ranges are very difficult to cast because of the extensive coring due to the large melting range of these regions.

Gold-copper.—The gold-copper system is one of the most interesting of the series, and is the most fundamental from a dental standpoint. The constitution diagram for the system is shown in Fig. 55. Above 450° C. (842° F.) all of the alloys form a continuous series of solid solutions, the system being unique in the fact that the liquidus

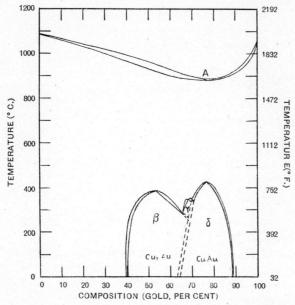

Fig. 55.—Constitution diagram of the gold-copper alloys.

and solidus fall to a minimum at A. In spite of the fact that the melting points of copper and gold are very similar, the addition of the former to the latter distinctly lowers the temperature of the melting ranges of the system; this is very important from a dental standpoint.

Throughout the entire system, the solidus and liquidus are very close together, approaching within 2° C. (3.6° F.) of each other at A; the temperature of the solidus at this point is 883° C. (1622° F.).[2] The minimum occurs at a composition of 75.6 per cent gold.

When the alloy is cooled slowly, according to the constitution diagram a change in phase occurs at approximately 450° C. (842° F.), the nature of the new phase depending upon the composition. This phenomenon may be designated as a *solid-solid transformation,* in which a reaction is thought to take place, producing a definite change in space lattice.

There are three possible phases which may form, all of which are intermetallic compounds: the β phase $AuCu_3$; the γ phase Au_2Cu_3, which exists in a pure form only in the temperature range of approximately 280° to 350° C. (536°–662° F.), unless quenched; and the δ phase AuCu. Only the last compound is of interest in dentistry, owing to the lack of nobility of the alloys containing more copper.

The range in composition limits of the AuCu compound, at room temperature, is from 64 to 88.2 per cent gold, or 36 to 11.8 per cent copper. In other words, the alloys of gold and copper may be heat treated within this range. For example, if a casting of composition 76 per cent gold and 24 per cent copper is quenched at a temperature of 700° C. (1292° F.), it will be in the solid solution condition, but if, instead, it is cooled slowly to room temperature, the AuCu compound will be formed. The first treatment will render the alloy ductile and comparatively soft. The second treatment will enhance its strength, elasticity, and moduli of elasticity and resilience, but the ductility is apt to be reduced radically. The quenched alloy may be hardened either by heating it above 450° C. (842° F.) and slowly cooling, or else by holding it at a temperature slightly below the transformation point for a period of time, either method being effective in producing the transformation. The hardened alloy may be softened by holding it at a temperature above 450° C. (842° F.) for a considerable period and then quenching it in water or oil. Such treatments are of vast importance in dentistry and their practical significance will be discussed later. The compound AuCu is quite soft, an attribute which is contrary to the general characteristics of this type of alloy.

The rate of change in phases occurring during heat treatment is rather slow and gradual; hence, the hardening process may be stopped at any time by quenching, thus offering a variety of physical properties directly under the control of the dentist.

Platinum-copper and Palladium-copper.—The constitution diagrams of the platinum-copper and palladium-copper systems are given in Figs. 56 and 57 respectively. It should be particularly noted that, although the copper does not lower the melting point as in the case of the gold-copper system, yet when it is present in amounts even greater than 50 per cent, it effectively prevents any sudden rise of the fusion range temperatures of the alloys. This effect is especially notable in the platinum-copper diagram.

When quenched from high temperatures, both systems form homogeneous solid solutions, but when cooled slowly, solid-solid transformations occur, which are quite analogous to those of the copper-gold system, in that intermetallic compounds of formulae $PdCu_3$, PdCu and $PtCu_3$, PtCu respectively are formed. As in the case of the gold-copper system, only the compounds PdCu and PtCu are of dental interest. They are definitely hardening agents, and the alloys may be heat treated in a manner similar to that of the gold-copper alloys, except that the temperatures of transformation are higher.

Dispersion Hardening.—*Dispersion hardening*, variously known as *age hardening, precipitation hardening*, etc., is a phenomenon occurring in alloy systems, which produces a hardening of the alloy, accom-

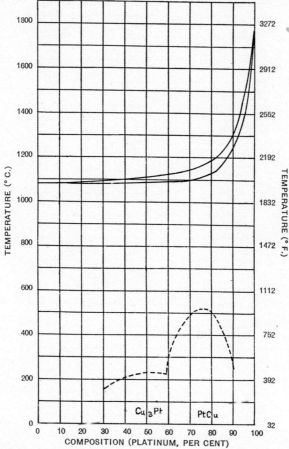

Fig. 56.—Constitution diagram of the platinum-copper alloys. (Adapted from work of Wise, Crowell, and Eash.)

plished by an allotropic change, or else a change in the solubility of some constituent which will cause hardening when expelled from the matrix.

Since hardness is, by definition, the resistance to permanent deformation, it follows that by any method whereby slip is decreased, hardness may be increased. Upon the basis of this reasoning, a theory of the mechanism of dispersion hardening may be built.

The exact nature of the expelled phase is often somewhat of a question, particularly in the case of the dental gold alloys. The mechanism of the changing or expelling of the phase must be thought of as a supersaturated condition of the alloy, which fact, of course, tacitly assumes the latter to be a solid solution when the phenomenon occurs. For example, consider again the silver rich copper alloy of composition 5 per cent copper and 95 per cent silver, studied on pages

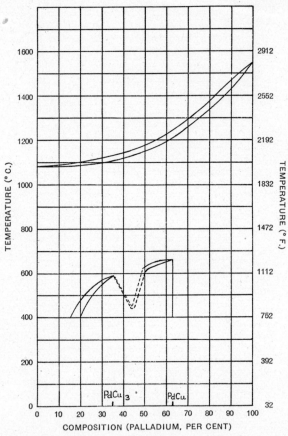

Fig. 57.—Constitution diagram of the palladium-copper alloys. (Adapted from work of Wise, Crowell, and Eash.)

200 to 202. As previously described, a slow cooling of the alloy results first in its solidification as a solid solution, and then a precipitation occurs, approximately at or below 630° C. (1170° F.) for the 5 per cent copper alloy. This is definitely caused by the fact that the alloy becomes supersaturated with respect to copper below 630° C., hence, the latter is expelled from the lattice. The ultimate result is a hardening of the alloy. Since the action involved is clearly a pre-

cipitation effect analogous to any liquid-solid precipitation in chemistry, the phenomenon is sometimes called *precipitation hardening.*

The illustration used above is distinctly a precipitation phenomenon, clearly demonstrated as such by microscopic examination. The precipitation of an excess phase in this manner assumes a definite though perhaps localized formation of a space lattice, characteristic of the hardening agent.

Now consider, for example, the hardening action of the compound AuCu. In discussing the mechanism of such dispersion hardening, Merica[3] assumes that the atoms of the excess phase, copper in this case, slowly diffuse toward common centers randomly situated, thus possibly forming nuclei, or embryonic molecules of the new phase. He further points out that the local concentrations of the copper atoms will produce a definite lattice distortion which will interrupt slip, *whether or not* the space lattice of the new phase is formed; he aptly terms such groupings as "knots."

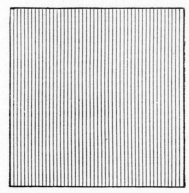

Fig. 58.—Set of planes of easy slip in a crystal having no internal keys. (Jeffries and Archer: *The Science of Metals,* McGraw-Hill Book Co., Publishers.)

Whether the hardening agent be "knots," a definite crystal space lattice of a different type and orientation from the matrix, or a single atom of a solute, the resulting hardness is due to a lack of ability of the space lattice to slip. Another way of expressing a similar idea is that slip may be rendered difficult by the crystals acting as *keys.* Jeffries and Archer[4] explain the action as follows:

Let Fig. 58 represent the potential slip planes in a given crystal grain capable of heat treatment. Now let a substance be dispersed throughout the grain in the form of spheres. It is assumed that this disperse phase has a space lattice of a different type from and differently oriented with the space lattice of the rest of the grain. Fig. 59 shows the result; as may be noted, not a single slip plane exists whose length is not interrupted by one of the particles or keys. Since the keys do not offer distinct planes of weakness in a direction comparable to those of the grain, slip does not readily occur. A little thought will show that the greater the number of the particles, and, within limits, the smaller their size, the more brittle the material will be; the effect of a single large particle is shown in Fig. 60.

In the light of such a theory, the mechanism of dispersion hardening by the soft compound AuCu is very clear, and it makes little difference whether an actual space lattice transformation occurs, or whether the atoms exist as the "knots" of Merica. In either case, slip is interrupted.

However, DeWald[5] points out that an atomic grouping or knot "might permit gradual stoppage of slip within the knot, rather than the abrupt stop produced by the sharply defined surface of a discreet

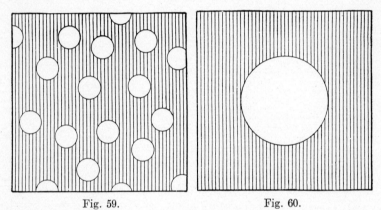

Fig. 59.   Fig. 60.

Fig. 59.—Slip planes keyed by hard particles. (Jeffries and Archer: *The Science of Metals,* McGraw-Hill Book Co., Publishers.)

Fig. 60.—Hard constituent gathered into a single large particle, leaving many planes unkeyed. (Jeffries and Archer: *The Science of Metals,* McGraw-Hill Book Co., Publishers.)

particle," as described in the previous paragraphs. Such a condition would, therefore, allow for greater ductility in the hardened condition than as though discrete particles of AuCu had been formed. DeWald further offers rather convincing evidence for the fact that there may be two types of hardening in the hardenable precious metal alloys, one caused by knots, and the other by a diffusion of the copper atoms to the vicinity of the grain boundaries where precipitation results. The latter type causes brittleness by slip interference, whereas the former definitely hardens and strengthens the alloy, yet only makes slip more difficult, without actually preventing it.

The theories given for the gold-copper compound as a hardening agent also apply to the dispersion hardening of the palladium-copper and platinum-copper systems.[6]

LITERATURE

1. Hodgen, J. D., *Practical Dental Metallurgy* (7th ed.) p. 28.   The C. V. Mosby Company.

2. Wise, E. M., Crowell, Walter S., and Eash, J. T., *The Role of the Platinum Metals in Dental Alloys.* Trans. A. I. M. E., Inst. of Metals Div. 99 (1932).

3. Merica, P. D., *The Age-hardening of Metals.* Trans. A. I. M. E., Inst. of Metals Div. 99: 13–54 (1932).

4. Jeffries, Zay, and Archer, R. S., *The Science of Metals,* p. 397.   McGraw-Hill Book Company.

5. DeWald, L. H., *Phasic Conditioning and Its Effect on the Ultimate Physical Properties of Some Dispersion Hardenable Systems.* Thesis, School of Mines and Metallurgy of the University of Missouri, 1935.

6. Harder, O. E., *The Constitution of Gold-Copper Alloys.* National Metals Handbook (1933 ed.) p. 1259.   American Society for Steel Testing.

14

CHAPTER XXV

CORROSION OF METALS AND ALLOYS

By *corrosion* is meant the attacking of the surface of a metallic body by some medium with which it is in contact, such as the fluids of the mouth. In time, the structure may be completely disintegrated, or it may suffer only a surface stain or discoloration; in the latter event it is said to *tarnish*.

One of the first requirements of a metallic dental restorative material is that it resist tarnish and corrosion under all conditions of usage in the mouth. The human mouth undoubtedly offers the most complicated and varied opportunities for corrosive action to which a metal can be subjected. The food eaten in one meal will be alternately alkaline and acid, varying in temperature from that of hot coffee to ice cream. The mouth fluids themselves are not entirely constant as to acidity and alkalinity, and will vary in this regard from mouth to mouth, as well as in an individual mouth from day to day. It is little wonder then that the noble metals have been used so extensively in dental work. This does not infer that base metals and alloys cannot be found which will not do as well. In fact, stainless steels, aluminum, and certain alloys of tungsten, chromium, and cobalt have been used satisfactorily as denture base materials, but their corrosion resistance depends upon certain other factors which will be discussed later.

The exact mechanism of corrosion in the mouth is not known, but the problem is being attacked at the present time from several angles, and it is hoped that considerable information may be forthcoming in the near future. All that can be done at the present time is to discuss some of the elementary facts concerning corrosion.

Electrolytic Theory.—According to modern theories, corrosion is distinctly an electrolytic phenomenon. For example, pure zinc will not "dissolve" in hydrochloric acid, yet if it is touched with copper while in the acid, the chemical action will start immediately. Such a phenomenon can be explained upon the basis of ionization or solution potential as studied in general chemistry. Textbooks on the latter subject should be consulted for a more detailed account of the theory than can be given here.

Whenever a metal is placed in contact with an electrolyte, metallic ions either tend to go into or out of solution, depending upon the *solution potential* of the metal. Assume that a strip of pure zinc and a strip of pure copper are immersed in a normal solution of hydrochloric acid from which oxygen is excluded. If the two metals are pure, as stated, nothing will happen, but if they are connected by a metallic conductor, two things will happen: (1) the zinc will go into solution, and hydrogen will collect on the copper; (2) an electrical current will flow, thus creating a voltaic cell. The presence of an electrical current indicates an electrical circuit in which differences in potential exist from point to point. Conventionally, an electrical current always flows from points of higher potential to points of lower potential. The nature of the current through the wire, or "external circuit" may be neglected for the present, except to state that the copper pole will be at a higher potential, or positive, with respect to the zinc, which will be negative. Hence the current flows from the copper to the zinc. The present interest is mainly upon the electrolytic action between the zinc and copper, or the "internal circuit." The current through the electrolyte is carried by ions. A zinc ion (Zn^{++}) goes into solution from the metallic zinc on which two electrons are left, thus charging the zinc negatively and the solution near the pole positively; hence, in agreement with the convention adopted for the external circuit, the solution must be at a higher potential than the zinc electrode. The difference in potential between the solution and the zinc is known as the solution potential of zinc, and is a negative quantity.

The positively charged hydrogen ions collect at the copper electrode, give up their charges, and deposit on the copper, thus rendering it positive; hence, the copper pole is at a higher potential than the solution. As before, the difference in potential between the copper and the solution is the solution potential of copper, and is a positive quantity. This example illustrates a law which may be stated for all metals as follows: those metals which exhibit a negative solution potential tend to pass into solution, whereas those metals which have a positive solution potential tend to go out of solution, but such action cannot take place unless an electrical current is present.

All metals exhibit solution potentials, when in contact with an electrolyte, which are characteristic of each individual metal. Potential as a physical entity cannot be measured, but differences in potential, commonly expressed in volts, can be measured. The difference in potential will depend upon the concentration of the electrolyte, hence, normal solutions are always used in its measurement. Furthermore, since there must always be two electrodes, hydrogen is usually selected as a standard for purposes of comparison, and is therefore rated a solution potential of zero. Table XXX shows the electromotive series of metals of particular dental interest, giving the solution potentials with respect to hydrogen and normal solutions.

Theory of Corrosion.—In the case of the zinc electrode discussed above, it was tacitly assumed that the zinc was 100 per cent pure. It is a well-known fact that hydrochloric acid will ordinarily react with zinc with the evolution of hydrogen, an action which is brought

TABLE XXX

ELECTROMOTIVE SERIES OF THE METALS

Metal.	Ion.	Solution potential (volts).
Lithium	Li^+	-2.96
Potassium	K^+	-2.92
Calcium	Ca^{++}	-2.76
Sodium	Na^+	-2.71
Magnesium	Mg^{++}	-1.87
Aluminum	Al^{+++}	-1.24
Manganese	Mn	-1.04
Zinc	Zn^{++}	-0.76
Chromium	Cr^{+++}	-0.55
Iron	Fe^{++}	-0.44
Cadmium	Cd^{++}	-0.40
Nickel	Ni^{++}	-0.23
Tin	Sn^{++}	-0.13
Lead	Pb^{++}	-0.12
Hydrogen	H^+	0.00
Antimony	Sb^{+++}	$+0.1$
Bismuth	Bi^{+++}	$+0.2$
Arsenic	As^{+++}	$+0.3$
Copper	Cu^{++}	$+0.34$
Mercury	Hg^{++}	$+0.80$
Silver	Ag^+	$+0.80$
Palladium	Pd^{++}	$+0.82$
Platinum	Pt^{++}	$+0.86$
Gold	Au^{++}	$+1.36$
Gold	Au^+	$+1.5$

about by impurities. For example, assume that a minute particle of iron occurs on the surface of the zinc. An *electric couple* will thus be formed between the zinc and the iron, and electric currents will be set up with the evolution of hydrogen, as in the case of the simple voltaic cell previously described; the zinc will go into solution, and the hydrogen will pass off from the iron which acts as the positive electrode.

Such phenomena are examples of the simplest type of corrosion, and are characteristic of the metals above hydrogen in the electromotive series. The first metals listed in Table XXX are the most active chemically, but as hydrogen is approached in the list, the metals become more resistant to corrosion. Iron corrodes only in the presence of oxygen and an electrolyte. It is common knowledge that water "rusts" iron, but as a matter of fact it is the absorbed gases in combination with the liquid which bring about the corrosion; a piece of iron or steel may be kept indefinitely in distilled water in the absence of air without the least suggestion of corrosion occurring.

As may be noted from the table, the noble metals are the most resistant to corrosion, gold being the most noble. However, some of these metals (silver for example) may be attacked by certain acids which occur in the mouth in the presence of dissolved oxygen, in a similar manner as described for iron. Although gold is immune from tarnish by the mouth fluids, it is readily attacked by free chlorine (*aqua regia*), bromine, and the cyanides. It is apparent, therefore, that the solution potential is, after all, of secondary importance to the composition and concentration of the electrolyte, since all metals will corrode, provided that the environment is such as to bring it about.

Passivity.—Some metals form an oxide coating in air, which protects them from further corrosion; such a metal is said to be *passive*. A metal can be rendered passive only if such a surface film will not attack the atomic layers below.

Aluminum is probably an outstanding example of a passive metal. As noted in Chapter XIV, aluminum may be used as a denture base plate material, yet it occurs very high above hydrogen in the electromotive series. When freshly polished, aluminum exhibits a silvery surface for a very short time only; because of its strong affinity for oxygen, it tarnishes rapidly in air, the tarnish film being strongly adherent. If the formation of the film is prevented by amalgamating the surface of the metal with mercury, oxidation in air occurs so rapidly as to raise the temperature of the metal radically with the occurrence of a feathery growth of oxide in the course of a few minutes.

Chromium is a very important metal exhibiting passivity. Iron, steel and certain other metals which are subject to corrosion may be electroplated with chromium, thus rendering them noncorrosive. The so-called "stainless steels," to be discussed in Chapter XXXVII, are alloys of steel with chromium, or with chromium and nickel, in amounts sufficient to passivate the alloy. Since the presence of two separate metallic materials is necessary for corrosion, the metallic mixtures of the eutectiferous alloys are obviously the least resistant to corrosion of the three types of alloys described in Chapter XXIII. Each component will be a potential electrode for voltaic action.

A homogeneous solid solution will obviously be the most resistant alloy to corrosion, all things being equal, since it is a one-phase system. It should be noted that the alloy must be homogenized; the "as cast" condition is likely to be much less resistant to corrosion due to coring than the properly annealed casting. The resistance to corrosion of a solid solution alloy will, of course, depend considerably upon the nature of its components. In general, the components may be attacked unequally. In the case where gold is one of the constituents, it will exert a protective influence upon the less noble metals up to a certain limiting value. For example, at least 46 weight per cent of gold[1] must be present in a copper-gold alloy in order to prevent chemical action by weak oxidizing agents at room temperature. In the presence of ammonium polysulphide, at least 50 weight per cent of gold is necessary to prevent corrosive action in such an alloy.

Under certain conditions of the grain boundaries, any type of alloy may corrode badly. The localization of certain impurities in a precipitated phase, and the diffusion of the atoms to the grain boundaries may result in the establishment of a couple between the grain boundaries and the grain proper. Such action is usually called *intergranular corrosion*. At best the grain boundaries are always potential sources of corrosion, probably due to their amorphous character. A regularity of atomic arrangement such as occurs in a space lattice is much less subject to attack than is the more heterogeneous arrangement of the atoms in the intergranular substance. This is borne out by the fact that in etching metallographic specimens, the amorphous grain boundaries are always the first to be attacked.

The final conclusion regarding the corrosion resistance of alloys may be summed up in a single statement: the more nearly homogeneous the alloy, the greater will be its resistance to corrosion. The statement obviously applies to metals as well. For example, properly annealed metals (and alloys also) will resist corrosion better than cold worked metals, all things being equal. The strains introduced by strain hardening cause localized inhomogeneities which form couples with other portions of the metal. In other words, the closer a metallic substance approaches its equilibrium condition, the better is its resistance to corrosion.

Corrosion of Metallic Dental Restorations.—The electrolytes in the mouth vary from acids to alkalis. Some of them are present in the foods taken in the mouth, and others are present in the mouth fluids. Eggs, as one of the staple food products, are high in sulphur content. The hydrogen sulphide resulting will attack silver, copper, mercury, and many other metals present in the alloys from which the restoration is fabricated. Acids which may be present are carbonic, lactic, and phosphoric. Since free oxygen is always present, oxidation is very likely to occur. Obviously metals and alloys which are corroded badly by these agents cannot be used. Metals and alloys which form a protective coating by means of a tarnish film may be used in posterior restorations which are not exposed to view. This point will be discussed more fully in connection with amalgams in Chapter XXXV.

The possibility of electrolytic action between restorations of definitely different composition, such as amalgams and gold inlays, is of interest. The effect of "galvanic shock" is well known in dentistry. For example, assume that an amalgam restoration is placed on the occlusal surface of a lower tooth directly opposing a gold inlay in an upper tooth. Since both restorations are wet with saliva, potentially an electric couple exists, with a difference in potential between them. Obviously, when the teeth are not in contact, the external circuit must be through the tissues, which are very poor electrical conductors, thus rendering the currents very small in magnitude. But if the two fillings are brought into contact, the circuit is suddenly completed through the two alloys, with a surge of current resulting. The result is sharp pain; if the process is repeated often enough, devitalization of the pulp and corrosion of the amalgam may ensue.

A similar effect may be observed by touching the tine of a silver fork to a gold foil or inlay restoration, at the same time allowing some other portion of the fork to come in contact with the tongue.

Differences in potential can be demonstrated between any number of restorations of different compositions in the mouth, or even the same composition. For example, two gold foil fillings will exhibit slight differences in potential because of their difference in strain hardness.

As to whether any significance is to be attached to such effects of potential differences between restorations not in contact, this question is being subjected to research at the present time.

Lain[3] has presented convincing evidence in case reports of mouth lesions which may be correlated with restorative structures of different solution potentials. He found that every case exhibiting such "electrolytic" lesions completely recovered after the mouth was restored with either nonmetallic materials or metallic materials of the same solution potential. It is a scientific fact that electrical currents exist between dissimilar metals in the mouth, but in consideration of the electrical constants involved, they must be so minute that further study is necessary before final conclusions can be drawn as to their relation with the above pathological conditions.

Tests for Corrosion.—Corrosion by the mouth fluids is not very well understood at the present time. As yet, the best testing laboratory is the mouth of the patient. In industry, certain "accelerated" corrosion tests have been devised, but they have not been completely successful in many cases. Such tests have also been devised by the American Dental Association Research Commission, and are described as follows:[2]

"(a) Immerse the alloy in 30 per cent solution of hydrogen peroxide for twenty-four hours. Observe the oxidation if present. (b) Place the alloy in egg yolk and allow it to remain during decay. Observe stains. The final and most satisfactory test was: (c) Saturate 100 milliliters of ammonium hydroxide with hydrogen sulphide gas. Then add another 100 milliliters of ammonium hydroxide and dilute to 500 milliliters. Place clean strips of alloy in a vertical position beside a beaker containing the solution in a closed desiccator. After ninety-six hours' exposure, wash the alloy strips with carbon disulphide, then with acetone, and dry. Compare the color of the exposed strip with a control strip not exposed to the vapors."

The last test is obviously based upon the assumption that sulphur is the principal tarnishing agent in the mouth. Its chief fault in thus comparing the tarnish and corrosion resistance of various dental alloys is the fact that no quantitative method has been devised for determining the degree of the action. Furthermore, no definite conclusions can be drawn from the tests as to the manner in which the material will react in the mouth. Since the advent of the dental palladium alloys, the subject of corrosion by mouth fluids is receiving considerable attention by various investigators, and it is hoped that this important problem may eventually be solved.

Protection Against Corrosion.—Gold always has been, and probably will be for some time to come, the basic element in dental alloys insuring protection against corrosion. Hence the surest protection against corrosion and tarnish in the mouth is the use of those gold-colored dental alloys which have withstood the test of time in this regard. It is not impossible that a nongold alloy can be discovered which will withstand corrosion in the mouth; it is further possible that an entirely base metal alloy can be produced which will meet such requirements, but such a material has not been invented up to the present date, without its fabrication requiring such expensive and complicated equipment that its manipulation is limited to the commercial dental laboratories.

Electroplating with gold, chromium, or any other noncorrosive metal offers certain possibilities, but its use has not been very extensive in dentistry, nor has the use of enamels, paints, shellacs, etc., been practiced as it has in industry.

LITERATURE

1. Tammann, Gustav, *A Text Book of Metallography* (Translated from the Third German Ed. by Dean and Swenson) p. 305. Chemical Catalog Co.

2. Souder, Wilmer, *Standards for Dental Materials*, J. A. D. A., 22: 1873–78 (Nov.) 1935.

3. Lain, E. S., Paper read at the Winter Meeting of the Chicago Dental Society (1936).

CHAPTER XXVI

DENTAL WROUGHT GOLD ALLOYS

DENTAL wrought gold alloys are used for a variety of prosthetic purposes, such as denture base materials, clasps, lingual bars, saddles, etc. However, many of these structures may also be cast instead of being fabricated from wrought metal; hence, it is the orthodontist to whom the use of wrought gold alloys is absolutely indispensable.

Wires are by far the most extensive form of wrought metal used in dentistry, hence, the discussion will be centered largely around their composition and properties.

Composition.—The chemical composition of eighteen commercial brands of dental wrought gold alloy wires are given in Table XXXI, as determined by the National Bureau of Standards Staff and the American Dental Association Research Associates.[1] As may be noted, the alloys are extremely complex, alloy A containing eight different metals, with alloy K having the smallest number of constituents (four). It is obviously impossible to study such complex systems systematically as in the case of the binary alloys, since the combinations necessary in order to establish all phase relationships would run into the millions. However, it must not be thought that the compounding of such alloy formulae is entirely by "cut and try" methods, as there are many empirical ideas to be gained from certain combinations of metals, which are guide posts in determining the next procedure to be followed in such research.

For example, certain systematic studies have been made upon the effects of varying the palladium and platinum content of alloys in combinations with gold, copper, and zinc, which are of great help in determining the general physical contributions of these metals. However, oftentimes the addition of a small amount of a single metal as an impurity may change the entire character of the alloy, thus effectually masking the effects of all other metals. For example, a minute trace of metals such as lead, antimony, arsenic, etc., will render gold uselessly brittle. Hence any discussion of alloys in relation to their constituent metals must be extremely general and limited to those metals which are most commonly used in the alloys.

General Effects of Constituent Elements.—Gold is, of course, the principal constituent of the "gold-colored" alloys. It not only contributes its characteristic color to the alloy, but it also increases the specific gravity and raises the melting point, providing its melting point is higher than that of the metal or alloy to which it is added. It also contributes ductility and malleability, and it is a factor in

217

TABLE XXXI

Composition of Dental Wrought Gold Alloys
(Per cent by weight)

Alloy No.	Gold.	Silver.	Copper.	Platinum.	Palladium.	Nickel.	Zinc.	Iron.	Iridium.	Manganese.	Tin.
A	57.6	4.3	11.7	17.2	8.9	....	0.10	0.02	0.13	....	0.11
B	64.3	5.2	10.5	16.7	2.2	....	1.00	0.02	....		
C	58.9	7.0	13.3	16.5	4.4	....	0.05	....	0.20		
D	54.5	6.2	13.0	17.7	7.2	....	1.20	....			
E	60.0	7.8	12.8	18.0	1.5	....	0.06	0.06			
F	54.6	7.1	12.3	17.2	7.3	....	1.50	....	0.20		
G	66.2	11.1	9.0	10.5	1.9	....	1.00	....	0.20		
H	58.8	8.5	12.9	17.3	2.6	....					
I	54.3	7.9	12.5	17.0	7.1	....	1.20				
J	58.3	7.5	14.1	16.2	3.8	....	0.06				
K	60.4	15.2	9.0	15.5	....						
L	68.1	10.2	13.9	5.0	2.8						
M	54.9	14.3	10.1	14.8	5.2	0.04	0.74				
N	63.1	9.1	13.5	6.9	4.9	2.00	0.53				
O	74.8	....	1.9	....	....	18.40	4.30	0.20	....	0.4	
P	63.2	14.9	11.3	10.6	....	....	....	....	0.10		
Q	61.9	13.0	12.5	7.9	3.9	....	0.70				
R	63.2	12.4	14.9	4.3	4.5	....	0.60				

heat treatment in combination with copper. It must not be thought that the metal, although essential to all commonly employed dental restorative alloys, is always a major constituent in percentage composition; some of the modern "white golds" may contain 25 per cent or less of gold.

Copper tends to give the alloy a reddish tinge. It is a good hardener, but its principal function is its contribution to heat treatment in combination with gold, platinum, and palladium. Brumfield[2] estimates that the amount of copper in the alloy necessary to promote heat treatment of sufficient benefit should be from 8 to 17 per cent, depending upon the alloy. Copper, in general, lowers the upper limit of the melting range, for reasons noted in Chapter XXIV.

Silver imparts a whitish color to dental alloys. It tends to raise the melting range only if the alloy melts below its own melting temperature. It is usually credited with contributing to ductility. Silver also acts as a controlling element over the rapidity and intensity of the reaction of the alloy to heat treatment.[2]

Platinum and palladium both impart a white color to the alloy, palladium being more effective in this regard, since as little as 5 or 6 per cent of the latter, under certain conditions, will render the alloy totally white in color.[2] Both of the metals increase the fusion point of the alloy. Although palladium fuses at a lower temperature than does platinum, it is more effective in this regard than is the latter, as its percentage composition is increased. Since high fusion temperatures are desirable in wrought metals, the addition of these elements is unrestricted in this regard. Both metals are splendid strengtheners, platinum being somewhat superior to palladium in this respect. Both platinum and palladium react with copper in the hardening heat treatment. The two metals also reduce the grain size of the alloys, platinum being the most effective.[3]

Zinc is introduced, in small quantities, to promote soundness and workability,[3] and may possibly be a strengthener as well. It is also an effective scavenger for oxides during melting.

The advisability of using nickel in wrought alloys is somewhat in question at the present time. Alloy O in Table XXXI offers an interesting study in this regard and it will be discussed more fully in a later section. The general tendency is to substitute nickel for platinum for economic reasons. DeWald[4] finds that dental alloys containing nickel have a low tarnish resistance, unless the nickel content is offset by sufficient amounts of platinum and palladium, the metals for which the nickel is substituted. He attributes the lack of resistance to tarnish to the fact that the nickel phase concentrates at the grain boundaries during slow cooling, thus opening regions for attack by the mouth fluids. According to Souder,[5] nickel-bearing gold alloys exhibit low percentage elongation and resilience. Nickel raises the melting point, and is an effective whitener and strengthener of the alloys.

Specific Gravity.—Brumfield[2] found that the specific gravity was affected by each of the alloying elements, almost in proportion to their content by volume. In other words, the specific gravities of the alloys may be computed, the values being very nearly identical with the specific gravities determined experimentally, as shown in Table XXXII.

TABLE XXXII

COMPUTED SPECIFIC GRAVITY IN COMPARISON TO EXPERIMENTAL SPECIFIC GRAVITY

Alloy.	Composition (per cent by weight).						Specific gravity.	
	Au.	Ag.	Cu.	Pt.	Pd.	Ni.	Experimental.	Computed.
1............	63.0	11.5	13.5	10.0	2.0	...	15.78	15.4
2............	65.0	13.0	17.0	1.0	2.0	2.0	14.39	14.5
3............	65.2	10.5	24.5	....	....	2.6	13.70	13.75
4............	66.0	13.5	14.5	4.5	1.5	...	15.87	15.1
5............	47.0	36.0	....	....	17.0	...	13.97	13.8

The formula used for computing the specific gravities is as follows:

$$\text{Specific gravity} = \frac{100}{\dfrac{P_{au}}{S_{au}} + \dfrac{P_{ag}}{S_{ag}} + \dfrac{P_{pt}}{S_{pt}} + \dfrac{P_{cu}}{S_{cu}} + \text{etc.}}$$

Where P_{au} = percentage gold, P_{ag} = percentage silver, etc.
and S_{au} = specific gravity of gold, S_{ag} = specific gravity of silver, etc.

All things being equal, a low specific gravity is more desirable than a high one, particularly when large metallic restorations are involved because of the less weight involved in the former. In this respect, at least, the newer "white golds," which are high in palladium* content, are distinctly superior to the other types, since palladium is the lightest of the important metals commonly associated with the dental gold alloys.

Fusion Temperature.—Instead of determining the fusion range by obtaining a time-temperature cooling curve as described in Chapter XX, a process which is both laborious and expensive, a "fusion temperature" is established by the "wire method."† The fusion temperature is the lowest temperature at which a wire, from 0.028 to 0.032 inch in diameter and approximately $\frac{1}{16}$ inch long, will break when subjected to a cross bending load of 3 ounces avoirdupois. Such a temperature is probably close to the solidus line of the alloy, and is a measure of the highest temperature to which the alloy may be subjected in soldering.

*Sp. gr. 11.5.
† See American Dental Association Specification No. 7, Appendix, page 390

TABLE XXXIII

Physical Properties of Dental Wrought Gold Alloys

Alloy.	Fusion temperature, wire method.		Vickers hardness numbers (10 Kg. load).			Elastic limit.			Ultimate tensile strength.			Increase from quenched to "oven-cooled."	Elongation in 2-inch gauge length.		
	Fahrenheit.	Centigrade.	As received.	Quenched.	Oven-cooled.	As received. Lb. per sq. in.	Quenched. Lb. per sq. in.	Oven-cooled. Lb. per sq. in.	As received. Lb. per sq. in.	Quenched. Lb. per sq. in.	Oven-cooled. Lb. per sq. in.	Per cent.	As received. Per cent.	Quenched. Per cent.	Oven-cooled. Per cent.
A	1998	1092	267	217	231	109,500	73,000	77,500	132,000	105,500	118,000	12	2.0	21.0	20.5
B	1861	1061	226	226	324	91,500	78,500	117,000	120,000	106,500	164,000	54	15.5	20.5	7.5
C	1877	1025	272	236	322	110,000	90,000	134,000	142,000	121,000	174,000	43	14.0	16.5	8.5
D	1911	1044	330	247	367	120,500	83,500	131,500	161,000	119,000	173,000	45	24.0	20.0	7.5
E	1834	1001	256	229	336	112,500	84,500	135,500	135,500	117,500	178,000	52	4.5	15.5	4.5
F	1882	1028	268	249	362	107,500	84,500	140,500	143,500	120,000	184,000	53	11.5	20.5	6.5
G	1780	971	215	210	289	68,000	65,500	103,000	114,000	100,000	144,000	44	20.0	14.0	5.0
H	1850	1010	278	233	353	119,000	85,000	144,000	150,000	120,000	182,500	52	13.0	17.5	3.5
I	1893	1034	302	224	367	117,500	77,500	136,500	156,500	115,000	183,000	59	5.0	20.5	5.0
J	1872	1022	263	215	332	91,000	72,000	123,500	119,000	107,500	172,500	60	18.5	22.5	6.5
K	1801	983	237	197	252	95,500	63,500	92,500	132,500	99,000	128,000	29	1.5	18.5	11.0
L	1731	944	238	174	292	81,000	50,000	102,000	116,000	87,000	138,500	59	17.5	32.0	6.5
M	1863	1017	266	213	323	107,000	77,000	129,000	140,000	109,500	167,000	52	8.0	19.0	5.5
N	1742	950	322	230	346	125,000	73,500	129,500	168,500	112,000	170,000	52	6.0	19.5	4.0
O	1688	920	251	261	287	95,000	92,000	117,000	133,000	128,500	146,000	14	14.0	16.0	6.5
P	1731	944	257	205	264	99,000	80,000	93,000	128,500	111,500	148,000	33	6.0	15.0	2.0
Q	1765	963	259	203	317	98,000	68,000	116,500	119,500	104,000	155,000	50	10.0	21.5	3.5
R	1711	933	209	173	305	55,500	53,500	105,000	97,500	86,500	143,000	65	25.0	34.5	4.5

Such fusion temperatures for the alloys whose composition is given in Table XXXI, are shown in the second and third columns of Table XXXIII.[1] In general, they are quite high, at least in comparison with those given for the casting gold alloys in the next chapter. The American Dental Association specification for dental wrought gold wire alloys requires a minimum fusing temperature, wire method, of 1750° F. (954° C.).

Hardness.—The hardness of the alloys shown in Table XXXIII, columns four to six inclusive, are given in terms of Vickers hardness numbers, which are, for all practical purposes, comparable to the Brinell number as determined by the micro-Brinell equipment. The numbers range from 173 (R, quenched) to 367 (I and D, oven-cooled). As may be noted from column four, many of the wires were received in a strain-hardened condition.

The investigators[1] found the hardness numbers to be directly proportional to the elastic limits and tensile strengths of the alloys.

Tensile Properties.—The elastic limits ranged from 50,000 pounds per square inch (L, quenched) to 144,000 pounds per square inch (H, oven-cooled), and the tensile strength ranged from 86,500 pounds per square inch (R, quenched) to 184,000 pounds per square inch (F, oven-cooled). These values are surprisingly large for such alloys, the higher figures being comparable to similar properties of many steels.

The values for percentage elongation, as an indication of ductility, are satisfactory for the most part. The specification requirements state that the elongation must not be less than 15 per cent on quenched specimens, and not less than 4 per cent on oven-cooled specimens. Obviously, the greater this value, the less likely is the wire to break while contouring.

HEAT TREATMENT

The theory of heat treatment, as given in Chapter XXIV for binary systems, applies in general to the complex systems under discussion. The effect of heat treatment upon the physical properties of alloys containing gold, copper, and zinc with platinum or palladium in varying amounts, has been studied quite extensively,[3] but the addition of other metals, even in small amounts, often changes the phenomena involved to a surprising extent. Hence it is not always possible at the present time to predict whether or not an alloy may be successfully heat treated by merely examining its composition.

There are two types of heat treatment; the softening heat treatment, or annealing, and the hardening heat treatment.* The hardening heat treatment may be carried out by oven-cooling or by aging.

* Occasionally the term "tempering" is used in place of "hardening heat treament," assuming that the latter is analogous to the tempering of steel. Inasmuch as the two terms are not synonymous, the longer terminology has been adopted as being more accurate.

In oven-cooling, the alloy is carried from a specified temperature, usually 450° C. (840° F.) to a lower temperature of 250° C. (480° F.) over a period of thirty minutes or less, followed by quenching. In the aging treatment, the alloy is held at a constant temperature for a definite time, and then quenched.

Softening Heat Treatment.—The standard softening heat treatment, given by American Dental Association Specification No. 7, is to place the alloy in a furnace at 700° C. (1292° F.) for ten minutes and immediately quench in room temperature water. This treatment will thoroughly anneal the wire or plate, presumably transforming the alloy into a solid solution. All of the physical properties will be decreased, with the exception of ductility which is enhanced. The alloy should be in this condition whenever the restoration or appliance is to be contoured, swaged, polished, or cold worked in any manner. However, more than one such treatment may be necessary in order to remove strain hardening occurring during such cold work. In practice, merely heating the alloy to redness and immediately quenching is usually sufficient, the longer method being employed only in testing procedures.

The quenching temperature of 700° C. (1292° F.) is practically standard for all ordinary dental wrought alloys; however, when platinum or palladium are present in large amounts (20–30 per cent), higher annealing temperatures are needed in order to obtain maximum percentage elongation values. For example,[3] an alloy containing 30 per cent palladium may require 800° C. (1472° F.) in order to give the proper ductility. This is of particular interest when heat treating the "white gold" alloys, which are high in palladium content.

Hardening Heat Treatment.—As described in Chapter XXIV, the purpose of the hardening heat treatment is to control the solid-solid transformations, which are supposedly the formation of the $AuCu$, $PtCu$, and $PdCu$ intermetallic compounds from the solid solution. A softening heat treatment must always directly precede a hardening heat treatment, in order that such control may be assured.

All of the physical properties are enhanced by this treatment with the exception of ductility, which may be alarmingly reduced, even rendering the alloy brittle, unless the proper treatment has been used. Inasmuch as the modulus of resilience is markedly increased, the advantage of such a heat treatment with respect to expectant life value is obvious.

Electric furnaces, especially equipped with thermoregulators and timing devices, may be purchased for carrying out such heat treatments, but they are likely to be quite expensive. A salt bath[6] made of equal parts by weight of potassium nitrate (KNO_3) and sodium nitrate ($NaNO_3$) may be used. The mixture melts at approximately 400° F. (204° C.), and may be heated to temperatures ordinarily used with this treatment.

The oven-cooling method for hardening heat treatment, as outlined above, is the standard method for determining the physical properties as given by the A. D. A. Specifications. In specifying such a treatment, it is not claimed that it is the best method for hardening all alloys, but rather that it practically assures the dentist that the alloy will not become brittle from the indiscriminate heat treatment to which it is often subjected in practice.

The differences in physical properties resulting from a softening heat treatment, followed by an oven-cooling hardening treatment are shown in Table XXXIII. As may be noted, all of the alloys except A and O responded quite well to heat treatment. It is interesting to observe that A and F had very similar compositions (see Table XXXI), yet the former practically failed to respond to heat treatment, whereas the latter increased 53 per cent in tensile strength after oven-cooling. Furthermore, the elongation of alloy A remained practically unchanged during hardening, whereas this property was reduced 50 per cent or more in the case of all other alloys.

Wise, Crowell, and Eash[3] have studied the effect of platinum and palladium upon the physical properties of a number of alloys in connection with age-hardening heat treatments. The alloys were annealed at 700° C. (1292° F.) for five minutes, quenched, and then aged for fifteen minutes at temperatures varying from 200° to 500° C. (392°–932° F.). They found the aging temperature, producing the maximum strength during the fifteen-minute-time interval, to be 300° C. (572° F.) for the alloy containing gold, copper, silver, and zinc, whereas it rose to 450° C. (840° F.) for alloys with considerable amounts of either platinum or palladium. Furthermore, it was discovered that, by the introduction of the proper quantities of platinum or palladium, alloys can be produced which will show excellent properties in spite of a considerable deviation from the optimum age-hardening temperature. Certain wrought wires on the market at the present time may be air-cooled from red heat, producing very satisfactory properties in a hardened condition, whereas formerly such a treatment would render the alloy quite brittle. The investigators further demonstrated that in the case of the palladium alloys, the aging method of treatment was superior to the oven-cooled treatment from the standpoint of ductility, the strengths being practically identical in both treatments.

The temperatures at which physical changes take place in some of the alloys whose compositions are given in Table XXXI have been studied.[1] The samples were first annealed at 700° C. (1292° F.) for ten minutes and then quenched, after which they were held at various temperatures for sixty minutes and again quenched. The variation of hardness with different soaking periods for seven alloys is shown in Figs. 61 to 64 inclusive.[1] As might be expected from the data given in Table XXXIII, alloy A (Fig. 61) responded very little. It is of interest to note that soaking treatments at temperatures of 100° C. (212° F.) and below softened the alloys slightly in every case. The curve for alloy O (Fig. 63), which contained 18.4 per cent nickel,

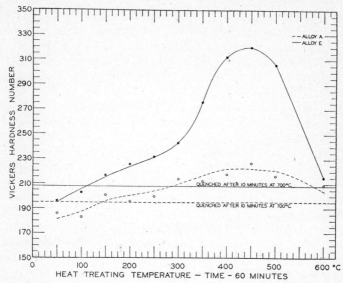

Fig. 61.—Effect of heat treatment on hardness of wrought gold alloys. (Paffenbarger, Sweeney, and Isaacs: Jour. Amer. Dent. Assoc., December, 1932.)

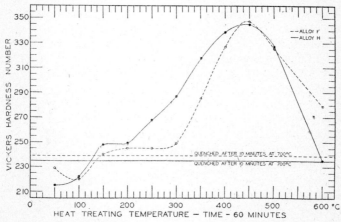

Fig. 62.—Effect of heat treatment on hardness of wrought gold alloys. (Paffenbarger, Sweeney, and Isaacs: Jour. Amer. Dent. Assoc., December, 1932.)

gave two maxima, and decreased in hardness considerably below that of the annealed condition, when treated at temperatures of 550° to 600° C. (1022°–1112° F.). It is very evident that no treatment other than annealing is needed for this alloy. As may be noted from Table

15

XXXIII, the oven-cooling treatment fails to give it any appreciable increase in hardness or strength, yet it radically reduces the percentage elongation from the softened condition.

Permanence of Properties After Heat Treatment.—Certain alloys of aluminum age-harden at room temperature, and the question has been raised as to whether the physical properties of gold alloys may

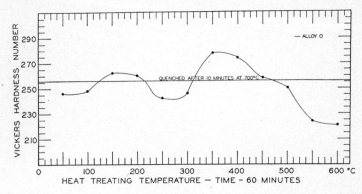

Fig. 63.—Effect of heat treatment on hardness of wrought gold alloys. (Paffenbarger, Sweeney, and Isaacs: Jour. Amer. Dent. Assoc., December, 1932.)

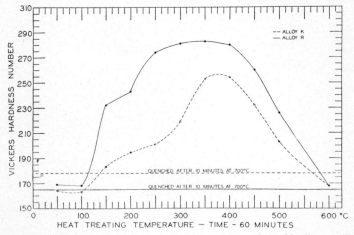

Fig. 64.—Effect of heat treatment on hardness of wrought gold alloys. (Paffenbarger, Sweeney, and Isaacs: Jour. Amer. Dent. Assoc., December, 1932.)

not change after heat treatment while vulcanizing or subsequent use in the mouth. Brumfield[2] reports certain changes in tensile strength which he observed for two months after slow cooling. One of the alloys showed a 35 per cent increase in strength whereas the other exhibited a 22 per cent decrease in strength. The percentage compositions of the alloys were as follows:

	Au	Ag	Cu	Pt	Pd
Alloy showing decrease in strength	63.0	11.5	13.5	10	2
Alloy showing increase in strength	62.5	10.5	24.4		

This phenomenon has also been studied by the American Dental Association Research Associates[1] for the alloys whose composition is given in Table XXXI. They observed the hardness changes occurring in the alloys over a period of six months after an oven-cooling treatment. Although slight changes were observed, they were of no practical importance. They further submitted specimens of the alloys to various temperatures and times such as they might be subjected to in vulcanization, curing of synthetic resins, etc. Very few changes of practical importance were demonstrated under such conditions. It may be inferred, therefore, that, in general, such properties are permanent, and are not changed by use or any normal conditions of heating at temperatures below those at which the physical changes occur.

Specifications.—American Dental Association Specification No. 7. See Appendix, page 390.

LITERATURE

1. Paffenbarger, G. C., Sweeney, W. T., and Isaacs, Aaron, *Wrought Gold Wire Alloys: Physical Properties and a Specification.* J. A. D. A., 19: 2061–2086 (Dec.) 1932.

2. Brumfield, R. C., *Precious Metal Alloys.* Trans. A. S. S. T., 19: 333–367 (Feb.) 1932.

3. Wise, E. M., Crowell, W. S., and Eash, J. T., *The Rôle of the Platinum Metals in Dental Alloys.* Trans. A. I. M. E., Inst. Metals Div. 99 (1932).

4. DeWald, L. H., *Nickel in Precious Metal Alloys.* Metals and Alloys, 6: 331 (Nov.) 1935.

5. Souder, Wilmer, *Nickel in Dental Alloys.* Metals and Alloys, 6: 194 (July) 1935.

6. Paffenbarger, G. C., and Sweeney, W. T., *Dental Research at the National Bureau of Standards in Relation to Orthodontia.* Int. Jour. Ortho., 20: 1166–1172 (Dec.) 1934.

CHAPTER XXVII

DENTAL CASTING GOLD ALLOYS

ONE of the most widely used methods of fabricating metallic restorations outside the mouth is by casting. Castings with gold alloys may be made with considerable accuracy for anything from as large as a denture base to the smallest inlay. Obviously, the gold alloys employed for this purpose must have certain characteristic properties which render them suitable for this use. As previously noted, they may be extremely complex in structure, containing as many as six or more metals. Little can be stated definitely concerning their constitution, except as the study of the binary alloys is related to the more complex systems.

Carat and Fineness.—The carat of a gold alloy is determined by the parts of pure gold present, on the basis of 24 as unity. For example, 24-carat gold would be pure gold; 22-carat gold would be an alloy of which 22 parts would be pure gold, and the remaining 2 parts would be other metals. Similarly, 18-carat gold would consist of 18 in 24 parts pure gold; 14-carat, 14 parts pure gold, etc.

Fineness of gold alloys is measured on a basis of parts of pure gold per 1000; hence, 1000 fine would be pure gold; 900 fine would be 900 parts gold, etc. In order to express the gold composition on a percentage basis, the fineness value is divided by 10.

Carat values may be changed to fineness, and *vice versa*, by means of a simple mathematical proportion as follows:

$$\frac{\text{Carat}}{24} = \frac{\text{Fineness}}{1000}$$

Table XXXIV shows the equivalent fineness for each carat value. Twenty-four carat gold is seldom used in dentistry other than in the form of gold foil, as it is lacking in strength and hardness.

TABLE XXXIV
FINENESS OF GOLD ALLOYS IN TERMS OF CARAT

Carat	Fineness	Carat	Fineness
1	41.667	13	541.667
2	83.333	14	583.333
3	125.000	15	625.000
4	166.667	16	666.667
5	208.333	17	708.333
6	250.000	18	750.000
7	291.667	19	791.667
8	333.333	20	833.333
9	375.000	21	875.000
10	416.667	22	916.667
11	458.333	23	958.333
12	500.000	24	1000.000

TABLE XXXV

PROPERTIES OF GOLD ALLOYS FOR CAST INLAYS

Type or use, No.	Alloy composition, per cent by weight. Gold and platinum group.	Silver.	Fusion range, degrees F.	Melting point (wire method) degrees F.	Castings quenched from 1290° F. (700° C.). Brinell No.	Elastic limit, lbs. per sq. in.	Ultimate strength, lbs. per sq. in.	Per cent elongation 2-inch gauge length.	Brinell No. (oven-cooled) reheated to 842° F. and cooled to 482° F. in 30 minutes.
1	100.0		....	1987	33	3,000	16,000	18.5	34
2	95.0	4.0	....	1904	32	3,500	16,500	14.5	34
3	87.8	11.2	....	1881	39	4,500	25,500	25.5	38
Soft Inlays									
4	95.0	3.5	....	1884	42	5,000	23,000	23.5	38
5	91.4	5.8	....	1827	42	7,500	25,000	16.5	
6	89.8	8.1	....	1850	47	6,500	27,000	21.0	46
7	91.5	5.7	....	1834	50	7,500	31,000	24.5	47
8	90.8	4.0	....	1783	52	10,500	28,000	17.5	
9	90.1	6.3	1812-1751	1778	68	11,500	35,000	24.5	64
10	89.5	6.2	....	1812	63	11,500	34,000	19.0	59
11	82.9	12.0	....	1753	67	13,500	36,500	26.0	64
12	82.4	11.6	....	1746	67	13,500	39,500	25.5	67
13	87.8	6.8	....	1758	60	15,500	38,500	22.5	59
14	90.1	0.4	....	1729	69	14,000	33,500	16.0	
15	83.2	10.1	....	1739	71	16,000	38,000	18.0	75
Medium Inlays									
16	83.3	8.3	....	1686	77	19,000	38,500	26.0	91
17	83.2	11.0	....	1735	88	19,500	36,500	11.0	97
18	81.3	9.3	1702-1627	1650	85	19,500	46,000	30.5	88
19	84.4	10.1	1872-1731	1791	85	22,000	45,500	18.5	87
20	85.7	7.1	....	1767	98	22,000	49,500	22.0	110
21	80.2	13.0	....	1738	95	22,500	46,500	21.0	119
22	83.0	9.1	1830-1704	1753	89	23,000	43,000	10.5	104
23	73.9	17.3	1782-1679*	1679	96	23,500	41,000	21.5	106
24	84.7	7.5	....	1746	98	23,500	41,000	11.0	126
25	79.0	14.4	....	1789	96	25,500	45,500	10.0	117
26	83.4	9.0	1830-1704	1728	97	27,000	46,500	15.0	108
Hard Inlays									
27	84.1	7.0	1828-1690	1756	101	25,500	48,000	16.5	120
28	80.2	12.7	....	1708	116	30,500	51,500	11.5	151
29	79.5	9.3	1735-1656	1693	124	30,500	47,500	12.5	145
Denture Gold									
30	75.5	9.4	1740-1616	1663	149	41,000	57,000	5.5	205

* Alloy formula changed after original tests were made. The fusion sample had the following composition: gold and platinum group, 74.8 per cent; silver, 20.2 per cent.

Composition.—Table XXXVI shows the chemical composition of 30 dental casting gold alloys as published by Coleman,[2] and in Table XXXV is shown the gold and platinum group content, and the silver present according to a later analysis also made at the National Bureau of Standards.[1] Comparing with the chemical compositions for wrought alloys given on page 218, the chief differen'ces lie in the platinum and palladium content. In casting alloys, the fusion temperature must be kept sufficiently low so that the metal may be melted with a gas-air flame, a factor which is of no importance in the case of wrought metals.

TABLE XXXVI

CHEMICAL COMPOSITION OF CASTING GOLD ALLOYS

(per cent by weight)

Alloy.	Au.	Ag.	Cu.	Pt.	Pd.	Ni.	Zn.	Ir.	Sn.
I......	71.3	7.1	9.9	10.62	....	....	0.08	0.14	0.83
II......	78.0	10.0	5.9	6.1	....	....	....	0.1	
III......	60:0	11.0	8.8	13.1	5.94	....	0.72	0.10	0.14
IV......	71.4	6.0	15.6	2.78	....	1.98	2.38		
V......	62.8	13.9	18.9	.....	....	2.57	1.92		
VI......	59.3	8.1	12.7	15.95	3.55	....	0.08		
VII......	59.8	13.5	13.6	5.22	7.10	....	0.67	0.20	
VIII......	65.9	5.9	10.2	10.58	5.69	....	1.34	0.03	
IX......	64.9	12.5	10.0	12.23	....	....	0.03	0.14	0.10
X......	68.3	11.1	13.9	2.86	2.89	0.93	0.05		
XI......	64.4	7.2	10.4	11.15	5.74	0.16	1.07		
XII......	65.4	5.4	11.8	10.80	5.04	0.05	1.09		
XIII......	72.0	9.8	8.8	7.92	....	0.95	0.15	0.07	
XIV......	66.3	9.7	12.9	2.06	7.78	....	1.18	0.07	
XV......	75.6	.....	10.6	10.14	....	2.73	1.08		
XVI......	67.8	11.7	10.5	10.12					
XVII......	67.0	16.8	12.2	3.92	....	....	....	0.05	
XVIII......	69.6	18.4	4.1	7.72	....	....	....	0.10	
XIX......	81.1	11.0	4.0	3.75	....	....	....	0.10	
XX......	76.3	5.1	9.8	8.00	....	....	0.82		
XXI......	79.6	4.5	8.0	7.80	....	....	0.06	0.03	
XXII......	63.1	10.5	11.9	3.15	9.75	0.22	1.68		
XXIII......	81.8	7.2	7.2	3.95					
XXIV......	67.8	16.5	8.9	2.96	2.82	....	0.94	0.08	
XXV......	83.2	8.4	8.3	.....	....	....	....	....	0.18
XXVI......	89.8	0.04	10.0	0.08					
XXVII......	91.7	7.8	0.5						
XXVIII......	91.7	4.6	3.7						
XXIX......	75.0	21.8	3.2						
XXX......	75.0	18.8	6.2						

The general effect of the individual metals upon the physical properties of the alloys is much the same as outlined in the previous chapter, with the additional effect of gas absorption while in the molten state. Copper, silver, palladium, and platinum all dissolve oxygen while molten. The formation of cuprous oxide (Cu_2O) while casting is particularly to be avoided, as it forms a eutectic with copper. Palladium and platinum also dissolve hydrogen in large quantities. The occlusion of gases is to be avoided during casting, since it causes porosity; this point will be discussed more at length in a subsequent section.

As may be noted from American Dental Association Specification No. 5,* there are certain restrictions placed upon the chemical composition of these alloys; however, little significance can be attached to such a requirement, aside from its indications as to color and resistance to corrosion or tarnish. As in the case of the wrought alloys, the results of tests for physical properties are much more important in judging their suitability for dental purposes than is their composition.

As to the use of nickel in casting alloys, DeWald[3] states as follows:

"A nickel-bearing casting gold may be used with some success if the ratio of platinum metals to nickel is sufficiently high, but this invariably raises the casting temperature, thus jeopardizing the soundness of the alloy by excessive oxidation of the other constituents. Nickel increases the strength of the alloy in the quenched condition but inhibits its capacity to harden at higher temperatures, although nickel itself imparts considerable hardness with low temperature hardening treatments. The equilibrium conditions of nickel with gold and silver, both important constituents of dental alloys, are such that it forms heterogeneous alloys which are, obviously, not conducive to successful dental castings."

Heat Treatment.—The theory and practice of heat treatment is the same for these alloys as outlined in the last chapter. The properties of some of the alloys whose physical properties in the quenched condition are given in Table XXXV, are shown in Table XXXVII, after being oven-cooled. By comparing the values in the two tables, it may be seen that the hardness, elastic limit, and tensile strength are increased, whereas the percentage elongation is decreased by the hardening heat treatment.

TABLE XXXVII
PROPERTIES OF OVEN-COOLED ALLOYS

Alloy.	Brinell No.	Elastic limit, lbs. per sq. in.	Ultimate strength, lbs. per sq. in.	Percentage elongation, 2-in. gauge.
21	119	27,500	56,000	7.5
27	120	26,000	48,000	12.0
28	151	36,500	62,000	1.5
29	145	36,000	55,000	3.5
30	205	69,000	94,000	1.0

* See Appendix, page 387.

If the hardness numbers in the quenched and oven-cooled condition in Table XXXV be compared with the similar values for wrought metals on page 221, it will be noted that, in general, the casting alloys do not respond to hardening heat treatment to as great a degree as do the wrought wires.

Although a hardening heat treatment undoubtedly increases the modulus of resilience of the cast alloy, its use in operative restorations is somewhat questionable because of the increase in hardness. For example, an occlusal inlay of any type is likely to become so hard after such a treatment, that the restoration will abrade more slowly than the tooth enamel during mastication, thus producing a "high spot," which, if not ground off, will cause trauma and other pathological disturbances. Hence some authorities[1] feel that it is better to use inlay golds in the softened condition only, controlling the strength and other properties as needed by a proper selection of materials. However, large restorations which do not extend appreciably over the occlusal surfaces of the teeth, such as partial or full dentures, lingual bars, etc., may be considerably benefited by such a treatment.

Physical Properties.—The hardness of a dental casting gold may be made almost any desired value, governed by the manner in which the material is to be used. As in the case of the wrought alloys, the Brinell hardness number is proportional to the elastic limit and the tensile strength.[1]

As may be noted from Table XXXV, the elastic limits and tensile strengths of these alloys are not as great as similar values for the wrought wires. Very likely this cannot be accounted for *entirely* by differences in composition.

One of the causes for such a decrease in tensile values, aside from a difference in composition, might be attributed to the method of preparing the specimens, although no data are at hand to substantiate such an opinion. In determining the tensile properties of cast samples, the specimens are cast in the form of rods, 5 to 6 inches in length, with a diameter between 0.070 and 0.090 inch. It is probably difficult, if not impossible, to cast such a specimen without introducing a certain amount of internal flaws. Naturally, such flaws might create a weakness in the specimen at the location of its occurrence, thus markedly lowering the tensile properties as observed in testing.

Furthermore, the grain structure of the cast alloy is not so conducive to high strength. As noted in Chapter XX, the solid solution grain structure is characteristically dendritic. When fabricated to a wire form, such grains are recrystallized and elongated, thus any flaws are likely to disappear and a much more homogeneous structure with increased strength results. By similar reasoning it is very likely true that a wrought restoration has better physical properties than a cast structure, even though the two might have identical chemical compositions.

Furthermore, the corrosion and tarnish resistance of a wrought structure will also very likely be better than the cast restoration. While the latter is solidifying, a certain amount of coring is likely to occur for reasons given in Chapter XXI. Such a condition can be homogenized only by annealing, a procedure which is not generally practiced by the dentist. On the other hand, the very fact that a wire or plate has been fabricated by the manufacturer from a cast ingot necessarily implies a thorough homogenizing in order that the fabrication may be carried out successfully. Inhomogeneity is exhibited clinically by localized areas of tarnish or corrosion, presumably caused by localized segregation of the baser metals or coring.

In Table XXXV, a tendency toward smaller percentage elongation values may be noted, as the platinum and palladium content becomes greater. The percentage elongation and hardness number are properties indicating whether or not the alloy may be burnished in the mouth; the greater the elongation and the less the hardness, the more readily the alloy may be burnished.

Classification of Dental Casting Gold Alloys.—As may be noted from Table XXXV, the casting gold alloys may be classified as *very soft, soft, medium, hard* and *denture golds*. The very soft alloys (B.H.N. below 40) are considered too soft for use as inlays with safety. The soft, medium, and hard gold alloys are usually designated as type A, type B, and type C respectively, and are used almost exclusively as inlay golds with the exception of some of the last type which may be employed for certain types of partial dentures. The classification by types is chiefly based upon hardness values, and does not include the denture gold alloys, which are, in general, both harder and stronger than type C alloys. The so-called "white golds" will be treated separately, although some of them classify as type B or C so far as physical properties are concerned.

Very Soft Inlay Gold Alloys.—As previously mentioned, these alloys, with a hardness number below 40 (alloys 1–3 inclusive, Table XXXV), are considered to be unsatisfactory for use as inlays. They are comparatively weak and inelastic, and exhibit no greater elongation values than do the type A alloys. They were formerly used quite extensively because of their ability to withstand considerable burnishing, but in the present era of greater accuracy in casting, such extensive burnishing should be unnecessary. Ill-fitting inlays, such as were formerly produced, were burnished and spread out over the margins of the prepared cavity to an extent causing the formation of a thin layer of strain-hardened metal which fractured easily.

Type A, Soft Inlay Gold Alloys.—The type A alloys* are the familiar 20 to 22 carat golds, with hardness ranging from Brinell numbers 40 to 75. Although the hardness numbers and tensile proper-

---

* Alloys number 4–15 inclusive, Table XXXV.

ties cover a rather wide range, the elongation values are quite high in comparison with the next group.

The alloys can all be burnished within reason, with the expectation of obtaining smooth and strong margins. They are all inlay golds for use in the simpler types of restorations, the softer members being used for restoring cavities formed by structural defects in the teeth not subject to great stress, such as simple proximal incisor and cuspid cavities, and gingival third cavities,* whereas the harder members may be used as inlays for cavities in the proximal surfaces of bicuspids and molars, and those occurring in the proximal surfaces of the incisors and cuspids which require the removal and restoration of the incisal angle,† thus subjecting the restoration to greater stress than in the simpler cavity types previously noted.

Type A alloys contain little or no platinum or palladium, their main constituents being gold, silver, and copper. As may be observed from the table, they are generally not amenable to heat treatment.

Type B, Medium Inlay Gold Alloys.—The alloys belonging to this group have Brinell numbers ranging from 70 to 100. Their tensile properties are considerably higher than the type A alloys, and their elongation values are much less in comparison. As a result of their higher hardness and lower ductility, they are difficult if not impossible to burnish; hence, castings must be made very accurately in order to obtain tightly sealed margins Alloys number 16 to 26, in Table XXXV, are included in this group.

These alloys may be used for all types of inlays, and some of the harder members may be used for three-quarter crowns. They are very popular with the operative dentists.

The composition of these alloys is such that most of them may be heat treated.

Type C, Hard Inlay Golds.—Alloys number 27 to 29 inclusive, with a Brinell hardness range of 90 to 140, are included in this group. Their tensile properties are the highest in the entire series, with low elongation values. Hardening by oven-cooling decreases their ductility markedly. Obviously, they cannot be burnished in the mouth.

Their use is confined mainly to three-quarter crowns with thin walls, fixed partial denture abutments, and mesio-occluso-distal inlays in the mouths of those few patients who exert abnormally large forces of mastication. In general, their fusion ranges are higher than is conducive to the successful production of large denture castings.

Cast Denture Gold Alloys.—These alloys should exhibit a high modulus of resilience and tensile strength in order to withstand the impact forces to which they are subjected, particularly in the case of large removable partial dentures with lingual bars, palatal arches, and many clasps. Their melting points should not be excessively high, as it is difficult to maintain a large bulk of gold in a molten condition

* Classes 1, 3, and 5 respectively.
† Classes 2 and 4 respectively.

without oxidation at higher temperatures, when the usual gas-air blow torch is employed.

This type of gold alloy has not been subjected to as much study as have the other types, only one example being included in Table XXXV. However, these alloys are likely to be lacking in ductility, possibly because of a comparatively low gold content. Their Brinell hardness numbers should probably be placed at 130 as a minimum, with a possible maximum of 200 or above.

"White Golds."—The so-called "white golds" are essentially alloys of palladium, gold, copper, silver, and zinc, their chief difference from the "gold-colored" alloys being their relatively low gold content and high percentage of silver and palladium. Since palladium is the essential constituent in these alloys, they should be more properly designated as *palladium alloys*.

Undoubtedly the prime object of the manufacturers in introducing this type of alloy was economy in price over the gold-colored alloys, which have almost doubled in cost since the inauguration of the new governmental monetary policies. It so happened that when the price of gold was increased, palladium, due to certain advances in industrial refining methods, was very plentiful, its cost being only one half that of gold. Consequently the refiners have been very active in their search for outlets for the consumption of this metal. However, if economy in price were the only recommendation for these alloys, they would hardly merit discussion, because in many cases such economy is very likely to prove false from the standpoint of service to the patient and profit to the dentist. Any discussion of these materials must of necessity be rather conservative, both because of the rather limited information available concerning their physical properties, and because they have not been in general use for a sufficient length of time to obtain conclusive clinical evidence of their success or failure.*

The alloys may be classified into two types: type I being comparatively low in gold content, whereas type II contains more gold. Type I is somewhat cheaper in price than the other type, and, due to the lower gold content, it is less ductile than the other. Confining the discussion for the present to casting alloys, the following chemical composition may be given as typical of a type I alloy: gold, 15 per cent; palladium, 24 per cent; silver, 45 per cent; copper, 15 per cent; and zinc, 1 per cent. The type II alloys contain more gold as previously mentioned, and the higher priced alloys of this group may have their palladium content considerably reduced.

At the present time, no casting alloys with a melting point sufficiently low for ordinary laboratory use have been successfully formulated without the addition of precious metals. It is not to be inferred that such an alloy is entirely impossible of formulation, but until such an alloy is approved by an impartial testing agency, the dentist is

* As nearly as can be determined, the first alloy of this type was introduced into England in 1932, and into this country in 1933.

warned to beware of false claims by certain unscrupulous manufacturers in this regard.* Furthermore, the sale of certain base metal alloys, to which gold "scrap" is to be added, is to be deplored as false economy. From the discussion given in the preceding chapters on gold alloys, it should be evident that the melting together of miscellaneous scrap gold is entirely contraindicated, as there is absolutely no criteria by which the physical and chemical nature of the resulting alloy can be predicted. The folly of adding such scrap gold to a previously prepared base metal alloy of unknown constitution should be even more evident on this basis.

In general the palladium alloys are, of course, white in color, which is considered by many patients to be superior esthetically to a gold color. Aside from this slight advantage, there is little or no reason for using such alloys for simple inlay restorations; their use should be confined to large one-piece castings, such as partial dentures or denture bases. Their chief advantage in the latter cases is their lightness in weight, when compared with the gold-colored alloys.

TABLE XXXVIII

SPECIFIC GRAVITY OF CERTAIN PALLADIUM ALLOYS IN COMPARISON WITH A GOLD-COLORED ALLOY AND PURE GOLD

Alloy.	Specific gravity.	Weight in comparison with alloy A (100%) (per cent).	Weight in comparison with pure gold (100%) (per cent)
Gold colored:			
A.	17.75	100	92
Type II:			
C.	11.60	65	60
I.	13.22	74	69
K.	11.50	65	60
M.	11.80	66	61
Type I:			
B.	11.24	63	58
D.	11.50	65	60
E.	12.22	69	63
H.	11.60	65	60
L.	11.30	64	58
P.	10.20	58	53
V.	14.33	81	74

Table XXXVIII shows the specific gravity of one gold-colored alloy and 11 palladium alloys, all of which were purchased on the open market. Columns 3 and 4 give their weights on a percentage basis in comparison with the gold-colored alloy and pure gold. For example, a restoration constructed from alloy P would be only 53 per cent as heavy as though the restoration were constructed from pure gold, and 58 per cent as heavy as a similar denture constructed from alloy A.

* For example, see the report in J. A. D. A., 22: 348, 349 (Feb.) 1933.

The hardness of these alloys is, in general, rather high, placing them in the denture gold classification.* They can be heat treated, but the advisability of so doing is questionable due to the large reduction in elongation, which renders them quite brittle in the majority of cases. Table XXXIX shows the Brinell hardness numbers of certain

TABLE XXXIX

HARDNESS OF SOME PALLADIUM ALLOYS

Alloy.	Brinell hardness number.	
Gold colored:	Quenched.	Oven-cooled.
A	146	222
Type II:		
B	158	232
Type I:		
C	142	220
D	144	228
E	147	263
F	169	237
G	157	232

of these alloys in the quenched and oven-cooled condition. The tensile properties of a few of the alloys as given by the manufacturers, are shown in Table XL.

TABLE XL

TENSILE PROPERTIES OF PALLADIUM ALLOYS

Alloy.	Tensile strength, lb./sq. in.		Prop. limit, lb./sq. in.		Elongation, per cent.	
	Quenched.	Oven-cooled.	Quenched.	Oven-cooled.	Quenched.	Oven-cooled.
Type II						
A	86,000	115,000	53,500	65,000	9.0	3.0
B	69,000	107,500	41,500	84,500	11.0	1.0
C	75,400	113,200	36,700	58,000	4.0	1.5
D	77,000	100,000	47,000	81,500	7.0	1.0
Type I						
E	......	......	......	......	7.0	1.0
F	85,000	105,000	49,000	71,000	4.0	1.0

One of the disadvantages of the type I alloys is their high melting points, which are in the neighborhood of 1800° F. (1000° C.), caused,

* B.H.N. 130 or above.

of course, by the relatively high palladium content. Furthermore, the large palladium and silver content causes considerable occlusion of gases, particularly oxygen. The inclusion of oxides is likely to render the solidified alloys extremely hard and brittle. However, if special precautions are observed, these difficulties are not insurmountable, and castings can be obtained comparatively free of such inclusions.

The question of resistance to corrosion and tarnish in the mouth is somewhat open at the present time. Some manufacturers claim that their alloys are as resistant to discoloration as are the 22-carat golds, whereas others are of the opinion that the cheaper alloys are unsafe for mouth restorative purposes. The alloys most certainly tarnish badly under the ammonium sulphide test* unless they have been properly manipulated while casting; oxides and other types of inclusions lower their tarnish resistance considerably.

In the wrought condition, more palladium may be added, and many of the above objections may be overcome, and generally a very satisfactory and reliable product results.

Casting Shrinkage.—Gold and its alloys shrink when cooling from the molten state to room temperature. The shrinkage occurs in three stages: (1) the thermal contraction of the liquid metal to the solidification point; (2) the contraction of the metal while solidifying, and (3) the thermal contraction of the solid metal in cooling from the freezing point to room temperature. The first contraction is of no dental importance, since more molten gold may be fed into the mold while cooling to compensate for such shrinkage. The third stage was studied by Coleman,[2] whose results are shown in Table XLI. In

TABLE XLI

LINEAR THERMAL CONTRACTION OF GOLD ALLOYS

Material.	Melting point (solidus).		Contraction from melting point to 25° C. (77° F.) (per cent).
	° C.	° F.	
100% gold...............	1014	1845	1.76
90% gold, 10% silver....	973	1784	2.03
90% gold, 10% copper...	860	1580	1.62
90% gold, 10% nickel....	886	1627	1.91

order to determine whether the second stage was of significance, Coleman further measured the total linear shrinkage from the liquid state to room temperature, using an alloy of composition 90 per cent gold and 10 per cent copper; the results are shown in Table XLII.

* See page 215.

TABLE XLII

CASTING SHRINKAGE OF A GOLD-COPPER ALLOY

Approximate temperature of the mold.	Casting temperature of the alloy.	Casting pressure (lb. sq. in.).	Casting shrinkage (per cent).
40° C. (104° F.)........	Moderate	20	1.24
40° C. (104° F.)........	Moderate	10	1.24
300° C. (572° F.)........	Moderate	10	1.26
300° C. (572° F.)........	High	10	1.28

The average linear casting shrinkage was 1.25 per cent, and it was evidently independent both of the temperature of the mold when the alloy was cast and of the pressure under which the alloy was forced into the mold. This casting shrinkage value was recently confirmed[5] at the National Bureau of Standards using different shapes of castings, different mold investment materials, and gold alloys of varying compositions, the final figure arrived at being 1.25 ± 0.1 per cent. The practical significance of this figure is very great indeed, as will be pointed out in the next few chapters. In brief, if an inlay is cast into a mold which is accurate at room temperature, the inlay will be 1.25 per cent too small after it has cooled to room temperature. The methods of accurately compensating for this shrinkage offer one of the most interesting problems for study in the entire field of dentistry.

The term "casting shrinkage" must not be confused with linear thermal shrinkage; the latter term refers to the shrinkage which occurs from the solidus temperature, whereas the casting shrinkage includes all contractions occurring from the molten state to room temperature. Furthermore, it should be observed that the casting shrinkage is less than the thermal shrinkage; for the alloy of composition 90 per cent gold and 10 per cent copper, the former is 1.25 per cent, whereas the latter is 1.62 per cent (Table XLI). Coleman explains these rather anomalous results as follows:[2]

"(1) There may be sufficient friction or interlocking between the casting and the walls of the mold to hold and stretch the casting while it is cooling through that range of temperature within which the metal is very soft or weak, thus preventing the full normal shrinkage, and (2) the compensation of part of the total shrinkage of the solid metal may be dependent upon a difference in the rates of cooling of different parts of the casting. If part of the metal in the mold solidifies and cools to some temperature below the melting point before the metal in the sprue freezes, the shrinkage due to cooling of this solid metal may be compensated by the addition of metal from the crucible."

Porosity in Castings.—There are two causes of internal porosity in dental castings: (1) localized shrinkage and (2) the occlusion of gases.

The cause of localized shrinkage is essentially described in the preceding section. Due to the different rates of cooling of the molten metal, and the "stretching" of the casting at the walls of the mold as described above, internal voids will appear if additional liquid metal is not supplied.

While it is in the molten state, the alloy will absorb gases from the air and flame. For example, gold, copper, and silver will absorb oxygen in large amounts, and platinum and palladium have a strong affinity for hydrogen, as well as oxygen. Upon cooling, the gases are expelled, and form internal voids.

Such porosity causes weakness of the casting; methods for avoiding these porosities will be described in Chapter XXXI.

Remelting of Casting Alloys.—Dental gold alloys may be remelted time and again without changing the composition, unless zinc is present. This point has been studied by Coleman,[6] and his results are given in Table XLIII. There is probably little danger in volatiliza-

TABLE XLIII

CHANGE IN COMPOSITION OF A DENTAL GOLD
CASTING ALLOY DUE TO REMELTING

Metal.	Composition (per cent).		
	Not remelted.	Remelted at moderate temperature.	Remelted at high temperature.
Au	60.5	60.5	60.8
Ag	11.0	11.0	11.0
Cu	8.5	8.6	8.6
Zn	0.64	0.56	0.32

tion of even the zinc upon remelting, unless the temperature is raised abnormally high. The analysis given in the fourth column of the table was obtained after holding the alloy at the high temperature for five minutes, during which period small particles were flying off from the molten metal to the extent that the total loss in this manner was approximately one half of the original weight. This treatment is much more severe than is likely to occur in ordinary dental practice. Coleman concludes that a good alloy may be remelted and cast two or three times without seriously changing the proportions of the constituent metals.

Specifications.—American Dental Association Specification No. 5. See Appendix, page 387.

LITERATURE

1. Taylor, N. O., Paffenbarger, G. C., and Sweeney, W. T., *Inlay Casting Golds: Physical Properties and Specifications.* J. A. D. A., 19: 36–53 (Jan). 1932.

2. Coleman, R. L., *Physical Properties of Dental Materials.* Research Paper No. 32: 893. U. S. Gov. Printing Office (1928).

3. DeWald, L. H., *Nickel in Precious Metal Alloys.* Metals and Alloys, 6: 331 (Nov.) 1935.

4. Reference (2), pp. 908–911.

5. Souder, Wilmer, *Fifteen Years of Dental Research at the National Bureau of Standards.* J. A. D. A., 21: 58–66 (Jan.) 1934.

6. Reference (2), p. 897.

16

CHAPTER XXVIII

INLAY CASTING WAX: COMPOSITION, PROPERTIES, AND MANIPULATION

THE first important step in the actual construction of a cast restoration is the preparation of a pattern, usually constructed of wax. There are many different types of waxes used in dentistry, but none of them require such care in manufacture and manipulation as do the inlay waxes.

In practice, the wax is softened by heat and then forced into the cavity preparation under pressure where it is held until rigid. It is then burnished and carved to the anatomy of the tooth, obtaining as nearly as possible an exact reproduction of the finished restoration. Since these types of restorations are comparatively small, it is not difficult to understand why slight warpages or other types of distortion in such a pattern produce an ill-fitting casting. The cast restoration can be no better than the wax pattern; hence, it is essential that these waxes have certain properties which render them as stable and rigid as possible while being manipulated. After the pattern has been constructed, it is removed from the prepared cavity and invested.

Desirable Properties of Inlay Waxes.—In consideration of both the method of preparation of the patterns and the limited possibilities of production of suitable wax formulae, the American Dental Association Research Associates at the National Bureau of Standards have indicated the following characteristics as being desirable for inlay casting waxes:[6] "1. The waxes should soften without becoming flaky or laminated. 2. They should be sufficiently plastic at temperatures slightly above mouth temperature to permit forcing them into all the details of the cavity walls. 3. They should harden sufficiently at mouth temperature to permit withdrawal from the cavity without distortion. 4. They should carve without chipping or flaking. 5. The color should be such that it facilitates the carving of patterns in the mouth through contrast with the hard and soft tissues of the mouth. 6. The thermal expansion characteristics should be known to insure the correct use of the material in any technic requiring wax expansion." Two other requirements might be added: 7. The waxes should be cohesive but not adhesive. 8. They should vaporize at temperatures compatible with normal casting practice without leaving any residue other than carbon.

Composition.—The exact composition of these waxes is a commercial secret; however, they probably contain at least some of the following ingredients: paraffin, beeswax, carnauba, ceresin, dammar resin (gum dammar), and stearin. Paraffin is the basic ingredient, with other materials, notably carnauba, which are added as hardeners or stiffeners and to raise the melting and softening points. It is not always an easy matter to formulate a good inlay wax, since many of the ingredients are natural waxes and are subject to fluctuation in properties. For example, a certain formula will be found satisfactory, but with a new batch of constituent ingredients, the mixture may show very poor properties indeed until altered by a change in formula.

Coleman[1] gives the following composition of an inlay wax which he compounded for experimental purposes: carnauba, 25 per cent; paraffin, 60 per cent; ceresin, 10 per cent; refined beeswax, 5 per cent; and a small amount of coloring matter. The wax withstood handling without distortion at ordinary temperatures, and could be carved without chipping or flaking; it became soft and plastic between 45° and 50° C. (113°–122° F.), and was completely eliminated from a casting mold at 250° C. (480° F.). However, the wax is not completely satisfactory for clinical use, and it does not comply in its entirety with the American Dental Association Specification No. 4. Most commercial varieties of inlay waxes start to smoke at temperatures[2] of 115° to 143° C. (240°–290° F.), and have a flash point approximately 83° C. (150° F.) higher.

Flow.—Probably flow is the most important physical property of inlay waxes from a practical standpoint. Flow is, in this instance, identical with and is measured in the same manner as the flow of modeling compound discussed in Chapter IX.

These waxes are very nearly amorphous in character, hence, they may be considered as being essentially super-cooled liquids.* Like liquids then, these waxes flow. However, the lower the temperature, the more nearly their properties resemble those of a solid, and, conversely, the higher the temperature, the more do the properties of liquids predominate, yet at no ordinary temperatures do the latter properties entirely disappear. For example, a stick of inlay wax will snap between the fingers as so much glass, when bent suddenly at room temperature; this certainly is a property proving the wax to be solid. However, if the stick is suspended at its ends between two supports at room temperature for a number of days, it will bow under its own weight, thus exhibiting the liquid property of flow.

* That these waxes are not entirely amorphous is shown by the fact that their time-temperature cooling curves exhibit an arrest point similar to that of a pure metal or, in some cases, a solid solution alloy. However, the temperature of this "solidification" point is considerably above the working range temperature as specified by American Dental Association Specification No. 4, and it can be of little or no practical importance since the waxes are seldom manipulated at temperatures above the working temperatures specified. Presumably when the waxes are worked at the lower temperatures, any crystal formations are broken up, and therefore they contribute little to the structural characteristics of the material. Hence, for all practical purposes, the waxes may be treated as "super-cooled liquids."

The practical significance of flow lies in the construction of the wax pattern. The wax must be sufficiently plastic at temperatures tolerable to the mouth, in order that it may be flowed or forced into the prepared cavity with every minute detail of the latter impressed into its form. During this stage, the predominance of the liquid property is highly desirable indeed. After the pattern has been constructed, it must be withdrawn from the prepared cavity in one piece without the slightest flow or distortion. Obviously, the properties of a solid are now required; hence, the pattern is chilled with water in order to provide rigidity before it is withdrawn. Experiments have

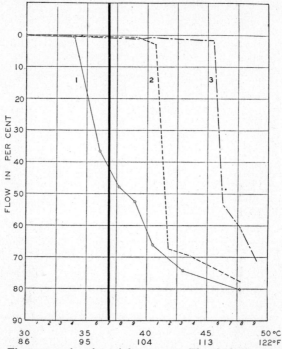

Fig. 65.—Flow curve for three inlay waxes. The dark line represents body temperature. (Volland and Paffenbarger: Jour. Amer. Dent. Assoc., February, 1932.)

shown[3] that, regardless of the temperature of the water used in chilling the pattern in the mouth, the wax returns to mouth temperature before it can be withdrawn; hence the requirement that the waxes exhibit a minimum of flow at *mouth temperature.*

According to American Dental Association Specification No. 4,* the maximum flow allowable at mouth temperature is 1 per cent. The flow is measured by determining the percentage shortening in length of a cylindrical specimen 10 mm. in diameter, and 6 mm. long when placed under a load of 2 kg. at the specified temperature.

* See Appendix, page 386.

In order to determine the softening point of the wax and its working range, the test is continued at higher temperatures, and the flow in per cent is plotted as a function of the temperature, as shown in Fig. 65.[7] The softening temperature, as determined from the graph, is the temperature at which the flow exceeds 5 per cent, and must fall between 38° and 42° C. (100°–108° F.). Similarly the working range is defined as the temperature at which a flow of 50 to 60 per cent is exhibited on the curve, and it must be at or below 43° C. (110° F.).

Observation of the three flow curves in Fig. 65 demonstrates clearly that the wax represented by curve 1 is very nearly useless for inlay purposes. The heavy vertical line represents body temperature. At body temperature, this particular wax flows approximately 42 per cent. Curve 2 represents an almost ideal wax; it flows but very little at body temperature, yet its softening temperature and working range both occur at only a few degrees above this temperature. Curve 3 is for a wax which is unnecessarily hard, and it would be very difficult to work.

Thermal Expansion.—Inasmuch as accuracy of reproduction of the wax pattern is such an important element in the casting procedure, and since the pattern is subjected to changes in temperature as when removing the pattern from mouth to room temperature, a knowledge of the thermal properties of waxes is highly desirable. The thermal conductivity of all of these waxes is very low, and their linear coefficients of thermal expansion are high; in fact they are higher than any of the other materials used in dentistry. Curve A, in Fig. 66, shows a typical linear thermal expansion curve for an inlay wax. Its lack of uniformity at certain temperatures should be noted. It is very evident that any thermal changes in dimension must be computed from the curve, and not by the conventional method of using a linear thermal expansion coefficient.

Furthermore, the amount of thermal expansion or contraction during temperature change depends somewhat upon the manipulation of the wax. Curve A in Fig. 66 represents the thermal expansion of a specimen prepared by allowing the wax to cool from the liquid state under pressure, whereas curve B shows the same wax prepared similarly, except that it was cooled without pressure. As may be noted, the latter specimen exhibits less expansion. Had the wax been softened, then stretched and allowed to harden in the stretched condition, an actual contraction would occur as the temperature was raised, usually followed by a relatively small expansion.

Wax Distortion.—One of the greatest difficulties in modern casting procedure is to obtain a homogeneous wax pattern. In the preceding experiments, in general the wax was manipulated in a manner to give complete homogeneity, which is not entirely possible when working in the mouth. For example, consider the method employed for obtaining a pattern from a proximal cavity preparation. A thin strip of metal, called the matrix, is inserted between the teeth, and the wax is forced into the preparation, held under pressure, and chilled. Some regions are compressed more than others. Perhaps the pattern is short at the gingival margin and more hot wax is added, which is allowed to cool without pressure. The pattern is carved, and this further changes the molecular configuration locally. Under such conditions, it is evident that considerable heterogeneity will result; when the pattern is withdrawn, some parts of it will flow more than others,

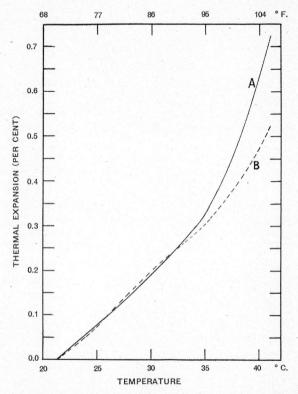

Fig. 66.—Thermal expansion of an inlay wax. Curve A represents the thermal expansion when the wax was held under pressure while it was solidifying from a liquid condition, and curve B is the expansion of the same wax when cooled as before without pressure.

and when its temperature is changed to that of the room, some parts of it will change thermally more than others. Hence, even under the best of conditions, some distortion is bound to occur.

That the above discussion is not entirely theoretical is shown by some experiments by Maves.[4] A series of mesio-occluso-distal wax patterns were prepared in the usual manner. Each of them was placed in a water bath, and an image of the patterns was projected onto a screen. The temperature of the bath was varied, and the outline of the projected image was traced at each temperature. The tracings were then superimposed on one another, with the results shown in Figs. 67 and 68. Such discrepancies are very serious in casting work, and are accounted for in the manner outlined above. Although the changes in temperature to which the pattern is ordinarily subjected

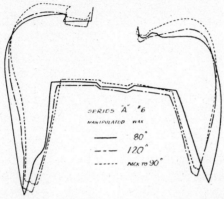

Fig. 67.—Distortion of a wax pattern under heat. (Maves: Jour. Amer. Dent. Assoc., April, 1932.)

in modern casting procedures is not so great as those used by Maves, yet the temperature changes which do occur are sufficient to cause distortion.

Another type of wax distortion is caused by its elasticity, which persists even while it is in a plastic condition. For example, if a stick of inlay wax is softened, bent into a horseshoe shape, and

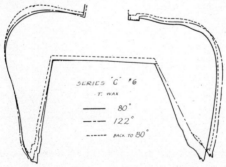

Fig. 68.—Distortion of a wax pattern under heat. (Maves: Jour. Amer. Dent. Assoc., April, 1932.)

then suddenly released, a tendency to return to its original shape may be noted. It is for this reason that the wax must be held under pressure while solidifying. The wax further exhibits the peculiar property of distorting elastically at higher temperatures than the temperature at which it is adapted. For example, if a stick of inlay wax is softened at a definite temperature and bent into a horseshoe shape as before, chilled in that position, and then placed in a water bath, the temperature of which is gradually raised, the wax will begin to distort at or slightly above the temperature at which it was manipulated. Distortions of this type can be partially avoided by manipulating the wax at the highest practicable temperature.

The effect of distortion as caused by elasticity at lower temperatures is shown in Fig. 69, which was prepared by P. B. Taylor of Western Reserve University. Figure 69a represents two castings made in the same operation, from wax patterns which were chilled from the molten condition, *under pressure*. In Fig. 69b, the casting on the left was made from a wax pattern constructed as before, but the wax pattern on the right was allowed to cool *without pressure*. Although both castings were made in the same mold under identical

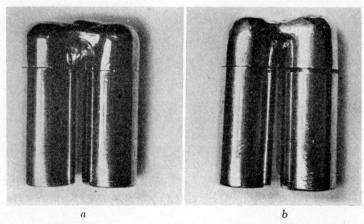

a   b

Fig. 69.—Castings from differently manipulated wax patterns.

conditions, the casting constructed from the pattern which solidified without pressure does not fit the model, whereas the other one does. Presumably, in the first case, the exerted pressure flowed the wax to an extent that all elasticity was overcome, whereas in the second case the wax slowly solidified, and was stretched elastically over the model, so that, when it was removed, the stresses caused it to become smaller than its original size. This effect undoubtedly occurs in any three-surface or full-crown pattern, and additional compensation is needed to overcome it.

Another factor, aside from temperature, which enters into the distortion of wax, is the element of time. Stresses and strains introduced by manipulation may be relieved over a period of time, even though the temperature remain constant. This can be demonstrated in a measurable amount by allowing a measured specimen of wax to harden while held in a vise. If it is measured carefully with a micrometer at certain intervals after removal, it will be found to increase in dimension quite rapidly at first, and then more slowly. Often a slight change may be detected for as long as twenty-four hours. Furthermore, a certain amount of wax flow will take place over a period of time at room temperature as previously noted. To avoid such distortions, the pattern should be invested as soon as possible after obtaining it.

A Working Hypothesis for Wax Distortion.*—It is postulated that a normal or average molecular distance normally exists between certain of the molecules scattered over the entire mass of the wax. When this average or normal distance is disturbed in any manner, the molecular forces tend to reestablish the original configuration and distance. It has been stated that the waxes are essentially supercooled liquids; that the liquid state by no means exhibits a completely random molecular configuration has been demonstrated by Stewart.[5] Although it cannot be stated that the amorphous configuration under discussion is identical with that of the liquid state, yet it is logical to assume a certain similarity, since the waxes exhibit a molecular mobility of flow, which to all appearances is similar to a liquid flow of considerable viscosity.

In other words, it is assumed that a major number of the molecules of the entire mass of the wax tend to maintain an average distance between themselves, and in so doing, cause distortion, anomalous expansions, contractions, etc., when disturbed.

In the application of such a hypothesis, the case of the stick of wax suspended between two supports at room temperature may be first considered. This phenomenon is simply a flowing of the material under its own weight, the molecules merely sliding over one another as they do in the flow of a liquid. The normal molecular distances are maintained, and no stresses or strains are introduced at any time other than those incurred by the weight of the wax itself.

If the wax is cooled under pressure, certain of the molecular distances may be decreased by compression. When heat is applied, a large expansion occurs due to two factors: (1) the reestablishment of the normal or average molecular distance, plus (2) the normal thermal expansion which usually takes place with increase in temperature. Such a statement implies that the contraction to room temperature should be less than the total thermal expansion from room to mouth temperature by an amount approximately equal to the expansion caused by factor (1) above. Preliminary experiments by P. B. Taylor† seem to indicate this supposition to be true. In other words, the thermal expansion of an inlay wax is equal to its contraction over identical temperature ranges, only if the normal

---

* This hypothesis is advanced by the author as a means of rationalizing and accounting for the wax distortion phenomena mentioned. The validity of the theory is, at the present time, being subjected to further study and research.

† Data not yet published.

molecular distance is maintained. When the wax solidifies homogeneously without pressure, presumably such a normal distance is maintained, and the wax may be heated and cooled repeatedly without distortion.

When the stick of wax is softened and bent into a horseshoe shape, the normal molecular distance is again disturbed, and, because of its tendency to overcome this effect, the wax exhibits "elasticity."

Furthermore, over a period of time at a constant temperature, such a molecular disarrangement tends to become normal, more or less, by a process of flow.

With these illustrations, it is evident that any type of manipulation which disturbs the normal molecular distances will cause distortion because of the tendency for a molecular rearrangement to take place, brought about either by change in temperature or by time. In other words, as R. H. Volland aptly expresses it, the molecules are "uncomfortable" and tend to rearrange themselves into more "comfortable" positions.

Manipulation of Inlay Wax.—The wax may be softened in a water bath, or over a Bunsen burner. If the latter method is used, great care must be taken not to volatilize any of the constituents. The safest method is to hold the wax between the thumb and first finger of the hand above the flame and to rotate it until it becomes thoroughly plastic. The plastic mass is then forced into the prepared cavity under considerable pressure at as high a temperature as is consistent with comfort to the patient; the pressure should be maintained until the wax is thoroughly cooled to mouth temperature. Ideally, the cooling should be done with decreasing temperatures of water. For example, the pattern may be first cooled with water at approximately 40° C. (104° F.), then with water at an approximate temperature of 38.5° C. (101° F.), and finally with water at mouth temperature. Such a process is much less likely to introduce distortional strains, as it allows for an "annealing" process. In practice, the assistant may prepare three syringes containing water approximately at the three different temperatures, each being used in turn by the operator. Whatever is the method of obtaining the pattern, it should be accomplished with the aim of doing as little carving and repairing as possible.

The pattern may be removed with an explorer, care being taken to lift it directly outward from the preparation, so as to produce a minimum of flow. It should then be laid upon a towel or a piece of gauze for inspection, and invested as soon as possible. At no time should the pattern be touched with the hands, as this introduces an unnecessary temperature change, which is to be avoided at all times.

Other Dental Waxes.—In some instances softer waxes are necessary for convenience in manipulation; they are prepared by varying the ingredients as necessary, paraffin being the basic ingredient. "Sticky" wax usually contains rosin, to give it a certain amount of adhesion. Formulae for these various types of waxes may be found in Prinz, *Dental Formulary* (Lea and Febiger).

Specifications.—American Dental Association Specification No. 4. See Appendix, page 386.

LITERATURE

1. Coleman, R. L., *Physical Properties of Dental Materials. Research Paper* No. 32, U. S. Gov. Printing Office.
2. Harder, O. E., *Modern Dental Metallography*, p. 104, Burgess-Roseberry Company.
3. Taylor, N. O., and Paffenbarger, G. C., *A Survey of Current Inlay Casting Technics.* J. A. D. A., 17: 2058–2081 (Nov.), 1930.
4. Maves, T. W., *Recent Experiments Demonstrating Wax Distortion on All Wax Patterns When Heat Is Applied.* J. A. D. A., 19: 606–613 (April) 1932.
5. Stewart, G. W., *X-Ray Diffraction in Liquids.* Rev. of Modern Physics, 2: 116–122 (Jan.) 1930.
6. Taylor, N. O., Paffenbarger, G. C., and Sweeney, W. T., *A Specification for Inlay Casting Wax.* J. A. D. A., 18: 40–52 (Jan.) 1931.
7. Volland, R. H., and Paffenbarger, G. C., *Cast Gold Inlay Technic.* J. A. D. A., 19: 189 (Feb.) 1932.

CHAPTER XXIX

DENTAL CASTING INVESTMENTS

AFTER obtaining the wax pattern, it is used for preparing a casting mold. A small length of wire, called the *sprue former*, is attached, and the pattern is painted with an *investment*, which is essentially a material composed of plaster of Paris and silica. After forming a thin coating of investment on the pattern, it is placed in a flask and surrounded by investment, which sets to a hard mass. The sprue former is then removed, and the wax is eliminated by heat, thus leaving a mold, with an *ingate* or *sprue* formed by the space left after removing the sprue former. This process will be discussed in detail in Chapter XXXI. Investments are used for both dental soldering and casting, but the present chapter will deal primarily with casting investments.

As will be discussed in detail, the casting investments are not only refractory materials for withstanding the comparatively high temperatures met with during the casting procedure, but they are also used to provide compensation for the pattern and gold shrinkages previously discussed.

In order to be efficient in modern dental casting practice, an investment should have the following properties: (1) The constituents should segregate neither while in the container nor during manipulation. (2) The investment should mix with the water so as to give a smooth consistency, and (3) it should not set too rapidly or too slowly. (4) It should have a fineness of particles and a composition such that the surface smoothness of the casting will not be impaired. (5) It should contain no ingredients which are injurious to the casting metal. (6) It should neither crack nor give off offensive odors when heated. (7) It should have sufficient setting and/or thermal expansion for shrinkage compensation. (8) The temperature of maximum thermal expansion (*i. e.*, casting temperature) should not be critical, and such a temperature should be within the range of normal dental practice. (9) It should have a reasonably high crushing strength. (10) It should have sufficient porosity to vent the air from the mold during casting.

Composition.—The chemical composition of 39 casting investments[7] is shown in Table XLIV. As previously mentioned, the main constituents are plaster of Paris and silica; the approximate amount of the latter is shown in column three of the table. The boric acid is introduced to produce more uniform thermal expansion as will be discussed later, and possibly to increase the strength; graphite is

TABLE XLIV
PROPERTIES OF CASTING INVESTMENTS

Sample.	Chemical composition.*				Setting expansion (per cent).	Thermal expansion from room temperature to 700° C. (per cent).	Crushing strength (lb./ sq. in.).
	Plaster of Paris (per cent).	Insoluble matter† (per cent).	Boric acid (per cent).	Graphite (per cent).			
1	54.5	42.0	0.2	...	.28	+.08	1880
2	54.0	35.0	0.3	...	.25	−.64	1560
3	49.5	50.0	...	...	.16	−.01	1280
4	46.0	50.0	...	...	.24	−.20	760
5	45.5	54.0	...	...	.26	.03	1810
6	41.5	52.0	...	...	.18	.17	500
7	40.0	50.0	...	...	.25	.58	730
8	37.5	59.0	1.8	...	.33	.66	640
9	37.5	60.0	...	...	.38	.61	1700
10	37.5	57.0	...	5.0	.45	.32	590
11	36.5	54.0	...	...	.27	.68	1160
12	35.5	60.0	...	...	.01	.60	780
13	35.0	58.5	0.3	...	.25	−.15	210
14	34.5	58.5‡	...	...	.21	−.21	340
15	34.0	62.5	...	1.8	.23	.53	1090
16	33.5	61.5	...	2.1	.16	.59	1160
17	32.5	45.5	...	...	.18	.47	870
18	32.0	35.0§	...	...	.08	.48	2140
19	32.0	66.0	1.5	...	.32	.78	360
20	31.0	64.0	1.0	...	.02	.68	440
21	30.5	65.5	...	...	.34	.78	470
22	30.5	69.0	...	...	.25	.59	1070
23	29.0	71.0	...	...	.24	.82	720
24	29.0	57.0	...	3.0	.27	.57	1350
25	28.0	69.0	...	0.6	.33	.76	980
26	27.5	69.5	...	...	.25	.62	1230
27	26.5	72.0	0.5	...	.30	.75	300
28	26.5	70.0	...	...	.31	.81	570
29	26.0	73.0	...	...	.26	.64	770
30	26.0	71.5	...	...	.30	.63	900
31	26.0	70.0	...	...	.30	.82	820
32	25.5	73.0	0.8	...	.37	.80	440
33	25.0	74.0	...	...	.32	.89	260
34	24.5	75.0	...	...	.34	1.27	990
35	24.5	68.5	1.1	...	.12	.73	340
36	24.5	74.5	...	...	.49	.85	560
37	22.5	75.5	...	...	.18	.76	260
38	20.0	79.5	...	...	.31	.70	540
39	19.5	78.5	1.8	...	.29	.82	250

* No attempt was made to determine coloring matter or small amounts of impurities.

† Mainly silicious.

‡ Contains asbestos fiber.

§ 29.5 per cent magnesium oxide.

supposed to provide a reducing atmosphere when casting. Other materials occasionally used for this purpose are copper, aluminum, and calcium and barium oxides.[3]

The following formulae, taken from patent specifications, are probably indicative of the composition of modern investments:

I[4]	Grams.
Silica 200–400 mesh......................................	65
Alpha gypsum (ball milled about three hours)...............	30
Andalusite, finely ground................................	5
Boric acid...	2
Alundum..	1

II[5]	Grams.
Alpha gypsum..	40
Powdered silica..	60
Gum arabic...	$\frac{1}{2}$

III[6]	Per cent.
Plaster of Paris..	45.0
Silica..	54.2
Sodium chloride..	0.8

Plaster of Paris.—The plaster of Paris or alpha gypsum acts as a binder in the investment, and thus provides strength. Any quick-setting variety of plaster of Paris may be used; the chemistry and physics of these varieties were discussed in Chapters VI to VIII.

Silica.—Silica, SiO_2, occurs in at least four varieties of dental interest: quartz (sand), tridymite, cristobalite, and fused quartz. All of these varieties are chemically identical, but are physically different; all are crystalline in nature with different space lattices, with the exception of fused quartz, which is amorphous. Quartz and cristobalite are of particular interest in connection with dental investments. Cristobalite is found rarely in nature, and methods of producing it artificially at a low cost have only recently been perfected. It is now produced by heating certain forms of silica above 1470° C. (2678° F.), when the quartz changes by inversion to cristobalite. As a matter of fact, such inversions may occur between all four forms of quartz at suitable temperatures. Table XLV[1] shows some of the possible inversions of quartz, tridymite, and cristobalite at different temperatures.

TABLE XLV

INVERSIONS POSSIBLE WITH SILICA AT DIFFERENT TEMPERATURES

Temperature.	Quartz.	Tridymite.	Cristobalite.
Below 870° C. (1598° F.)..	No change.	To quartz.	To tridymite or quartz.
870–1470° C. (1598–2678° F.)...................	To cristobalite or tridymite.	No change.	To tridymite.
1470° C. (2678° F.) to melting point..............	To cristobalite.	To cristobalite.	No change.

The changes in dimension with temperature of these forms of silica are of interest, and are shown in Fig. 70.[2] The curves for quartz and cristobalite are fairly regular until a temperature is reached when an allotropic change, or inversion, takes place. This inversion temperature of quartz is approximately 500° to 600° C. (932°–1112° F.), whereas that of the cristobalite is approximately 210° to 246° C. (410°–474° F.).[1] The forms of silica, occurring before and after inversion are known as *low quartz* and *high quartz*, and *low cristobalite*

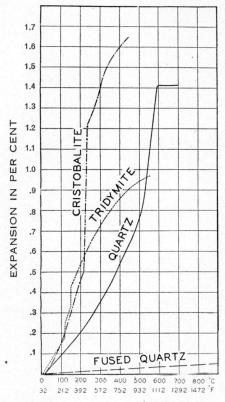

Fig. 70.—Thermal expansion curves of four forms of silica. (Volland and Paffenbarger: Jour. Amer. Dent. Assoc., February, 1932.)

and *high cristobalite* respectively, the inversion being accompanied by considerable expansion. . Tridymite is of interest only as it occurs purposely or as an impurity with cristobalite. Fused quartz exhibits no inversion at temperatures employed in casting, and further shows a very low thermal expansion. Any of these types may be used as refractory materials in the investment, but they must be selected upon the basis of other properties, such as thermal expansion, according to the use to which they are to be adapted.

The combinations of silica and plaster, as used in dental investments, are quite varied. The effect of varying the composition is so marked that it will be discussed somewhat in detail.

Crushing Strength.—The crushing strength of the investment is of importance, particularly in the case of large one-piece castings, where the investment may be required to serve as a cast. During the actual casting of the molten metal, the investment must obviously be strong enough to withstand the impact of the liquid metal as it pours into the mold.

In general, the greater the plaster content of the investment, the greater will be its crushing strength, although fineness and type of plaster used will also be factors in this respect. For example, the use of alpha gypsum definitely increases the strength of an investment over ordinary plaster, all factors being equal. Furthermore, the more water used in mixing, the less will be the strength of the investment.

Since the investments are always heated previously to casting, the effect of temperature upon the crushing strength is of interest. Coleman[8] has studied such an effect in connection with an investment of approximate composition 30 per cent plaster and 70 per cent silica, mixed in the proportion of 100 parts of powder to 46 parts of water by weight. His results are shown in Table XLVI. The mold tem-

TABLE XLVI

Effect of Temperature on Compressive Strength of an Investment Material

Temperature.	Crushing strength without cooling (lb./sq. in.).	Crushing strength at room temperature after rapid cooling (lb./sq. in.).	Crushing strength at room temperature after cooling slowly (lb./sq. in.).
Room temperature.	310		
150° C. (302° F.)	160	151	
200° C. (392° F.)	178	112	80
300° C. (572° F.)	246	85	72
400° C. (752° F.)	286	89	69.
500° C. (932° F.)	258	107	83
600° C. (1112° F.)	199	37	44
700° C. (1292° F.)	252		
800° C. (1472° F.)	252	39	50

perature, at which the casting is made, is usually 700° C. (1292° F.), at which temperature the crushing strength is but slightly lower than the original strength. However, if the mold is allowed to cool, the crushing strength of the investment decreases alarmingly; hence, a cooling of the mold before casting is not indicated.

American Dental Association Specification No. 2 requires a minimum crushing strength of 350 pounds per square inch for inlay investments, measured seven days after pouring. Most of the inlay investments on the market at the present time meet this requirement without difficulty; however, model investments should have a greater crushing strength than this.

Setting Time.—The setting time of investments is controlled in the same manner as described for plaster (pp. 47, 48), since the plaster content is the sole determinant in this regard. For casting purposes, the initial setting time should not be less than five minutes, or longer than thirty minutes, the longer setting times being used in wax expansion casting technics. For the more modern casting methods, the initial setting time may be from seven to ten minutes.

Fig. 71.—Comparator used in determining the setting characteristics of casting investments. (Taylor, Paffenbarger, and Sweeney: Jour. Amer. Dent. Assoc., December, 1930.)

Setting Expansion.—The setting expansion of investments is due to the plaster content, and the discussion of this phenomenon in connection with plasters, given on pages 48 to 50, applies equally well to these products. At the present state of progress in casting, a certain amount of investment setting expansion seems desirable, as a partial means of shrinkage compensation. For most investments, the setting expansion is approximately between 0.1 and 0.5 per cent in magnitude.

The setting expansion is measured for testing purposes by placing the investment in a trough lined with waxed paper. Markers are placed at either end upon which comparator microscopes are focused; such an equipment is illustrated in Fig. 71. The expansion so determined is the value generally claimed by the manufacturers, and

17

appears on the investment container; it will be hereafter designated as the *normal setting expansion,* since it is determined under conditions of complete freedom of movement.

Effective Setting Expansion.—It is questionable whether the normal setting expansion is always effective in expanding a wax pattern to the full amount as determined by the method outlined. The fact that the setting expansion may be considerably reduced by friction and other similar causes is well known to experimenters in this field. For example, the technic of placing the waxed paper in the trough of the apparatus shown in Fig. 71 may have considerable effect, from a research standpoint, upon the magnitude of the observed ex-

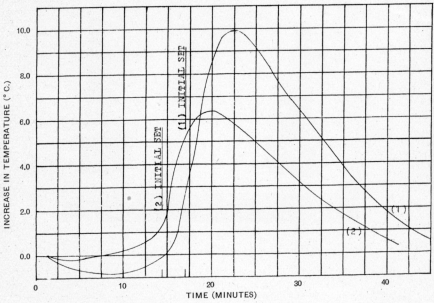

Fig. 72.—Temperature changes during the setting of two inlay investments. W/P ratio of 0.3 used in both cases.

pansion. It is evident, therefore, that such an expansion may be confined also by wax patterns, particularly the three or more surface types.

The actual mechanism by which a mesio-occluso-distal pattern is made larger during the setting of the investment is of interest. Since the setting expansion is so readily confined, it should be evident that the phenomenon is not entirely due to an actual stretching of the wax during set. If such were the case, presumably such an expansive force would be limited in value with the result that the thicker the pattern, the less its expansion would be, a fact which is observed in neither clinical nor laboratory practice. It has been shown[9] that the major portion of the effect of the setting expansion upon the wax pattern is due to the heat of reaction of the plaster during set. The action is one of thermal expansion of the wax pattern, by virtue of the rise in temperature occurring during the setting of the investment; the pattern thus expands thermally at the same time the investment setting expansion is taking place. Such a theory allows all inlay patterns, regardless of size, to expand equally in the same investment without confining the expansion, so long as heat is supplied from the chemical reactions involved.

Fig. 72 shows the heat evolved by two commercial dental investments during set when mixed by proportions and methods ordinarily employed in dental practice. Curve (1) represents Investment I, which contains 45 per cent plaster, and curve (2), Investment II, containing 25 per cent plaster. As may be noted, the rise in tem-

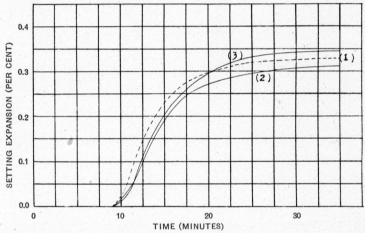

Fig. 73.—Normal and effective setting expansions of an investment containing 45 per cent plaster. Curve (1), normal setting expansion, curves (2) and (3), effective setting expansion, using pattern thickness 0.8 mm. and 2 mm. respectively. W/P ratio 0.3.

perature starts soon after the initial set, the major portion occurring before the final set. The effect of this temperature rise was studied by confining the investment in wax troughs closed at the ends, and observing the changes in dimension of the wax by means of a comparator similar to the equipment in Fig. 71. Using Investment I and a popular brand of inlay wax, the results shown in Fig. 73 were found. Curve (1) represents the normal setting expansion, whereas curves (2) and (3) represent the expansions obtained with wax patterns respectively 0.8 mm. and 2 mm. in thickness. As may be noted, the values of the respective expansions agree, within the limits of experimental error, regardless of the thickness of the wax. Assuming that the temperature change was 9.9° C. (17.8° F.) as shown for Investment I in Fig. 72, the thermal wax expansion, as computed from data for the particular wax used, is found to be 0.36 per cent, whereas the average setting expansion for the three trials shown in Fig. 73 is 0.33 per cent, which values are in agreement as well as might be expected.

However, if the expansion of the pattern during set is connected with thermal wax expansion as postulated, Investment II should expand the pattern less than its own normal setting expansion, since the maximum temperature reached during setting is only 6.3° C. (11.3° F.) (Fig. 72, Curve [2]). The expansion of the wax pattern when using this investment is shown by curve (2), Fig. 74, whereas curve (1) is the normal setting expansion. Only 52 per cent of the normal setting expansion is attained by the investment confined by the pattern; the exact value of the latter expansion is 0.17 per cent, whereas the thermal wax expansion, computed as before, is 0.16 per cent. Hence, it may be concluded that any wax pattern of a type which

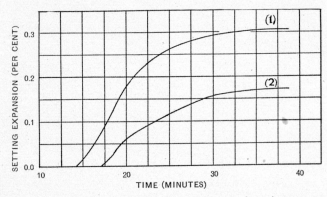

Fig. 74.—Normal and effective setting expansion of an investment containing 25 per cent plaster. Curve (1), normal setting expansion, curve (2), effective expansion, using pattern thickness 2 mm. W/P ratio 0.3.

confines the investment (three surface, full crowns, etc.) expands thermally during the investment setting expansion, its amount being dependent upon the heat of reaction between the plaster and water, the latter being, in turn, generally proportional to the plaster content of the investment. The actual expansion of the pattern during set will be hereafter designated as the *effective setting expansion,* in order to distinguish it from the normal setting expansion previously described.

The normal setting expansion may be controlled by the same methods as described for plaster of Paris. In general, the greater the amount of water used, the less will be both the normal and effective expansions, but not necessarily proportionately less. Within limits, the longer the mix is spatulated, the greater will be the normal setting expansion. A casting ring must always be lined with a strip of asbestos sheet, otherwise the setting expansion will be confined, with the result of distorting the mold. The asbestos acts as a cushion, thus allowing the setting expansion to take place unimpeded.

Hygroscopic Setting Expansion.—Another type of expansion which occurs during the setting of the investment under certain conditions is known as *hygroscopic setting expansion*.[10] It occurs if water is allowed to come in contact with the investment during or after the

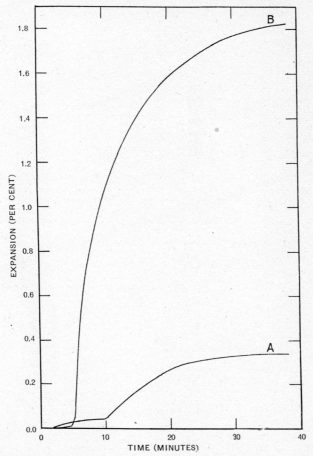

Fig. 75.—Hygroscopic expansion of an investment. Curve A, normal setting expansion. Curve B, hygroscopic expansion, water added five minutes after beginning spatulation. W/P ratio 0.3.

initial set. The magnitude of the expansion may be very large, even greater than 2 per cent in some cases. Fig. 75 shows this effect as exhibited by a popular commercial investment, curve A being its normal setting expansion, and curve B the hygroscopic setting expansion obtained by immersing a specimen in water at 39° C. (102° F.) five minutes after commencing spatulation. The reasons for this phenomenon are not specifically understood at the present time, although it may possibly be due to the absorption of water in the intercrystalline spaces during crystallization, similar to the phenomenon connected with the swelling of a dry sponge when it is immersed in water.

Thermal Expansion.—In modern casting methods, the principal means of shrinkage compensation is the thermal expansion of the investment mold; hence, a study of this property in connection with

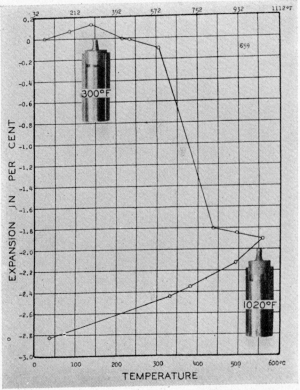

Fig. 76.—Thermal expansion curve of plaster of Paris. (Volland and Paffenbarger: Jour. Amer. Dent. Assoc., February, 1932.)

dental investments is very important. The thermal expansion is brought about by heating the mold to a temperature of 700° C. (1292° F.), when the alloy is cast. The amount of thermal expansion obtained is very largely a function of the plaster-quartz content of the investment.

The thermal expansion of plaster is shown in Fig. 76.[2] A small expansion occurs up to a temperature slightly above the boiling point of water, which is followed by a marked contraction as the temperature increases. As may be observed from the photographs of the castings made with molds at the various temperatures indicated, plaster of Paris is very poor as an investing medium. The observed contractions are undoubtedly connected with the loss of the water of crystallization of the plaster at the various temperatures.

Referring again to Fig. 70, the advantage of combining quartz or cristobalite with plaster of Paris becomes evident; their large thermal expansions may be employed not only to counteract the thermal contraction of the plaster, but also to produce an investment with con-

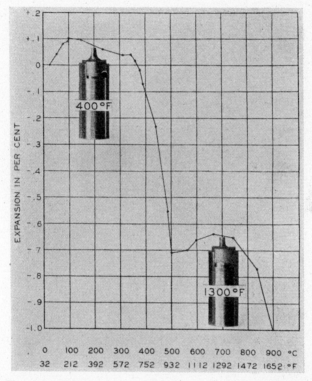

Fig. 77.—Thermal expansion curve of 55 per cent plaster of Paris investment. (Volland and Paffenbarger: Jour. Amer. Dent. Assoc., February, 1932.)

siderable thermal expansion. Figs. 77 to 79[2] show the effect of quartz upon the investment thermal expansion when combined with plaster as follows: plaster 55 per cent, quartz 45 per cent (Fig. 77); plaster 40 per cent, quartz 60 per cent (Fig. 78); and plaster 25 per cent, quartz 75 per cent (Fig. 79). As may be observed, the gradual increase in quartz content causes increased thermal expansion, but not until 75 per cent of quartz is added does the initial contraction of the plaster entirely disappear. In each case, it should be observed that the maximum expansion occurs at the inversion temperature of the quartz; furthermore, in no case is the thermal expansion sufficient to produce a well-fitting casting.

Fig. 80[2] shows the thermal expansion of an investment composition 25 per cent plaster and 75 per cent cristobalite. Cristobalite is very evidently more efficient as an expanding agent than the quartz; not only is its expansion much greater, but also its inversion occurs at a lower temperature, thus completely eradicating the initial contraction of the plaster. Furthermore, it reaches a sufficiently high

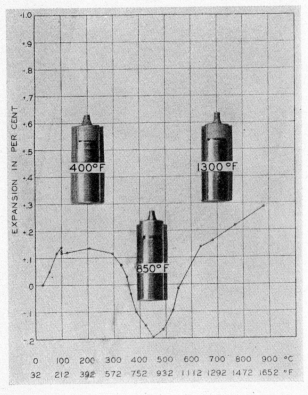

Fig. 78.—Thermal expansion curve of 40 per cent plaster of Paris investment. (Volland and Paffenbarger: Jour. Amer. Dent. Assoc., February, 1932.)

expansion value at a lower temperature than do the investments containing quartz; as may be noted from the castings, any temperature between 500° and 900° C. (932°–1652° F.) produces satisfactory results. It is not to be inferred, however, that a satisfactory investment cannot be made from quartz and plaster; if a setting expansion of 0.3 per cent is added to the thermal expansion of the investment shown in Fig. 79, for example, the compensation should be sufficient to compensate for the gold shrinkage. However, the cris-

tobalite investments are the only inlay mold materials available
which will give sufficient thermal expansion alone for this purpose.

Effect of Water : Powder Ratio.—Presumably, all of the curves
shown thus far were obtained by using identical ratios of investment
to water. The effect of varying water : powder ratios is shown in Fig.
81.[2] The ratios used are signified by proportions of water to powder;
for example, W/P = 0.30 would signify a mix of 30 parts of water to
100 parts of investment by weight, or 15 parts of water to 50 parts

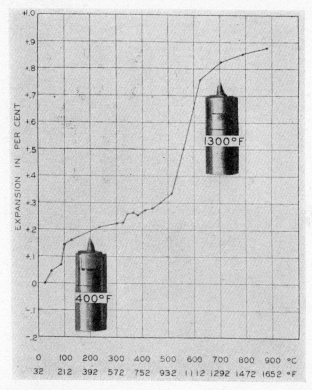

Fig. 79.—Thermal expansion curve of 25 per cent plaster of Paris investment.
(Volland and Paffenbarger: Jour. Amer. Dent. Assoc., February, 1932.)

of investment by weight, etc. Hence, in the figure the weight of the
water used, divided by the weight of the investment is in the proportion of 0.30, 0.40, and 0.50 respectively. As may be noted, the more
water used in the mix, the less is the thermal expansion. From a practical standpoint this means that the water and investment must be
carefully weighed before each operation, if the thermal expansion is to
be controlled accurately.

American Dental Association Specification No. 2 requires a minimum thermal expansion of 0.7 per cent at 700° C. (1292° F.), no

contraction less than the original size above 200° C. (392° F.), and at no temperature must a contraction greater than 0.15 per cent occur. A good casting investment will more than meet these requirements for thermal change. Another desirable feature of an investment is that it should come to its maximum thermal expansion value at or less than 700° C. (1292° F.), and maintain a relatively uniform size as the temperature rises higher, within limits. This insures that the casting

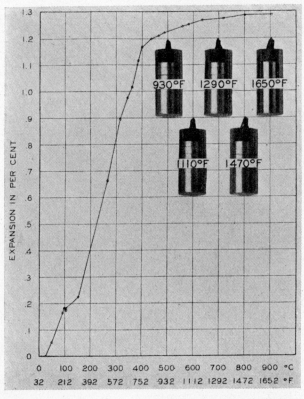

Fig. 80.—Thermal expansion curve, cristobalite investment. (Volland and Paffenbarger: Jour. Amer. Dent. Assoc., February, 1932.)

temperature is not critical, and that it can be gauged by the color of the mold, rather than requiring the use of a pyrometer.

Effect of Chemicals.—The introduction of certain chemicals, such as boric acid or sodium chloride, is quite effective in preventing the initial thermal contraction, even though the plaster content may be comparatively high. The effect of sodium chloride upon the thermal expansion of an investment of composition 45 per cent plaster and 55 per cent quartz is shown in Fig. 82.[11] The elimination of the initial contraction with the addition of sodium chloride in very small amounts is striking. It is evident that the addition of more than 0.8 per cent of the chemical has but little effect. An investment of approximate composition 45 per cent alpha gypsum, 54.2 per cent quartz, and 0.8 per cent sodium chloride exhibits a thermal expansion of approximately 1.05 per cent at 700° C. (1292° F.) when mixed with a water : powder ratio of 0.28. This expansion, together with a setting expansion of approximately 0.38 per cent, is sufficient for most casting compensation. The large alpha gypsum content gives the investment a dry crushing

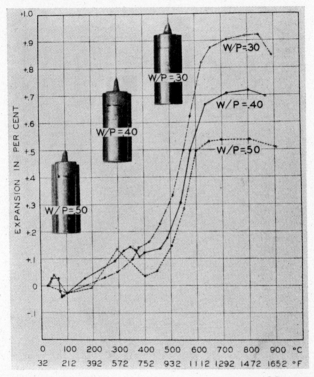

Fig. 81.—Thermal expansion curves, 20 per cent plaster of Paris investment, with varying water :investment ratios. (Volland and Paffenbarger: Jour. Amer. Dent. Assoc., February, 1932.)

strength of approximately 2500 pounds per square inch, which is of advantage, as the material may be used universally for inlays or large one-piece castings.

Thermal Contraction.—After an investment is heated to 700° C. (1292° F.), its thermal contraction curve tends to follow the expansion curve, to some extent at least, as illustrated in Fig. 83. This fact is of considerable importance in casting, as will be pointed out later. In general, the thermal contraction of investments to room temperature, after being heated to 700° C. (1292° F.), is usually greater than the thermal expansion to this temperature; in many cases the mold may be 1 per cent or more smaller than it was originally at room temperature. Hence, the necessity of casting into a hot mold is evident. Upon reheating an investment after it has cooled in air, it generally recovers its original expansion; however, such reheating is somewhat unsafe,

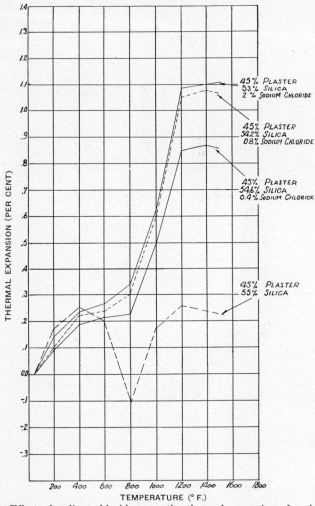

Fig. 82.—Effect of sodium chloride upon the thermal expansion of an investment. (Courtesy of the Ransom and Randolph Co.)

as the investment may have cracked while cooling, a condition which would obviously lower its crushing strength and cause surface roughness of the casting.

Fineness.—The fineness of the investment powder is very important in connection with the obtaining of smooth castings. In fact, the

finer the investment, the smaller will be the number of surface irregularities which may be expected. Specification requirements for
fineness are that all the powder shall pass a No. 30 standard sieve,
95 per cent shall pass a No. 100 sieve, and 85 per cent must go through
a 200-mesh sieve.

Porosity.—When the molten metal is forced into the mold, obviously, the air must escape if the mold is to be completely filled.
The common method for venting is through the pores of the investment; hence, the porosity of the molding material is of importance.

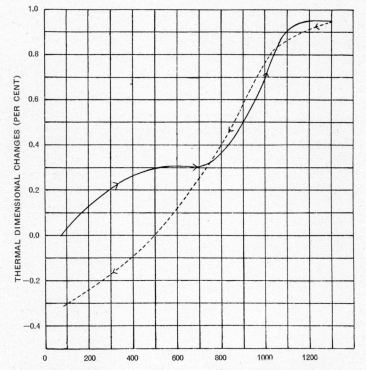

Fig. 83.—Thermal contraction of an investment, W/P ratio 0.28.

In general, the more plaster present in the investment, and the
less water used in mixing, the less will be the porosity.[12] Although
it might be thought that the coarser the investment, the greater is the
porosity, such is not necessarily the case. It has been found[7] that the
porosity is more nearly a function of uniformity of particle size, than
of the size of the largest particles. Many of the finely ground casting
investments of uniform particle size exhibit greater porosity than do
some of the coarser soldering investments.

Manipulation.—As with plaster of Paris, investments must be kept
dry and clean in air-tight containers, in order that the physical and

chemical properties may be maintained reliably constant as long as the investment may last.

In order to control the setting and thermal expansions with any pretension of accuracy, the investment and water must be proportioned accurately; the investment should be weighed on scales which are sensitive at least to one-tenth of a gram, and the water may be measured by means of a graduated cylinder. If the tap water of the locality in which the work is done contains sufficient chemicals to change any of the properties of the investment, distilled or rain water should be used.

The water and investment are placed in the plaster bowl and jarred for the purpose of removing any trapped air. A hand spatula is then slowly moved through the mixture, until the water has soaked through all of the powder, after which it is mechanically spatulated for a specified time. The avoidance of large air bubbles is of prime importance in casting, hence the use of a mechanical spatulator is imperative. The amount of spatulation is standardized either by timing with a watch, or by counting the number of turns of the spatulator; such standardization should be maintained since the method and time of spatulation has an effect upon the magnitude of the setting expansion and setting time.

After completing the spatulation, the mix should be thoroughly vibrated so as to remove all incorporated air. The material is now ready for forming the mold, the method of which is to be described in Chapter XXXI.

Specifications.—American Dental Association Specification No. 2. See Appendix, page 382.

LITERATURE

1. Sweeney, W. T., *Cristobalite for Dental Investment.* J. A. D. A., 20: 108–119 (Jan.) 1933.

2. Volland, R. H., and Paffenbarger, G. C., *Cast Gold Inlay Technic.* J. A. D. A., 19: 185–205 (Feb.) 1932.

3. U. S. Patent 1,953,075.

4. U. S. Patent 1,901,052.

5. U. S. Patent 1,901,053.

6. U. S. Patent 1,924,874.

7. Taylor, N. O., Paffenbarger, G. C., and Sweeney, W. T., *Dental Inlay Casting Investments: Physical Properties and a Specification.* J. A. D. A., 17: 2266–2286 (Dec.) 1930.

8. Coleman, R. L., *Physical Properties of Dental Materials.* Research Paper No. 32, p. 930. U. S. Government Printing Office.

9. Skinner, E. W., *The Role of Investment Setting Expansion in Gold Compensation Casting Techniques.* Dent. Cos., 75: 1009–1018 (Oct.) 1933.

10. Scheu, C. H., *A New Precision Casting Technic.* J. A. D. A., 19: 630–633 (April) 1932.

11. U. S. Patent 1,924,874.

12. Reference (8), p. 932.

CHAPTER XXX

GENERAL INTRODUCTION TO DENTAL CASTING

ALTHOUGH gold castings of any size may be made from a complete denture base to the smallest inlay, in general only the construction of the smaller pieces will be discussed. The fundamental principles involved are the same for the large one-piece castings as for the inlays and crowns, but the manipulation in the construction of the former is slightly different from the latter.

Historical.—So far as can be ascertained, B. F. Philbrook of Iowa was the first to cast a gold inlay. He read a paper describing his methods in 1897 before the Iowa State Dental Society,[1] but for some reason his work failed to receive wide recognition. Hence Dr. W. H. Taggart is generally given the credit for first introducing the cast gold inlay to the dental profession, although Philbrook antedated him by ten years.

Nevertheless, it must be admitted that a new era in dentistry started in 1907, when Taggart read his now famous paper[2] before the New York Odontological Society on casting inlays in one piece. Although Taggart's method has been improved considerably, yet in its essence it is still in use, viz., the preparation of a wax pattern, the method of its investing and elimination, and casting under pressure.

Dr. Taggart realized that gold contracts when solidifying. After the gold has been melted and forced into the mold, he states:[2] "While it (the gold) is in this freshly molded condition the pressure is maintained for a few moments, in order to allow the molten gold to thoroughly congeal; either this continued pressure prevents the gold from contracting, or the amount of expansion in the hot mold is equal to it; at any rate the filling fits."

As the profession became more critical of this new invention, it became apparent that the inlays did not fit, and the reasons for the discrepancies were ardently sought. There are at least two pioneers in this field who should be mentioned: Doctors Weston A. Price and C. S. Van Horn.

In a paper by Price[3] at the National Dental Association Meeting in Denver, July 20, 1910, 12 variables were noted, all of which he recognized as contributing to faulty casting. Quoting from his paper the variables are as follows:

"(1) Change in the dimensions of the impression or the pattern by the cooling when removing.

271

"(2) Change in the dimensions of this impression or pattern material by change in temperature when investing.

"(3) Change in the shape of the pattern due to the elasticity of the wax.

"(4) Change in the dimensions of this investing medium in its process of setting.

"(5) Change in dimensions of this investing medium in the process of heating, or heating and cooling.

"(6) Effects of the wax or pattern material on the investing medium.

"(7) Change in the investment dimensions from the pressure of the gold when casting.

"(8) Action of the molten gold on the investing medium.

"(9) Change in dimensions of the gold with its change of state from liquid to solid.

"(10) Change in dimensions of the cooling gold.

"(11) Distortion of the mold in the investing medium by the cooling gold.

"(12) Stretching of the gold if held when cooling."

No better summary of the variables involved can be given at the present date. The paper was considerably ahead of its time, since with the materials available these variables could not possibly have been overcome; hence, the ideas were lost sight of and many of the variables have been rediscovered within the last few years.

Price attempted to control these variables, and gave considerable data concerning the thermal expansions of waxes and crushing strengths of investments. It should be noted that he is silent on wax flow as a variable.

Dr. Price's work was somewhat theoretical in nature, and he failed, in some degree at least, to apply his data to a casting technic which could be used by the practicing dentist. Van Horn presented the first paper[4] outlining a practical technic which would successfully compensate for the shrinkage of gold and wax. This paper was read before the Susquehanna Dental Association at its annual meeting on May 24, 1910. Van Horn recognized the most important of Price's twelve variables, although working independently.

He advocated taking advantage of the thermal expansion of the wax pattern together with that of the investment as means of shrinkage compensation. The technic consisted of investing the pattern in a warm investment mix made by mixing with water at 115° to 120° F. (46°–49° C.). While the investment was setting, the ring was immersed in a water bath at a temperature of 110° F. (43.4° C.), which expanded the wax thermally. The pattern was eliminated by heat, and the casting was made in a mold heated to redness. Dr. Van Horn has done extensive and valuable research in casting and has published numerous articles on the subject. He is undoubtedly one of the foremost investigators in this field at the present date.

The Dental Group at the National Bureau of Standards, together with the Cooperative Research Group under the auspices of the Dental Research Commission of the American Dental Association have made outstanding as well as fundamental contributions to this field.

Due to the standardization and improvement of materials, casting technic has reached a precision far in advance of a few years ago. However, there are still many refinements to be made.

Theory.—The one objective of the casting procedure is to cast an inlay which is an exact duplicate of the missing tooth structure.

It is a physical law that lowering the temperature of a body causes it to contract, and conversely, if heat is applied, it expands. As already noted (see page 239) gold alloys contract 1.25 per cent when solidifying. However, there are other contractions involved, the principal one being that of the wax. Room temperature is usually lower than mouth temperature; therefore, when the pattern is obtained in the mouth and removed, its contraction averages approximately 0.4 per cent from mouth to a room temperature of 68° F. (20° C.).* If the room temperature is higher than this, it will contract less. Whatever the contraction is it must be added to that of the gold.

A few years ago, dental clinics were surfeited with men demonstrating various casting technics. Many times they would get excellent results *on a model*, but it should be noted that such a test is unfair. In order to fit a model it is necessary to compensate only for the gold shrinkage, since the shrinkage of the pattern is negligible in this case, provided that the wax is manipulated properly. Many of these technics had to be either improved or discarded when used practically.

As in balancing a ledger, the shrinkage must be balanced by certain compensation methods, if the restoration is to fit in the mouth. Obviously, if a contraction is to be overcome, it must be done by a counteracting expansion. In the cases cited above, the wax pattern at room temperature will be too small by an amount equal to the wax contraction (0.4 per cent) plus the gold contraction (1.25 per cent), thus making a total contraction of 1.65 per cent. Therefore, in order for the casting to fit the tooth, the mold must be made 1.65 per cent larger at the time of casting than the pattern was at the room temperature of 68° F. This accomplishment is known as *compensation*.

The compensation may be achieved by any one, or combination, of the following three methods:

1. Thermal expansion of the wax pattern.
2. Setting expansion of the investment.
3. Thermal expansion of the investment.

In other words, the casting materials and procedure must be selected with the necessary compensation in mind. A hypothetical problem may be given as an example of the computation necessary: assume that a pattern, made in the mouth, is to be invested at a room temperature of 68° F. (20° C.). The investment has an effective setting expansion of 0.3 per cent, and a thermal expansion of 0.7 per cent at 1300° F. (704° C.). What technic shall be used?

* Assuming that the wax pattern is homogeneous, and cooled without pressure.

18

The contractions are first added up and then balanced against the compensations available in the investment:

Contraction.		Compensation.	
Wax contraction from 98–68°		Investment setting expansion.	= 0.30%
F	= 0.40%	Investment thermal expansion	
Contraction of gold	= 1.25	at 1300° F. (704° C.)	= 0.70
Total contraction	= 1.65%	Total investment expansion...	= 1.00
		Needed wax thermal expansion	= 0.65
		Total expansion	= 1.65%

When the investment setting and thermal expansions are added together, it will be noted that the compensation is 0.65 per cent short of balancing the contraction, which may be compensated by taking advantage of the thermal expansion of the pattern. A water bath is prepared at a temperature computed from the thermal expansion curve of the wax used, so that a wax expansion of 0.65 per cent will occur in the pattern while the investment is setting.

Wax Expansion Technic.—The entire technic will be somewhat as follows: the investment and water are mixed in the exact proportions required to give the correct setting and thermal expansions. The water should be at a temperature of approximately 5° F. (2.8° C.) above the computed temperature for the water bath, in order to allow for cooling while investing. The case is invested, and immediately placed in the bath at the computed temperature, until the investment has completely set.* At this stage, the amount of compensation which has taken place includes the wax thermal expansion (0.65 per cent) plus the investment setting expansion (0.3 per cent), or a total expansion of 0.95 per cent.

The flask is then placed in an electric furnace and slowly heated until the wax is eliminated and the mold has become cherry red in color. The investment thermal expansion has now taken place, giving the total required compensation of 1.65 per cent, and the gold is cast with the mold at this temperature. When the mold has cooled to room temperature the casting is 1.25 per cent smaller than the mold at red heat, and 0.4 per cent larger than the pattern at room temperature, i. e., it is the same size as the pattern at mouth temperature.

It should be noted that all three of the possible compensation methods have been employed. The use of thermal wax expansion is rather undesirable, due to the inherent wax distortions as discussed in Chapter XXVIII.

Investment Thermal Expansion Technic.—At the present time there is no investment on the market which exhibits adequate thermal expansion for complete compensation under all conditions of room temperature. However, when the effective setting expansion is com-

---

* Investments used in this technic must have a setting time of twelve to eighteen minutes, in order that the wax may expand thermally before the investment thickens sufficiently to cause distortion.

bined with the thermal expansion, there are several investments which give sufficient compensation without the use of wax thermal expansion. The technic is the same as previously outlined, except that the water bath is not used.

One of the disadvantages of this technic, as ordinarily employed, is the lack of flexibility of control of the expansion. In the wax expansion technic, as outlined, the compensation for the wax contraction for various room temperatures can be controlled by varying the temperature of the water bath, but it is not feasible to control the thermal expansion of the investment by varying the casting temperature. However, it may be controlled by varying the water content of the mix; most manufacturers specify at least two water:powder ratios for mixing their investments, one giving a "thick mix," with a comparatively high thermal expansion, and the other a "thin mix" with a lower thermal expansion. However, only two choices in this respect are often insufficient, and the manufacturers might well standardize their products further by giving as many as six different water:powder ratios with the corresponding setting and thermal expansions which the dentist may employ to his advantage.

Another method of controlling the thermal expansion of the investment is to combine two investments in proper proportions, one with a low thermal expansion, and another with a high thermal expansion. Such a technic has been developed by Phillips,[5] by combining a quartz investment with one containing cristobalite. In this manner, by gradually increasing the proportion of the cristobalite investment, thermal expansions varying from 0.7 to 1.4 per cent may be obtained.

Hygroscopic Expansion Technic.—The entire compensation may be procured by the use of hygroscopic expansion.[6, 7] The most precise method of employing this technic is to cover the pattern with a small amount of investment paste which has been carefully proportioned as to water and powder. Soon after the initial set occurs, the pattern thus partially invested, is placed in a water bath at 100° to 104° F. (37°–40° C.).* The warm water softens the wax, and at the same time causes the hygroscopic expansion. In practice, a total expansion of 1.6 per cent may be realized. According to Scheu,[6] the expansion may be controlled by regulating the time after starting spatulation, at which the partially invested pattern is placed in the water bath; ordinarily the time for doing this is fifteen minutes from the beginning of spatulation, but if the time is shortened, the expansion may be increased, and if it is lengthened, the expansion may be decreased. The partially invested pattern is now surrounded by additional investment in a casting ring; the wax is eliminated at a temperature of 700° to 800° F. (371°–427° C.), and the casting procedure is carried out as usual. The technic, as outlined, gives con-

* It should be emphasized that the investment has already attained an initial set before this is done. This method is *not* a wax expansion technic.

siderable precision. However, it should be noted that it.is a double investment technic.* A single investment technic may be used, which is more nearly comparable to the usual method, but it is doubtful whether it is as accurate as the double investment procedure.

One of the disadvantages of this technic is the fact that a special investment is needed, whose hygroscopic expansion has been standard-

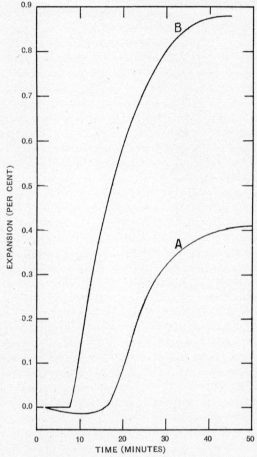

Fig. 84.—Curve A, normal setting expansion, curve B, hygroscopic expansion, due to wet asbestos liner.

ized. This is probably the reason why the technic has not been more widely adopted by the dental profession.

* *A double investment technic* is any casting technic where two different investments or powder : water ratios of the same investment are used. In general, the thicker mix is applied to the pattern as a thick coat, and then the partially invested pattern is invested in the casting ring, using a thinner mix. A *single investment technic* is distinguished by the fact that only one mix of one investment is used for the entire process.

Many dental investments exhibit considerable hygroscopic expansion when they should not, and the expansion is often a source of error in types of technics other than the hygroscopic method. For example, whenever a double investment technic is used, the thick mix may absorb water from the thin mix, and a higher total setting expansion may be obtained than is expected; in fact, the additional expansion may often act so as to cause serious distortion of certain types of patterns.[7] An unlooked for expansion may also occur in single investment technics, by the investment absorbing water from the asbestos liner while setting. Such an effect is demonstrated in Fig. 84, the lower curve (A) being the normal setting expansion of an investment, whereas the upper curve (B) represents the setting expansion of the same investment, when it is placed in an asbestos-lined casting ring. Although the asbestos is placed in the ring in order to allow an effective setting expansion to take place, as previously explained, yet it evidently may be a source of error in other respects. So far as is known, the only explanation for the effect shown in Fig. 84 is that some of the water in the asbestos is absorbed by the investment, thus causing a hygroscopic expansion. Some manufacturers have become cognizant of this error, and have eliminated the possibility of the occurrence of such an expansion in their investments.

Limitations of the Casting Theory.—The computation given in the technic illustrated above is highly theoretical; unfortunately the work is neither as simple nor as accurate as the theory would indicate. Even under the most scientifically controlled laboratory conditions, the error in casting is not less than 0.05 per cent. In a dental office, with the most skilled operator, the error will be in the neighborhood of 0.1 per cent. The perfect inlay has not been cast. By "perfect inlay" is meant the inlay which will fit the prepared cavity with an accuracy comparable to the dimensions of a single molecule of saliva; when an opening occurs larger than this dimension, there is always danger of leakage due to capillary action. Proper burnishing of the class A alloys will prevent such action, but such a procedure is not included in this discussion. Even the best inlays always show widely exposed margins under the microscope, whereas the openings should be submicroscopic in size. The greatest single uncontrolled factor is wax distortion, which cannot be entirely avoided under any conditions; hence, the inlay is likely to be inferior as a seal to the tooth structure in comparison to a correctly placed gold foil or amalgam filling. Other uncontrollable errors not under control of the operator are lack of standardization of materials by the manufacturer, and room humidity and temperature changes.

Literature

1. Philbrook, B. F., *Cast Fillings.* Trans. Iowa State Dent. Soc., pp. 277. 278, 1896–97.

2. Taggart, W. H., *A New and Accurate Method of Making Gold Inlays.* Dent. Cos., 49: 1117–1121 (Nov.) 1907.

3. Price, W. A., *The Laws Determining the Behavior of Gold in Fusing and Casting.* Dent. Cos., 53: 265–294 (March) 1911.

4. Van Horn, C. S., *Casting: A Review and Commentary, Including a Technique.* Dent. Cos., 52: 873–881 (Aug.) 1910.

5. Phillips, D. W., *A Scientifically Correct Inlay Technique.* Dent. Digest, 39: 72–81 (Feb.) 1933. *Controlled Casting.* J. A. D. A., 22: 439–451 (March) 1935.

6. Scheu, C. H., *A New Precision Casting Technic.* J. A. D. A., 19: 630–633 (April) 1932.

7. Scheu, C. H., *Controlled Hygroscopic Expansion of Investment to Compensate for Shrinkage in Inlay Casting.* J. A. D. A., 22: 452–455 (March) 1935.

CHAPTER XXXI

DENTAL CASTING PROCEDURE

OBTAINING THE WAX PATTERN

THERE are two general methods of obtaining a wax pattern, the *direct* method and the *indirect* method. There are other methods which are modifications of these, but their description is not within the scope of this book.

Direct Method.—As the name signifies, the direct method consists of constructing the pattern entirely in the mouth, as described on page 242.

After removing the pattern from the mouth, a sprue pin is attached; the pin is heated and then imbedded in the wax. Some authorities advocate attaching the sprue pin before removing the pattern from the mouth, a method which has certain advantages, inasmuch as the pin is applied while the pattern is in the prepared cavity, and any large distortions may be corrected before removal.

Whenever it is attached, it should be done with care and imbedded firmly in the wax. If the pattern is very thin, a small drop of wax may be added to give additional bulk. The position of attachment is not so important from the standpoint of the molten gold as might be expected; however, a good rule to follow is to attach the pin so that when the molten metal pours into the mold, it will always be traveling as nearly as possible in the same direction as the applied force.

Indirect Method.—The indirect method consists of obtaining an impression of the prepared cavity in modeling compound, from which a model is prepared. The compound is usually supplied in stick form, one end of which is softened and worked into the shape of a cone. A seamless copper matrix band is adapted around the tooth, and the softened compound is pressed into the enclosed cavity preparation. The compound is chilled, and the impression is withdrawn. The contraction of the compound from mouth to a room temperature of 25° C. (77° F.) averages approximately 0.3 per cent.

The materials usually employed for the construction of the model are quick-setting stone, investment, silver amalgam, and copper amalgam, all of which exhibit dimensional changes during setting; many of these changes are unpredictable in magnitude, which is likely to introduce unknown errors. For this reason the indirect method is generally conceded to be less accurate than the direct method.

Recently a copper electroplating method for making inlay models has been perfected. In brief, the method is as follows: the impression

279

is thoroughly dusted with bronze powder or lithographer's carbon in order that the surface may conduct electricity. The powder is applied with a brush and carried into every crevice and corner; at some place an electrical contact with the copper matrix band is made. A copper wire is wound around the band, and, after the copper band and the major portion of the wire have been insulated with a quick-drying varnish, the wire is attached to the negative pole of a direct current source; an anode of sheet copper is used. The two electrodes are placed in a copper sulphate bath. A current of 0.1 ampere is employed for electroplating. In approximately twelve hours a film of copper, $\frac{1}{64}$ inch in thickness, will be deposited on the impression.

The author has found the following electroplating bath to be excellent for this purpose:

Distilled water	350.0 cc.
Copper sulfate (U.S.P.)	52.5 g.
Sulfuric acid (conc., C.P.)	32.2 cc.
Ethyl alcohol	1.4 cc.

The plated impression is filled with a low-fusing alloy or quick-setting stone. If the latter is used, it should be mixed as thick as possible. The impression is then removed and a smooth accurate model will be found. An additional improvement may be made by holding the temperature of the electroplating bath at mouth temperature, which compensates for the shrinkage of the impression from mouth to room temperature. This latter refinement is particularly recommended for porcelain inlay models.

There are certain advantages in the use of the indirect method, provided that an accurate model of the tooth structure and prepared cavity can be made. The wax pattern can be obtained more easily, with the possibility of getting better adaptation. Furthermore, if an accident occurs, a new pattern can be made without calling the patient back to the chair. However, economy of time and general accuracy favor the direct method.

The pattern is made on the model in the same manner as in the mouth. If the wax is flowed on the model in a liquid condition and chilled under pressure in room temperature water, certain advantages are gained in freedom from wax distortion.

Preparation for Investing.—After the sprue pin is attached to the pattern, its other end is fastened to a *sprue base* or *crucible-former**which fits over the casting ring, and forms the crucible in the investment.

A spherical-shaped piece of wax is now placed on the sprue pin approximately $\frac{1}{16}$ inch from the pattern, in order to form a mold for a reservoir. This is done as a precaution against the occurrence of localized shrinkage. As noted on page 239, when the gold freezes,

* A typical crucible-former may be seen in the left hand of the operator in Fig. 85. The asbestos-lined casting ring is to the right in the figure.

it clings to the walls of the mold during a certain stage of the solidification, and this essentially results in a certain amount of shrinkage
toward the periphery, thus leaving voids near the center of the casting,
particularly in the region adjacent to the ingate. Hence, if the gold in
the sprue freezes before that in the casting, no more metal can pour
in from the crucible to fill up such voids. However, if a sufficient
bulk of gold remains in a reservoir, it is the last to solidify, thus permitting the voids to be filled; this fact should be borne in mind
while attaching the ball of wax to the sprue pin, as described.

The length of the sprue pin should be adjusted so that the pattern
extends to within one-third of the distance from the open end of the
casting ring, when the sprue base is placed on the latter. The case
is now ready to be invested, and this should always be done as soon
as possible after the preparation of the wax pattern, if excessive wax
distortion is to be avoided.

INVESTING THE PATTERN

The casting ring must be lined with asbestos, in order to allow the
investment setting expansion to take place. Furthermore, it is at this
stage that care must be taken to insure a smooth casting. There
are at least six causes[1] of surface roughness on castings: (1) coarse
investment; (2) too high a proportion of water used in the mix; (3)
excessive vibration of the pattern during the investing process; (4)
unclean patterns; (5) air bubbles in the investment; and (6) too
rapid rate of burning out.

All of the points except the last may be eliminated during the
investing process, assuming that the investment is sufficiently fine.
The pattern may be cleaned of all blood and other débris by washing
it with a solution of equal parts of tincture of green soap and hydrogen
peroxide.[2] Elimination of air bubbles from the investment may be
accomplished by proper spatulation as discussed on page 270, but the
avoidance of the collection of water on the wax is not so simple.

Prevention of the Collection of Water Droplets.—If a stick of
inlay wax is dipped into water, it will be noted that the water fails to
wet the surface of the wax, but rather tends to cling to it in droplets.
This results from the fact that the water exhibits little adhesion to
the wax, and, because of its high surface tension, it tends to become
spherical in shape. It is easy to understand, therefore, that such
droplets will form when placing the investment on the pattern, and,
when the wax is eliminated, every bubble thus formed will produce
a roughened area or nodule on the casting. Furthermore, the more
water present in the investment, the greater will be the danger of obtaining a rough casting in this manner; hence, extremely thin mixes of
investment for investing purposes are to be avoided.

Obviously, if the surface tension of the water can be lowered,
the liquid will have a greater tendency to form a film over the surface

of the wax instead of globulating. It is a physical fact that increasing the temperature of the water will decrease its surface tension. In this respect, any casting technic using a warm investment mix will tend to eliminate such trouble, but, as explained in Chapter XXVIII, such technics are likely to cause large distortions of the pattern; hence, any gain in smoothness is likely to be offset by poorly fitting castings.

The safest method for eliminating the collection of water on the pattern is by the use of the "investment wash." A very thin mix of investment is made of about the consistency of thick cream, which is painted thoroughly over the entire surface of the pattern with a camel's-hair brush. The excess is immediately blown off, and, if the slightest trace of wax shows through, the process is repeated, until

Fig. 85.—Coating the pattern with investment in preparation for investing. ("Metal Progress," August, 1934.)

the pattern is uniformly covered with a very thin coating of investment. The coating is so thin that it does not interfere with any subsequent setting expansion; yet when it sets, it effectively prevents any water from clinging to the wax during subsequent manipulation.

The theory underlying such a manipulation is very likely as follows: the plaster dissolves in the water, which lowers the surface tension of the latter to an extent that the mix will spread evenly over the wax.

Single Investment Technic.—The investment and water are carefully proportioned, and spatulated as described in Chapter XXIX. A small portion of the paste is transferred to the pattern by means of a camel's-hair brush as shown in Fig. 85, and is made to flow over the pattern by vibrating the sprue base; care must be taken that the viscous mass flows slowly into angles and depressions so as not to entrap air. This precaution must be observed especially in the case of full crowns; with such patterns, the investment should be added in small amounts which are flowed so that the investment runs down the inside and across the pulpal wall; this procedure is continued in this manner until the pattern is entirely filled. Excessive vibration is never indicated, particularly if the investment wash is not used, as it causes the formation of water bubbles. After the pattern has been thoroughly coated with investment, it is placed in the ring, and covered with investment. This may be done either by first filling the ring with investment, and then gently lowering the pattern with the sprue base into the investment until the end of the ring is closed, or by placing the sprue base over one end of the ring, and pouring the investment in the open end. The latter method requires more vibration than the former, to insure that the investment fills all parts of the unoccupied space in the ring. Obviously, the entire procedure must be completed before the investment approaches its initial set.

The investment is now allowed to harden for at least thirty minutes before proceeding further. Obviously the next step may be carried out at any time after the final set.

Double Investment Technic.—After applying the investment wash, a thick mix of investment may be vibrated on the pattern, which is then invested in a thinner mix; but this method is likely to present difficulties inasmuch as the first mix is apt to be unmanageably thick. One reason for the use of a double investment technic with modern investments is the increased setting and thermal expansions which are realized from the thick mix, or "core" as it is usually called.

An easier method of obtaining such a core is by means of the "dusting technic." A coat of investment is formed over the pattern as described in the previous section, but, instead of investing it at once, dry investment powder is dusted on the wet coating with the brush. The additional dry powder not only decreases the water:powder ratio of the mass, but also draws the water from the pattern, thus insuring a smoother casting. This process is continued until the pattern is entirely coated with a hard mass of investment, approximately the size and shape of a cherry. However, too much powder must not be added for the water present. Excess powder may be blown off with a blast of air.

The case is then invested immediately as described for the single investment technic. As mentioned in Chapter XXX, this method is likely to introduce an unknown amount of hygroscopic expansion with some investments; hence, the single investment technic is preferable and probably more accurate.

Influence of Relative Humidity.—It is important that a minimum amount of time be spent in investing the pattern, not only to insure that the investment does not become too thick, but also to prevent the thermal contraction of the pattern due to cooling by evaporation of the water. Of course, the higher the relative humidity, the less this effect will be, but the average dental office is very likely to have a low relative humidity, particularly when it is heated artificially.

The ultimate effect of evaporation is a definite contraction of the pattern up to the time when the investment gains its initial set; hence the pattern may be actually smaller at the time when the compensation begins than it was at room temperature.

The effect may be demonstrated by investing the bulb of a thermometer; various investing technics may be used and temperature

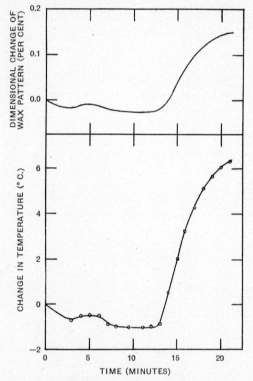

Fig. 86.—Effect of evaporation in a single investment technic. Case invested in the ring during the initial three-minute interval.

readings obtained at certain time intervals. Figs. 86 to 88 show the results of such experiments at relative humidities ranging from 35 to 45 per cent. The lower curves show the change in temperature with time, whereas the upper curves indicate the thermal response of the wax to such changes in temperature, as computed from wax thermal expansion and contraction data. An investment containing 45 per cent plaster was mixed with a water:powder ratio of 0.3 in all cases.

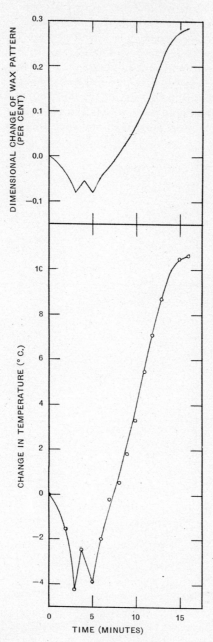

Fig. 87.—Effect of evaporation in a double investment technic. Case invested in the ring during the initial five-minute interval.

As may be observed from Figs. 86 and 87, the effect is very small if the pattern is invested at once; Fig. 86 represents the temperature change when a single investment technic is used, and Fig. 87,* the double investment powdering method. The initial set occurred at approximately the time when the temperature began to rise. A comparison of the two sets of data indicates that the effective setting expansion will be greater in the case of the double investment technic.

One casting technic advocates that the pattern be dusted with dry investment as previously described, and then that it be allowed to set

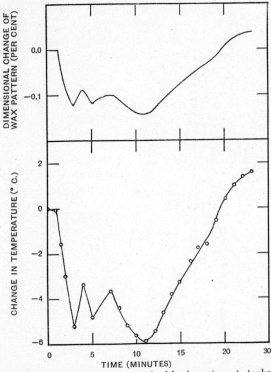

Fig. 88.—Effect of evaporation in a double investment technic, when the case is not invested in a ring. Pattern not touched after the initial ten-minute interval.

fifteen to twenty minutes before investing. Fig. 88 shows the fallacy of such a method; because of the increased surface exposed to evaporation, very little compensation by setting expansion can be realized.

All of the above theoretical considerations have been verified qualitatively by actual castings.

* The "peaks" in Figs. 87 and 88 are of interest as they occurred after dusting the pattern. The application of wet investment was always followed by a decrease in temperature which continued until dry investment was applied, when the temperature would increase slightly as shown.

ELIMINATION OF THE WAX AND HEATING OF THE MOLD

Source of Heat.—There have been many methods devised for the elimination of the wax, but most modern casting methods employ heat for this purpose. Electric heat is much superior to gas heat, as it is more uniform and easier to control.

The investment must be heated gradually, particularly at the start while the water is being driven off; otherwise steam is likely to collect in the interior, which may cause an explosion. Furthermore, too rapid heating may crack the investment, thus causing a rough casting. The cracks are formed by unequal heating. As an illustration, consider what happens if water is heated in a thick glass tumbler over a Bunsen burner; since glass is a poor thermal conductor, the portion adjacent to the flame becomes warm before the inside does. The outside portion therefore expands thermally more than the inside, and the glass cracks because of the unequal forces. The investment is also a poor thermal conductor, and cracks may occur for the same reason. Hence, the investment must be heated slowly, in order that the temperature gradient between the ring and the mold may be small.

As the temperature increases, the wax melts, boils, and finally burns. It completely volatilizes at a temperature of 700° to 800° F. (370°–427° C.) which is the casting temperature usually employed for the wax expansion and hygroscopic expansion technics. As may be noted from the investment thermal expansion curves shown in Chapter XXIX, comparatively little thermal expansion occurs in this temperature range, with the exception of cristobalite investment.

When the investment thermal expansion technic is used, the heating is continued until the sprue becomes cherry red in color, which indicates a temperature of approximately 1292° F. (700° C.). If properly observed, the color observation is sufficiently accurate for determining the casting temperature; it must be observed in a *shadow* and never under direct illumination. A good investment will maintain a constant thermal expansion value even though it is heated above its temperature of maximum expansion as much as 360° F. (200° C.). However, many investments will contract seriously when heated above their normal casting temperatures. The entire time required for thus heating the mold, starting with the heater at room temperature, is approximately forty-five minutes for the ordinary inlay case, but for large one-piece castings, the time may be as long as two to three hours, because of the large bulk of investment involved.

When the casting temperature is reached, the case is transferred to the casting machine and the casting is made immediately.

CASTING THE GOLD

Fig. 89 shows a diagrammatic picture of a cross section of the casting mold. Enough gold alloy must be used, to completely fill the mold and sprue, and leave an excess in the crucible; this excess is known as the *button*.

Time Allowable for Casting.—The operator should have all instru-- ments and materials at hand, in order that a minimum of time may be employed for the actual casting procedure. Obviously, the instant. the ring is removed from the furnace, it begins to lose heat with a consequent thermal contraction. As noted on page 267, the thermal contraction curve is somewhat similar to that of the thermal expan- sion curve at the higher temperatures. This is very fortunate, since, at this stage, the change in dimension is generally quite small in comparison with the decrease in temperature. Studies* comparing the investment thermal contraction curves as typically illustrated in Fig. 83 on page 269, with time-temperature cooling curves of the mold obtained under conditions of inlay casting procedure, indicate that little or no thermal contraction occurs within the first minute after removing the mold from the furnace at a temperature of 1292° F.

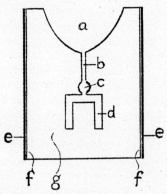

Fig. 89.—A diagrammatic representation of an inlay casting mold.   (a) Crucible, (b) ingate or sprue, (c) reservoir, (d) inlay mold, (e) casting ring, (f) asbestos liner, (g) investment.

(700° C.). The permissible time for casting will, of course, depend upon the bulk of investment used; hence, when casting large struc- tures, a longer time may be allotted.

The completion of the casting within¹ one minute is not difficult, particularly if the gold alloy is preheated. This is best done on a charcoal block; the gold is melted and fluxed if necessary. This also aids in removing the occluded oxygen (see page 240); the carbon unites with the occluded gas to form carbon dioxide and carbon monoxide which diffuse into the air.

By skillful synchronization of the work, the gold is thus preheated, then the casting ring is transferred from the furnace to the casting machine. Meanwhile, the gold will have solidified to an extent that it may be transferred quickly to the crucible, and the flame applied.

* Paper by the author at the Louisville Meeting of the International Associ- ation for Dental Research (1936).

In this manner, the casting may possibly be accomplished in a minute or less.

Casting Machines.—There are two types of casting machines in general use at the present time, air pressure and centrifugal. They

Fig. 90.—An air pressure casting machine. (Courtesy of the Detroit Dental Mfg. Co.)

are both satisfactory, and any choice between them is a matter of personal preference, rather than important differences in their efficiency.

Fig. 91.—Casting with the centrifugal machine. ("Metal Progress," August, 1934.)

An air pressure casting machine is shown in Fig. 90. The casting ring is placed on the base, the gold is melted in the ring crucible, and a plunger is brought down on top of the ring, which seals it; at the same instant, air under a gauge pressure of 8 to 12 pounds per square

19

inch is automatically applied, which forces the molten alloy into the mold.

When a centrifugal machine is used as illustrated in Fig. 91, the ring is clamped in an arm, and the gold is melted in a separate cup, instead of the crucible formed in the ring as in the case with the air pressure machine. When the arm is released, it is actuated by a spring and revolves rapidly; the gold is forced into the mold by centrifugal force.

Fusing the Gold Alloy.—The alloy is best melted by placing it on the side of the crucible rather than at the lowest point; in this position it is easier to melt, and the operator can more readily observe the completion of fusion. The fuel used by most dentists is illuminating gas and air, although other combinations may be employed such as illuminating gas and oxygen, hydrogen gas and air, acetylene gas and air, etc. The use of hydrogen gas offers certain advantages in casting when the flame is adjusted properly, inasmuch as the hydrogen may act as a reducing agent.

The *reducing zone* (see Fig. 92, page 298) of a brush flame should be used. The alloy is melted as quickly as possible by directing the flame steadily on the metal. A very slight motion of the flame will cause the gold to move slightly when it is thoroughly melted. When the gas-air blow torch is used, the danger of overheating the alloy is not great. The tendency of the beginner is to underheat the gold, with the result that the casting detail is not sharp. Little danger will result in heating the alloy 200° to 300° F. (100°–150° C.) above its fusion temperature, which gives the advantage of greater fluidity with less surface tension. At the proper casting temperature, the molten alloy exhibits a light orange color, with a clear mirror-like surface. If a film or "skin" appears, due to oxidation, a reducing flux should be quickly sprinkled over the surface of the molten alloy. Fused borax powder may be used, or else a mixture of equal parts of borax and powdered charcoal; the charcoal aids in the removing of the occluded gases.

The flame should be held on the alloy until the casting force is applied. When the casting has been accomplished, it should be quenched in water; this not only leaves the alloy in a softened condition, but also aids in freeing the pattern of investment. When the cool water comes in contact with the hot investment, a violent reaction ensues, and the investment becomes very soft and even granular. However, such treatment must not be used with large castings until the alloy is sufficiently strong that the structure will not be distorted.

After removing the casting from the investment, it is cleaned and then pickled in a 30 to 40 per cent solution of sulphuric or hydrochloric acid. The pickling removes any oxides and other débris in preparation for finishing; it is accomplished by boiling the casting in the acid.

Literature

1. Taylor, N. O., Paffenbarger, G. C., and Sweeney, W. T., *Dental Inlay Casting Investments.* J. A. D. A., 17: 2266–2286 (Dec.) 1930.

2. Dressel, R. P., *Principles of Fixed-Bridge Construction.* Reprint from Dent. Cos., June-Dec., 1930, Feb.-April, 1931, p. 25.

CHAPTER XXXII

THE JOINING OF METALS. FLUXES AND THEIR USES

WHATEVER is the method employed in joining two pieces of metal, it essentially consists of establishing cohesion between the atoms of the pieces, either directly, or indirectly through an intervening medium. *Welding* is the process of joining metals under pressure, whereas *soldering* is the process of uniting two metals by fusion, usually accomplished by the fusion of an alloy of lower melting temperature, called a *solder,* to the surfaces of the metal. *Autogenous soldering* is the process of joining by means of direct fusion of the two parts.

In any method of joining metals, the contiguous parts must be absolutely clean, and completely free of oxides. In order to dissolve such oxides and to prevent their formation while heating, a *flux* must be employed.

Welding.—The process of welding is usually carried out at a high temperature, gold foil being an exception. Hammer or forge welding consists of heating the metal to a high temperature, and then establishing cohesion by hammering; this method of welding finds little or no application in dentistry. Modern methods of welding used in industry employ electricity, either by use of the electric arc, or by the passing of an electric current of sufficient magnitude through the joint while it is held under pressure. *Spot welding* is an example of the latter method, and it is sometimes used in joining stainless steel orthodontic wires, as described in Chapter XXXVIII.

Selection of a Solder.—*Soft solders* such as are used by plumbers and tinsmiths are characterized by having a very low melting point, since they are essentially eutectiferous alloys of tin and lead; on the other hand, the solders normally used in dentistry are high fusing, and are usually classified as *hard solders.*

The requisites for a dental solder are as follows:

1. It must not be corroded or tarnished by the mouth fluids, which statement implies that it must be not only sufficiently "noble" in composition, but also that its composition must be such that its solution potential approximates that of the metal upon which it is used.

2. Its melting point must be lower than that of the metal upon which it is employed, in order that the latter may not be fused during the soldering operation. Most authorities agree that the fusion temperature of the solder should be at least 100° F. (56° C.) below that of the parts to be soldered. In most instances it is necessary

that its melting temperature be less than the recrystallization temperature of the metal.

3. Its color should match that of the metal employed.

4. It should flow promptly and smoothly over the surfaces of the parts to be joined. This property depends upon the surface tension, viscosity, and adhesive properties of the molten solder.

5. Its physical properties should be at least as good as those of the metal, in order that the joint may not be a source of weakness.

Gold Solders: Composition and Physical Properties.—The chemical composition of five commercial gold solders, as reported by Coleman,[1] are given in Table XLVII. The first three solders are recom-

TABLE XLVII
CHEMICAL COMPOSITION OF GOLD SOLDERS

Solder No.	Gold (per cent).	Silver (per cent).	Copper (per cent).	Zinc (per cent).	Tin (per cent).
I.........	65.4	15.4	12.4	3.9	3.1
II.........	66.1	12.4	16.4	3.4	2.0
III........	65.0	16.3	13.1	3.9	1.7
IV........	72.9	12.1	10.0	3.0	2.0
V.........	80.9	8.1	6.8	2.1	2.0

mended for soldering 18-carat gold, whereas the fourth is for soldering 20-carat gold, and the last for 22-carat gold. As may be noted, the fineness increases as the carat of the gold alloy to be soldered increases. The functions of the constituent metals in these compositions are essentially the same as those described for gold alloys (see p. 217); obviously, the zinc and tin are included primarily for control of the melting point, and the fineness of the alloy is governed largely by the extent to which these latter metals are introduced. Solders of varying melting ranges must be supplied for alloys of different melting points. Hence, when a manufacturer designates a solder as "18 carat," he does not usually imply that the solder itself is 18 carat, but rather that it is to be employed for soldering 18-carat gold alloy. Harder[2] gives the various finenesses of commercial solders to use with various gold alloys, as shown in Table XLVIII.

TABLE XLVIII
FINENESS OF GOLD SOLDERS AS USED FOR VARIOUS CARATS OF GOLD PLATE

	Range.	Most common.
For 22-carat gold plate.................	775–832 fine	810 fine
For 20-carat gold plate.................	715–750 fine	730 fine
For 18-carat gold plate.................	625–661 fine	650 fine
For 16-carat gold plate.................	531–569 fine	550 fine

The physical properties of the solders, whose composition is given in Table XLVII, are presented in Table XLIX. As may be noted,

TABLE XLIX

PHYSICAL PROPERTIES OF GOLD SOLDERS

Solders No.	Proportional limit (lbs./sq. in.)		Tensile strength, (lbs./sq. in.)		Elongation (3-inch gauge) (length) (per cent.)		Modulus of elasticity (lbs./sq. in.)		Brinell hardness number.		Melting range.	
	Softened.*	Hardened.†	Softened.*	Hardened.†	Softened.*	Hardened.‡	Softened.*	Hardened.†	Softened.*	Hardened.†	(° C.)	(° F.)
I........	27,000	55,000	42,500	63,000	14	1	11,000,000	12,000,000	111	185	745–785	1,375–1,445
II........	29,500	77,500	44,500	83,500	12‡	...	11,000,000	12,000,000	103	193	750–805	1,385–1,480
III........	30,000	77,000	44,000	92,000	9	...	12,000,000	13,000,000	111	199	765–800	1,410–1,470
IV........	24,000	61,500	36,000	70,000	7	...	11,000,000	12,000,000	103	180	755–835	1,390–1,535
V§........	20,500	......	37,500	......	18		11,000,000	....	78	...	745–870	1,375–1,595

* Softened by quenching in water from 700° C. (1292° F.).
† Hardened by cooling slowly from 450° C. (840° F.).
‡ Where no value for elongation is given, the value obtained was less than 1 per cent.
§ Not appreciably affected by heat treatment.

all of the solders except one are capable of heat treatment; however, the method of hardening, as employed by Coleman, rendered them extremely brittle. The problem of heat treating soldered joints will be discussed in a subsequent section.

Silver Solders.—Silver solders are often used in place of gold for technic work, and also in orthodontia for soldering nickel-silver wire or plate. With the exception of this use for temporary orthodontic appliances, their use in the mouth is very limited, because of their low corrosive resistance. They are not amenable to heat treatment, but otherwise all theoretical and manipulative discussions of gold solders will generally apply to silver solders as well.

The chemical composition of eight silver solders, as specified by the American Society for Testing Materials,[4] together with their melting points, is given in Table L.

TABLE L

CHEMICAL COMPOSITION OF SILVER SOLDERS

Grade No.	Silver (per cent).	Copper (per cent).	Zinc. (per cent).	Cadmium (per cent).	Melting point.	
					(° F.)	(° C.)
1	10	52	38	*	1510	820
2	20	45	35	*	1430	775
3	20	45	30	5	1430	775
4	45	30	25	nil	1250	675
5	50	34	16	nil	1280	695
6	65	20	15	nil	1280	695
7	70	20	10	nil	1335	725
8	80	16	4	nil	1360	740

* The addition of cadmium not to exceed 0.50 per cent, to assist in fabricating Grades Nos. 1 and 2, shall not be considered as a harmful impurity.

Fluxes.—In soldering, all parts must be kept spotlessly clean, in order for the solder to flow. In order to dissolve the metallic oxides and to keep the work covered while soldering, thus preventing the formation of oxides while working, the parts to be soldered are first covered with a flux. An ideal flux should meet the following requirements:

1. It should have a fusion temperature below that of the solder.

2. It should lie quietly on the work while it is being fused, and should not effloresce or perceptibly increase in volume.

3. After fusing, it should spread evenly over the surface of the work, and should remain in position during the soldering process without volatilizing.

4. It should be a solvent for all metallic oxides or other surface impurities likely to occur upon the metal.

5. It should be easily removed after soldering, without leaving any product which will be injurious to the metal at any subsequent period.

They may be classified as *oxidizing* and *reducing* fluxes. The oxidizing fluxes are used occasionally in dentistry for freeing precious metals of the baser elements; such fluxes unite with the base metals, and remove them from the molten alloy either by dissolving them and forming a *slag,* or by forming chemical compounds with them, which are either volatile or soluble in the molten flux.[5]

Reducing fluxes are used much more extensively in dentistry than the other type. Their purpose is to reduce any metallic oxides to the metallic state, without removing the metal from the alloy.

Fluxes may be supplied in the form of a powder, paste, or liquid.

Aside from their use for soldering purposes, they are also employed in casting for freeing the molten alloy of oxides, as described in the preceding chapter; a reducing flux is indicated for this purpose. Another important use for reducing fluxes is the cleaning of scrap gold. Casting buttons and other pieces of gold scrap may be melted up into one ingot of considerable purity, if cleaning and reducing fluxes are used. Aside from metallic oxides, the scrap may contain particles of investment, which must be dissolved as well. The scrap may be melted on a charcoal block, sprinkled liberally with flux, and any large pieces of impurity floating on the surface of the molten alloy may be removed with the point of a clean slate pencil.

Fluxes Used in Dentistry.—Borax, or sodium tetraborate, $Na_2B_4O_7.10H_2O$, is one of the most popular fluxes used in dentistry. However, because of the fact that it effloresces badly while heating, it is not very efficient. While the water of crystallization is being driven off, it becomes very light and feathery and is blown off the work, and this leaves regions of the metal unprotected; metallic oxides are formed in such exposed portions, and the solder either refuses to flow, or else a pit results.

The borax may be fused to a clear glass consisting of sodium pyroborate, $Na_2B_4O_7$, which, after it has' been ground to a fine powder, serves as an excellent fluxing material. At temperatures ordinarily employed in dental soldering and casting, the borax becomes molten, and acts as a general solvent for all impurities, but at higher temperatures (white heat) it combines with the metallic oxides, and forms borates. Such reactions are the basis for the "borax bead" tests for metals, which are used extensively in mineralogy.

Weinstein[6] gives the following formula for a soldering flux:

Borax glass	55 parts
Boric acid	35 parts
Silica	10 parts

The ingredients are fused together, and then pulverized to pass an 80-mesh sieve. The material may be used as a powder, incor-

porated with vaseline to form a paste, or dissolved in water to saturation and used as a solution. The flux melts at a higher temperature
than borax alone, and does not run off the work as readily as the
latter.[6]

By the addition of certain ingredients to the above formula, Weinstein[6] gives the following formula for a reducing flux:

Soldering flux (base) .... 40 parts
Borax glass .... 30 parts
Argol .... 25 parts
Animal charcoal .... 5 parts

For an oxidizing flux, he[7] gives the following formula:

Soldering flux (base) .... 55 parts
Potassium chlorate .... 20 parts
Sodium perborate .... 25 parts

Harder[8] recommends the following rather complex cleaning flux,
as being efficient for soldering, casting, and the cleaning of scrap
gold:

Calcium fluoride, CaF_2 .... 10 parts
Sodium fluoride, NaF .... 10 parts
Boric acid, H_3BO_3 .... 20 parts
Borax, fused, $Na_2B_4O_7$ .... 30 parts
Sodium bicarbonate, $NaHCO_3$ .... 10 parts
Sodium carbonate, Na_2CO_3 .... 10 parts
Sodium chloride, NaCl .... 10 parts

Both the fluorides and carbonates aid in removing the investment
from a gold button, since they both either react with or are a solvent
for the silicates. The ingredients may be mixed dry and ground together. Harder[8] is of the opinion that the flux might be used for reduction purposes if argol or charcoal are added.

An *antiflux* is any material which may be placed on the work, in
order to confine the solder and prevent its spreading beyond certain
limits. Such an area may be marked off with a soft lead pencil, the
pencil marks acting as an antiflux, provided that the temperature is
not high enough to allow the carbon to act as a reducing agent. Whit-
ing or rouge suspended in alcohol may also be used for this purpose.

The Soldering Flame.—As may be noted from Fig. 92, there are
four parts of a nonluminous brush flame from a gas-air blow torch.
The reducing zone is the portion which should be used in both soldering and casting. Not only is this the hottest portion of the flame, but
the gases present contain little or no oxygen, and aid in the prevention of oxidation. It should be noted that this region is just beyond
the combustion zone, which appears as a cone of greenish hue, whereas
the reducing zone is distinctly blue in color.

General Considerations.—The function of the flux has already been
discussed; it forms a protective coating for the metal while the solder

is applied. After fusion, the solder should flow over the metal between the parts and the flux. The direction of flow of the solder is determined by several factors. Gravity, of course, has considerable effect, but it is by no means the only factor involved. For example, solder may be "drawn" up a vertical wire by heating the wire adjacent to and just above the solder already joined to the wire. In other words, the direction of flow may be governed to some extent by the control of the flame, since the solder tends to flow toward the regions of highest temperature. This fact should not be lost sight of, as a means of the confinement of solder to a specific area. The reason for this effect of temperature upon the flow of solder is very likely because of the fact that, at the higher temperatures, both the surface

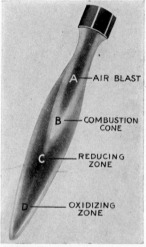

Fig. 92.—The soldering flame. A—Cone formed by air blast coming from center of blowpipe nozzle. B—Mixed air and gas in partial combustion. This part of the flame does not provide the maximum heat. C—Zone of reduction. The air from the blast has been exhausted, leaving a reducing excess of gas. Apply this portion of the flame when soldering. D—Zone where uncombined gas unites with oxygen from the surrounding air. This is an oxidizing zone, and is to be avoided in soldering operations. (Courtesy of Thomas J. Dee & Co.)

tension and viscosity of the molten solder are decreased and its affinity for the surfaces of the parts is increased, and thus its ability to flow is increased.

Another factor to be considered in soldering is capillary action. The molten solder will flow more readily between parts which are closely adjacent than when they are separated somewhat; this phenomenon is in accord with one of the physical laws of capillary action. Furthermore, the less the distance between the soldered parts, the stronger will be the joint.[9] The use of an excessive amount of solder is never indicated in dental soldering; an excess of solder is not only difficult to remove, but also it tends to weaken the joint.

Under no circumstances must the temperature be raised sufficiently high as to volatilize the base metals in the solder. Particularly the beginner is likely to have trouble in this respect; because of improper cleansing and fluxing, the solder refuses to flow and "balls up," and the temptation is to increase the temperature in an attempt to cause the solder to flow; this often results in solidification while it is in the flame. This occurs because of the volatilization of the zinc and tin, which considerably elevates the melting point. The author once observed a student in such a futile attempt to solder a brass wire with silver solder; the solder did not flow and solidified as described, and the wire finally melted, while the solder remained in the solid state.

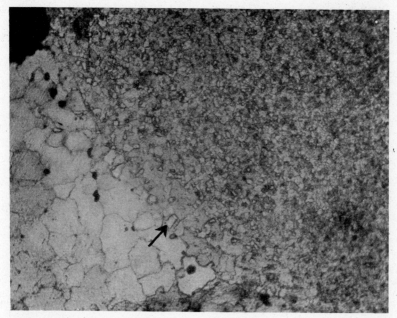

Fig. 93.—Cross section through a wire on which solder is flowed. × 200. (Courtesy of the J. M. Ney Co.)

The exact method by which the union between the solder and the metal is attained is not entirely clear. Very likely a superficial alloying between the solder and the soldered parts is essential to a strong joint. Fig. 93* shows a well soldered joint; although the line dividing the solder from the wire is quite distinct, the alloying is extremely slight indeed. As may be noted, some of the grains appear to be partly in the wire area and partly in the solder, particularly the one marked with the arrow. This indicates that the grains on the surface of the wire may act as nuclei of crystallization for the solder

* Figs. 93–105 were supplied by R. L. Coleman.

Fig. 94.—Typical fibrous structure of a normal wire. × 500. (Courtesy of the J. M. Ney Co.)

Fig. 95.—Microstructure of a high fusing wire (1925° F. or 1050° C., wire fusion method) after heating at 1750° F. (954° C.) for five minutes. The fibrous structure is beginning to recrystallize to an equiaxed structure. Both tensile strength and elongation were slightly decreased by this treatment, especially when the wire was subsequently given a hardening heat treatment. × 500. (Courtesy of the J. M. Ney Co.)

when it freezes. Such a possibility also might account for the metallographic structure of the soldered joint in Fig. 105. Prolonged heating or overheating will cause solution of the wire and grain growth, which greatly weakens the structure. Illustrations of the effect of such mishandling of gold wires, causing grain growth, are shown in Figs. 94 to 96.

Investment Soldering.—In brief, the process of investment soldering consists of waxing the parts together with sticky wax. Investment is then placed around the parts, with only those portions exposed which are to be soldered. After the investment hardens, the wax is flushed out thoroughly with clean boiling water. The invested

Fig. 96.—Another specimen of the same wire shown in Fig. 95, heated to 1850° F. (1010° C.) for five minutes. The fibrous structure has entirely disappeared, and grain growth has taken place. Both the strength and ductility of this wire were reduced radically, especially in the hardened condition. × 500. (Courtesy of the J. M. Ney Co.)

parts are then heated to redness, and the soldering is accomplished with the blow torch. Such methods are used in soldering backings for pontics in fixed or removable partial dentures, and in soldering clasps, etc. A large bulk of investment is never indicated as it retains the heat for too long a period after soldering.

The first requisite in successful soldering of any kind is cleanliness. The operator must not rely altogether upon the flux for cleansing purposes. The parts to be joined should be carefully scraped and preferably polished before beginning the operation. If wrought parts are used, they should be annealed in order to relieve any strain hardening.

The parts to be soldered may be placed in juxtaposition only if a thermally expanding investment is used. One of the errors arising from investment soldering is the danger of warpage. For example, if the parts are placed tightly together, and the investment contracts when heated, the parts may be drawn more tightly together, and at the same time the metal will expand thermally; both factors cause considerable warpage. Another cause of warpage may be the failure to anneal thoroughly any wrought metal parts before they are invested. Severely cold-worked structures often change in shape when subjected to the soldering temperatures normally employed. The

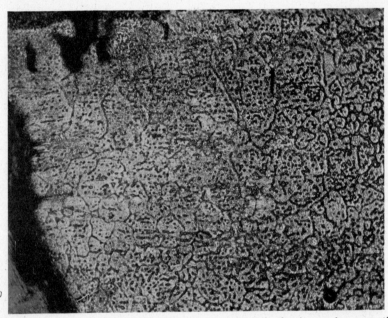

Fig. 97.—Microstructure of a clasp wire which broke in service near the soldered joint. The solder has completely dissolved in the wire and has formed an entirely different alloy with the latter. The wrought wire has been converted into the equivalent of a cast metal. × 500. (Courtesy of the J. M. Ney Co.)

use of an investment which expands thermally approximately 0.9 per cent at 700° C. (1292° F.) is generally indicated. This precaution not only permits the proper spacing of the parts by making allowance for their thermal expansion, but also aids in compensating for the shrinkage of the solder, which is comparable to that of a gold casting alloy (1.25 per cent).[12]

The parts to be soldered, as well as the solder, should be thoroughly but not excessively fluxed. An excessive amount of flux is likely to cause pitting, and prevents the confinement of the solder to the joint.

The solder may be applied in strip or wire form, but the piece should be sufficiently long so that it may be fed to the heated metal by holding it with soldering tweezers. A small pointed brush flame should be used, and confined as nearly as possible to the joint. As soon as the solder is seen to flow as desired, the flame should be removed at once. Whenever possible the case should be quenched in water in order to leave all alloys in the softened condition.

Undoubtedly, two of the most frequent causes of soldered clasp breakage are the prolongation of the soldering operation and the use of too high a temperature. Fig. 97 shows the microstructure of a wire clasp which broke in service adjacent to the soldered joint. The

Fig. 98.—Microstructure of a clasp wire which broke near the occlusal rest. The pronounced grain growth indicates that the wire was heated to a relatively high temperature, or held for a long time at the soldering temperature, possibly caused as a result of the employment of a solder with poor flowing qualities. × 100. (Courtesy of the J. M. Ney Co.)

solder used in this case was a low fusing variety of composition, gold 80 per cent, zinc 10 per cent, and nickel 10 per cent. When it is melted, this solder oxidizes badly, and the oxide film is extremely difficult to reduce by fluxing. As a consequence it is necessary to heat the work for a relatively long time, and to a high temperature, in order to make the solder flow, even though it exhibits a relatively low melting point as previously stated. Hence, a solder must not only be low in melting temperature, but also it must flow readily when it is melted. The figure demonstrates clearly that the cause of breakage was the formation of a different alloy and grain structure.

Improper heating technic does not always bring about failure because of solution of the metals, but also grain growth within the wire, as demonstrated in Figs. 94 to 96, may be a factor. Fig. 98 shows a photomicrograph of a clasp wire which failed for this latter cause. Very little solution of the wire may be noted, yet large equiaxed grains were formed from the characteristically fibrous structure of the wire, brought about by prolonged heating, or overheating.

Casting Against Wrought Metal.—Under certain conditions, clasps and other structures are united to a partial denture by casting a gold alloy directly into a mold in which the wrought structure is imbedded.

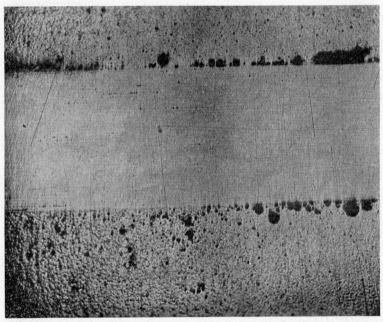

Fig. 99.—A longitudinal section of a high fusing wire, against which a gold alloy has been cast. The union and preservation of the wire microstructure are exceptionally good in this case, but nevertheless the union is faulty as may be noted. (Courtesy of the J. M. Ney Co.)

It is doubtful whether this procedure can be carried out successfully, with as strong a joint resulting as though the structure had been soldered. The casting alloy will undoubtedly have a higher melting point than a solder, and this, together with the time and temperature required during the heating and cooling of the mold, is very likely to produce grain growth and solution of the wire.

Fig. 99 represents a longitudinal section of a high fusing wire, against which a gold alloy was cast into a mold heated to approximately 1000° F. (538° C.). Although the wire has not been injured in this case, so far as can be discerned by change in grain structure,

Fig. 100.—A longitudinal section of a medium fusing wire on which solder was flowed, before it was cast against. Note the internal porosity. (Courtesy of the J. M. Ney Co.)

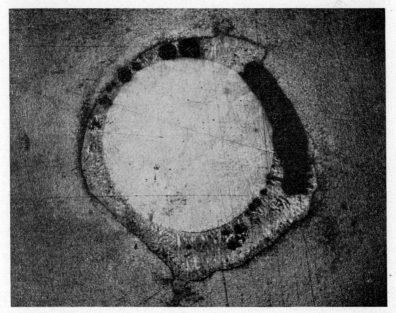

Fig. 101.—Cross section of the same wire shown in Fig. 100, showing the voids and incomplete union between the metals. (Courtesy of the J. M. Ney Co.)

20

yet the union between the gold and the wire is very poor indeed. It is very doubtful whether such a joint would prove satisfactory in service.

Some technicians advocate flowing solder over a wire before attempting to cast against it. A photomicrograph of a specimen thus treated is shown in Fig. 100. Although little solution of the wire is visible, a certain degree of recrystallization may be observed. Fig. 101 shows a cross section view of the same wire, which shows the voids and the incomplete bond between the metals. Fig. 102 shows what may sometimes happen when this technic is used; the solution

Fig. 102.—A longitudinal section of a medium fusing wire on which solder was flowed before casting against it. In this case marked solution of the wire and a very poor bond are noticeable. (Courtesy of the J. M. Ney Co.)

of the wire and lack of bond is very evident, although there is no perceptible grain growth.

It may therefore be concluded that the casting of gold against wrought metal is to be avoided, and that a soldered joint is preferable.

Free-hand Soldering.—This type of soldering is used quite extensively in orthodontic work. In theory it is quite similar to other soldering technics. No investment is used; the two parts are merely brought together and the solder is flowed between them.

For example, assume that two wires are to be soldered in a butt joint.* After the parts have been cleaned and fluxed as previously described, a bit of solder may be flowed on the end of one wire. Then

* A *butt joint* is a union of two materials end to end, or end to side, without overlapping, whereas a lap joint is made by overlapping the parts.

both wires are placed in the reducing flame; they are joined by flowing the solder between them while they are held with the hands or with soldering tweezers.

In this type of soldering, an orthodontic blowpipe may be used; such a blowpipe gives a very fine, but hot, gas-air flame, which may be regulated so as to heat only the parts to be soldered. Much better heat control can be assured with this type of soldering than with investment soldering.

Overheating or prolonged heating results in solution of the wire, as in other types of soldering. In Fig. 103 the solder was properly flowed on a wire with a blowpipe; both the solder and the wire were

Fig. 103.—A longitudinal section of a wire on which solder has been properly flowed with a blowpipe. The microstructure indicates no evidence of overheating or prolonged heating. × 30. (Courtesy of the J. M. Ney Co.)

properly fluxed, and the flame was removed as soon as the solder flowed. There is no solution of the wire, or perceptible change in its grain structure. The wire in Fig. 104 was treated in exactly the same manner, except that it was held in the flame for approximately forty-five seconds after the solder flowed. The solution of the wire by the solder is very evident, although the wire shows no evidence of grain growth. Since the diameter of the wire has been decreased, a soldered joint which exhibits such solution cannot be expected to give good service. Fig. 105 shows a correctly soldered orthodontic joint, which was accomplished by heating the parts rapidly, flowing the solder as quickly as possible without overheating, and then quenching in water.

According to Coleman,[11] in general, the longer the solder is kept

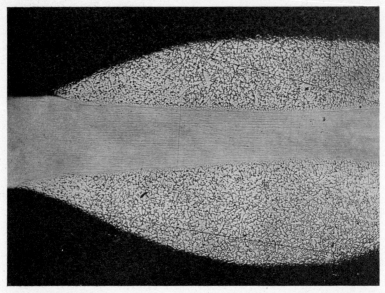

Fig. 104.—The same wire and solder as in Fig. 103 was used, with the same method of soldering, except that the solder was kept molten for forty-five seconds before the flame was removed. × 30. (Courtesy of the J. M. Ney Co.)

Fig. 105.—Cross section through an arch wire and longitudinal section through a fingerspring of an orthodontic appliance which had given satisfactory service, and was discarded after the completion of treatment. Note the microstructure of the solder. (Courtesy of the J. M. Ney Co.)

molten, the greater the solution will be. Furthermore, the amount of solution increases as the temperature is raised above the melting point of the solder. For example, it was found that a solder, whose liquidus temperature was 1430° F. (777° C.), dissolved a given wire more rapidly when heated to 1600° F. (871° C.), than did a solder of liquidus temperature 1590° F. (866° C.) when heated to 1650° F. (900° C.).

Heat Treatment of Soldered Joints.—The softening of soldered joints by heat treatment may be accomplished in the regular manner, but the method to be used in the hardening heat treatment is not so simple, because of the fact that the various portions of the joint may react differently to heat. Fig. 106 shows the effect of holding two wires of different composition for five minutes at each of the temperatures indicated. As may be noted, alloy No. 1 will be softened at any age-hardening treatment to which alloy No. 2 is subjected, so

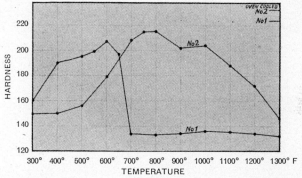

Fig. 106.—Hardening effect on two alloys by heating at various temperatures. (Coleman: Int. Jour. of Orthodontia, December, 1933.)

as to give the latter its maximum hardness. Alloy No. 1 is low in the platinum group metals, whereas alloy No. 2 contains these metals to a comparatively large degree. Hard solders exhibit a heat treatment somewhat similar to that of alloy No. 1. Hence, if the age-hardening treatment is employed, at least two treatments will be necessary. The wire of high platinum-palladium content must first be treated at approximately 800° F. (430° C.), and then the solder is treated at about 500° F. (260° C.), a temperature at which the already hardened wire will be affected only slightly, if at all.* These ideas are confirmed by the studies of Wesselhoeft[9] and Tichenor.[10]

Such treatments are obviously somewhat complicated for practical use, and it is very evident that the oven-cooling process should be able to accomplish the same result in one operation, provided that it can be carried out properly. As may be noted from Table XLIX,

* The data in Fig. 106 were obtained by treating specimens quenched from 1300° F. (704° C.).

the standard method of cooling from 450° C. (840° F.) to 250° C. (480° F.) over a period of thirty minutes is contraindicated, since such a treatment renders the solder uselessly brittle. However, a modification of this treatment might provide the required result. That soldered structures employed in dentistry would be greatly benefited by a proper hardening heat treatment goes without argument, since the modulus of resilience and general life value are definitely increased. However, this field requires more study before any definite technic can be recommended.

LITERATURE

1. Coleman, R. L., *Physical Properties of Dental Materials.* Res. Paper No. 32, p. 894. U. S. Gov. Printing Office.

2. Harder, O. E., *Modern Dental Metallography,* p. 162. Burgess-Roseberry Company.

3. *Ibid.,* p. 158.

4. *Standard Specifications for Silver Solders.* A. S. T. M. Designation: B 73–29. American Society for Testing Materials.

5. Hodgen, J. D. (Revised by Millberry, G. S., and Shell, John S.), *Practical Dental Metallurgy,* 7th Ed., p. 73, The C. V. Mosby Company.

6. Weinstein, L. J., *Dental Metallurgy,* in Peeso, F. A., *Crown and Bridge-Work,* 2nd Ed., pp. 461–463, Lea and Febiger.

7. *Ibid.,* p. 464.

8. Reference (2), p. 169.

9. Wesselhoeft, H. D., *Physical Properties of Soldered Joints in Orthodontic Appliances with Especial Reference to Heat Treatments.* Thesis, N. U. D. S.

10. Tichenor, E. R., *The Heat Treatment of Orthodontic Appliances.* Thesis, N. U. D. S.

11. Coleman, R. L., *Some Effects of Soldering and Other Heat Treatments of Orthodontic Alloys.* Int. Jour. of Ortho. and Dent. for Children, 19: 1238–1254 (Dec.) 1933.

12. *Gold,* p. 57. The J. M. Ney Company.

CHAPTER XXXIII

HISTORY OF DENTAL AMALGAMS. DENTAL AMALGAM ALLOYS

As defined in Chapter XX, an *amalgam* is an alloy, one of the constituents of which is mercury. By the term *amalgam alloy* is meant the metallic substance, supplied in the form of filings or shavings, which is mixed with the mercury to produce the amalgam.

The study of dental amalgams for restorative purposes is of great importance to the dentist. When the alloys are correctly compounded by the manufacturer and the amalgam is correctly manipulated by the dentist, a very serviceable restoration results. On the other hand, the most expert manipulation cannot produce a good restoration with a poor amalgam alloy. The best guide to the dentist that he is using a good amalgam alloy is to purchase only those products which are guaranteed to meet the American Dental Association Specification for Dental Amalgam Alloys.*

The principal physical properties of amalgams to be studied are crushing strength, flow, and dimensional changes. The flow of dental amalgams is a change in dimension occurring under a load over a period of time, and is merely a plasticity, thought by some authorities to be due to a lack of ability of the material to strain harden.

History.—The exact date when amalgams were first used in filling teeth is not known. However, there is a possibility that its use may have been an outgrowth of the work of M. Regnart who, in 1818, attempted to produce a low fusing alloy for filling teeth.

In 1826, M. Taveau's "silver paste" appeared, which was undoubtedly silver and mercury. This soon led to the shaving of silver coins, and mixing them with mercury, which meant the introduction of copper as well as silver. A similar amalgam† was introduced into the United States about 1833 and fell into the hands of charlatans and itinerant dentists who went from town to town leaving pain and misery in their wake.

In the face of such practices it is not to be wondered that the material fell into considerable disrepute. In fact, the feeling against its use became so acute that in 1845 the first national organization of dentists, the American Society of Dental Surgeons, passed a resolution as follows:

"Resolved: That any member of this Society who shall hereafter refuse to sign a certificate pledging himself not to use any amalgam,

* A. D. A. Specification No. 1, see Appendix, p. 381.
† The Crawours Brothers' "Royal Mineral Succedaneum."

and moreover, protesting against its use under any circumstances in dental practice, shall be expelled from this Society."

Some dentists believed the material to have possibilities and the resolution precipitated the famous "amalgam war" which fairly tore the newly organized profession asunder. Although the resolution was rescinded in 1855, the Society died a natural, yet agonizing, death.

The first important scientific studies of amalgam were by John Tomes of London in 1861. He packed seven different amalgams in cavities prepared in ivory, and observed the margins under a microscope. Six of them exhibited contraction, whereas the seventh, made of copper and mercury only, showed no contraction.

The next plan, suggested by Dr. Thomas Fletcher of Warrington, England, was to pack amalgams in glass tubing, and to observe the penetration of dye into the margins after setting. This is probably a good test for adaptation of amalgams, and it is being used with modifications at the present time. Dr. Fletcher found shrinkage in most of the specimens he tested.

The first quantitative measurement of dimensional changes was made by Charles Tomes, son of John Tomes. He determined the specific gravity before and after set, and calculated the volume change. This test, although rather tedious, is quite practical. He found that the alloys shrank in varying magnitudes. The accuracy of his method was later confirmed by Dr. G. V. Black.

Mr. A. Kirby in 1871 attempted to measure the changes directly with a **V**-shaped trough and a micrometer screw. He found that amalgams expanded when made with silver only.

Dr. Thomas B. Hitchcock of New York in 1874 designed the first indicating micrometer for determining dimensional changes. His instrument measured to within one thousandth of an inch. He used a 1-inch steel trough in which the amalgam was placed. The trough was closed at one end, and the micrometer fastened at the other end. Even with the much longer specimen than was later used by Black and others, the instrument was not sufficiently accurate. Dr. Hitchcock died before completing his work.

In 1895, Dr. G. V. Black began his fundamental work on this material which finally has resulted in the modern amalgam. He constructed and used an amalgam micrometer and other precision instruments for research purposes, which were far more accurate than any employed before. His work is so fundamental that it is of more than passing historical interest, and it must be discussed along with that of contemporary investigators.

Composition of Amalgam Alloys.—Silver and tin are the essential constituents of an amalgam alloy. Other metals employed in modern alloys are copper and zinc. An approximate idea of the limits of composition of these alloys may be gained from an inspection of the requirements of American Dental Association Specification No. 1 which are as follows:

Silver .... 65 per cent minimum
Copper .... 6 per cent maximum
Zinc .... 2 per cent maximum
Tin .... 25 per cent minimum

Table LI shows a chemical analysis reported by Taylor[1] for 26 commercial brands of alloy.

TABLE LI

COMPOSITION OF DENTAL AMALGAM ALLOYS

Sample No.	Composition. Per cent by weight.					
	Silver.	Tin.	Copper.	Zinc.	Gold.	Platinum.
1	56.3	39.0	3.7	1.0		
2	67.0	27.3	4.8	1.9	0.04	
3	57.7	38.9	1.9	0.9	0.50	0.10
4	63.9	32.45	2.7	0.9	0.05	
5	66.1	28.2	4.9	0.8	0.02	
6	70.2	26.3	3.5			
7	54.8	40.5	3.5	1.2	0.01	
8	65.2	29.0	4.8	1.0	0.04	
9	44.0	55.2	0.05	0.75		
10	67.9	26.7	4.9	0.5		
11	44.1	51.0	....	....	4.9	
12	60.2	39.2	....	0.6		
13	58.9	38.7	1.2	1.2		
14	68.2	27.1	4.0	0.6	0.04	
15	67.4	26.9	4.7	1.0	0.01	
16	66.8	28.2	3.9	1.1		
17	67.0	27.3	4.7	1.0		
18	66.9	27.1	5.0	1.0		
19	66.7	28.2	4.6	0.5		
20	66.6	27.4	5.1	0.9		
21	56.7	36.7	6.3	0.3	0.02	
22	53.0	42.7	1.9	....	2.3	0.12
23	67.6	26.8	5.5	0.1	0.02	
24	66.9	26.5	4.9	1.7		
25	68.7	26.1	5.0	0.2		
26	51.8	44.3	2.9	1.0		

The majority of the alloys in the table are of the "high silver" variety, but several "low silver" alloys are evident. The latter variety shrink under manipulations employed by the dentist, and they invariably exhibit low compressive strength and high flow values under test. These "low silver" alloys were very popular at one time, but no dentist worthy of the name uses them for restorative purposes in modern times.

Silver-tin Alloys.—The amalgam alloy can be considered essentially as a silver-tin system. Fig. 107 shows the constitution diagram for the silver-tin alloys as determined by Rosenhain and his co-workers* at the National Physical Laboratory of Great Britain.[2]   At first glance the diagram seems extremely complicated, but if it is considered as a mixed type alloy similar to the copper-silver system, its complicated structure resolves itself into two solid solution components, an intermetallic compound, and a eutectic.   The solidus is represented by the line ABMCDFEG, whereas the liquidus coincides with the line SELKA.   The eutectic composition at E is readily seen at the right.   For compositions to the right of E, the primary crystals will very evidently be pure tin, but for compositions less than E, the primary component must be discussed more at length.

As the amount of tin in the alloy increases from zero to the eutectic composition, three different phases appear consecutively.   The a

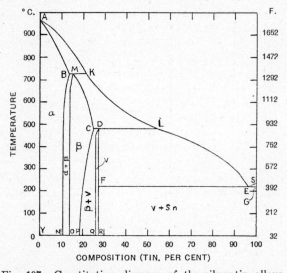

Fig. 107.—Constitution diagram of the silver-tin alloys.

substance represented by the area ABNY is substantially a solid solution of tin in silver.   Within the area OMCP another solid solution component freezes out, known as the β substance; between the areas of the pure a and β substances is a region in which a mixture of the two substances occurs.   The area QDFR represents a region in which the intermetallic compound Ag_3Sn occurs, which is designated as the γ substance.   To the left of this region, the β and γ substances occur together, whereas to the right, the eutectiferous alloy is formed with the components Ag_3Sn and tin.   Most modern amalgam alloys contain an amount of tin such that the composition lies approximately within the region of formation of the compound Ag_3Sn, the exact composition of the latter being 73.15 per cent silver and 26.83 per cent tin;[3]

* Investigated by Murphy, A. J., Jour. Inst. Metals, 35 (1926).

hence, this region of the constitution diagram is of considerable importance to the theory of dental amalgams.

Effect of the Alloy Constituents Upon the Amalgam.—The tin content of the alloy is somewhat critical, other factors being equal. In the opinion of Gayler,[3] the tin content is the composition factor which determines whether or not an amalgam is suitable for use as a filling material. She places the desirable tin content, irrespective of the silver and copper content (within limits), at not less than 25 per cent and not greater than 26.8 per cent by weight. However, the assumptions upon which Gayler bases these statements are somewhat restricted, and it is doubtful whether a complete generalization should be made in this respect.

Tin is probably a deleterious element so far as physical properties go. Its chief advantages are its strong affinity for mercury, and its ability to decrease the amalgamation time in combination with silver. It reduces the expansion under ordinary methods of manipulation.

Copper may be used to replace the silver in small amounts. It tends to increase the expansion of the amalgam in setting, to decrease the flow, and to increase the crushing strength. However, it must be used sparingly, as it is very effective as an expanding element when it replaces the silver.[3] Historically, it was undoubtedly introduced as a stabilizer because it was formerly thought that it formed a non-expanding and noncontracting amalgam with mercury. Modern research has shown that copper amalgams contract under all conditions thus far investigated.

The function of zinc as an element in the alloy is rather obscure. Black[4] found, when it was present in an alloy of silver 61.75 per cent, tin 33.25 per cent, and zinc 5 per cent, that it decreased the flow and increased both crushing strength and expansion. He noted that the wet mass of the amalgam tended to exhibit adhesion to the cavity walls during condensation.

However, he further noted a strong objection to its use, viz., its slow setting properties. In the sixth edition of his book (Vol. II, p. 308), he states: "Experiment in watching fillings for five years shows that one-half of 1 per cent of zinc is inadvisable for the reason that the amalgam will continue to change bulk very slowly for that time and perhaps much longer. Though this change is not large (not more than one to one and one-half points* per year with 1 per cent of zinc), it will finally destroy the usefulness of the filling." To the author's knowledge, this fact has been neither disproved nor confirmed. Gray[6] reports an expansion of 0.48 per cent for a non-zinc amalgam, his observations being taken over a year in time, whereas he found that an amalgam containing zinc expanded 1.28 per cent in eight months and was continuing to expand when the test was abandoned. In all fairness it should be mentioned that he did not attribute the

* 0.0001–0.00015 inches.

difference to the zinc content, yet he failed to make it clear what other factor could possibly have caused such a difference. More research is needed along this line with modern equipment before final judgment is passed.

The argument is occasionally raised that the presence of zinc in an amalgam renders the latter more electropositive, but this theory has been definitely disproved.[5]

Very likely the true reason for the use of zinc in the alloy is to aid the manufacturer in preventing the formation of metallic oxides during the process of manufacture. Zinc is known to have a scavenger action for metallic oxides, and it is used for this purpose in some industrial alloys. However, non-zinc alloys can be made with working and physical properties after amalgamation similar in all important respects to the amalgams made from alloys containing zinc.

Aging of Amalgam Alloys.—The true effect of aging of the amalgam alloy was first discovered by G. V. Black. He found that amalgams made from filings from an alloy of 65 per cent silver and 35 per cent tin neither expanded nor contracted when amalgamated the same day they were made, but if the filings were left on the shelf for a month, the amalgam from which they were made shrank. In the latter case less mercury was required for mixing, and a slower setting time resulted. Reasoning that the effect was in some manner related to the strain hardening of the filings while they were being cut, he placed the freshly cut filings in a test tube in boiling water, and discovered that the change noted previously over a month's time at room temperature occurred in fifteen minutes at the temperature of boiling water.

The discovery that the physical properties of an amalgam are dependent upon the aged condition of the filings is of utmost practical importance to the dentist who buys his alloys in large quantities. Even at the present date some of the widely used commercial alloys do not maintain their "balance" in this respect over a long period of time.

The exact reason for this effect is not known, although there is convincing evidence for the fact that it is connected in some manner with the mechanical deformation of the alloy filings during manufacture. According to Rosenhain[2] the farther the formula of the alloy departs from the composition of the intermetallic compound Ag_3Sn, the less marked are its aging properties, regardless of the additional metals ordinarily added. The effect is not due to any known type of deformation occurring during the mechanical working, nor do x-ray analyses throw important light upon the matter.

Aged filings require less mercury for amalgamation only because they react more slowly than do the unaged filings during the usual period of trituration. If both are given sufficient time, they will ultimately take up the same amount of mercury, but the unaged filings react with it more rapidly.

Manufacture of Amalgam Alloys.—Once the correct alloy formula has been established, there are at least four obstacles which must be overcome by the manufacturer of a reliable alloy: (1) obtaining sufficiently pure metals, (2) alloying the metals without oxidation, (3) correct annealing of the filings, and (4) standardization of production.

The metals are alloyed carefully in the absence of oxygen and cast into ingots, which are comminuted into filings or shavings. They are then annealed much in the same manner as described by Black. During the comminution process, an oxide film may form on the shavings because of the heat generated. This film may be removed by washing the filings in a solution of hydrochloric acid, which leaves the surface bright and silver-like. This process merely removes the surface impurities and insures nothing as to the internal purity.

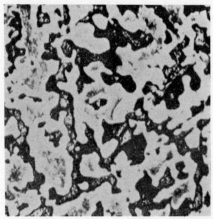

Fig. 108.—Microstructure of a hardened amalgam. (Rosenhain: *Dental Alloys*, Courtesy of Dental Board of the United Kingdom.)

In general, the over-annealing of the alloy filings tends to produce an amalgam which shrinks and flows badly, whereas under-annealing may cause the amalgam to expand and flow abnormally. It should be possible to compound an alloy which cannot be over-annealed, and yet will exhibit the proper physical properties when amalgamated. In cases where the annealing is not carried to completion, it may continue slowly at room temperature for periods of months or years. Hence, an amalgam alloy may be satisfactory at the factory, but by the time it is amalgamated by the dentist, its physical properties may be considerably changed; in other words, it exhibits a *shelf life*.

Because of the many variables entering into the manufacturing process, the careful manufacturer maintains a fully equipped testing laboratory, and conscientiously tests each batch of alloy before placing it on the market, thus completely insuring a constancy of production.

Metallography of Amalgams.—Fig. 108 shows the microstructure of a fully set amalgam. An exact interpretation of the picture cannot be made, since the silver-tin-mercury system has not as yet been fully studied because of the fact that many of the amalgams in such a system do not solidify at room temperature. Metallographic methods are limited in general only to the solid state, and this renders the study of liquid or semiliquid systems almost impossible. The photomicrograph very evidently shows filings surrounded by a sheath and imbedded in a matrix of some nature. The reaction of the filings with the mercury is not completed, and the former probably remain indefinitely in a solid-solid suspension, as may be noted in the figure.

Certain studies[7] of binary systems of tin and mercury indicate that a solid solution of mercury in tin (1 per cent) and free tin are formed. However, Hosford[8] is of the opinion that a compound of the approximate formula Sn_7Hg may occur; whatever is the nature of the tin amalgams they are very soft at room temperature. At least one of the products of a silver amalgam is an intermetallic compound Ag_3Hg_4. Assuming that such a compound occurs during the setting of a dental amalgam, it is not clear as to the ultimate form of the tin-mercury combination. According to one investigation,[7] free tin is formed in accordance with the following reaction:

$$Ag_3Sn + 4Hg \rightarrow Ag_3Hg_4 + Sn$$

The copper and zinc very likely may be classed with the silver as forming intermetallic compounds.

Setting of Amalgams.—The setting of amalgams is a solidification process, which is unique in the fact that it occurs with but very little change in temperature. In the light of the above theory, the mechanism of setting may possibly be one of reaction of the mercury with the filings to produce the intermetallic compound. As may be noted from Fig. 108, a sheath of the reaction product forms around the filings, which hinders further reaction, since the mercury diffuses through the sheath with difficulty. When the residual mercury becomes sufficiently altered by the reaction, the mass solidifies and the matrix is formed.

LITERATURE

1. Taylor, N. O., *A Survey of Amalgam Alloys. A Report to the Research Commission of the American Dental Association.* J. A. D. A., 16: 583–600 (April) 1929.

2. Rosenhain, Walter, *Three Lectures on "Dental Alloys,"* pp. 36–55. The Dental Board of the United Kingdom, 1926.

3. Gayler, Marie L. V., *The Setting of Dental Amalgams.* Brit. Dent. Jour., 58: 145–160 (Feb. 15) 1935.

4. Black, G. V., *The Physical Properties of the Silver-Tin Amalgams.* Dent. Cos., 38: 965–992 (Dec.) 1896.

5. Souder, W. H., and Peters, C. G., *An Investigation of the Physical Properties of Dental Materials.* Bureau of Standards Technologic Paper No. 157 (1920). Dent. Cos., 62: 305–335 (March) 1920.

6. Gray, A. W., *Contractions and Expansions of Amalgams with Time.* Phys. Rev. 18, series 2: 108–113 (Aug.) 1921.

7. McBain, J. W., and Joyner, R. A., *Amalgams Containing Tin, Silver and Mercury.* Dent. Cos., 54: 641–650 (June) 1912.

8. Hosford, H. H., *Composition of Crystalline Amalgams of Zinc, Lead, Tin and Cadmium.* Int. Jour. of Dent. Res., 14: 33–37 (Feb.) 1934.

9. McBain, J. W., and Knight, W. A., *The Chemical Constitution and the Physico-Chemical Properties of Dental Amalgams.* Dent. Cos., 57: 630–639 (June) 1915.

10. Fenchel, A., *Some New Researches into Amalgams, and Their Significance in Dental Practice.* Dent. Cos., 52: 30 (Jan.) 1910.

11. Ward, M. L., and Scott, E. O., *Further Studies of the Effect of Variations in Manipulation on Dimensional Changes and Flow of Amalgams.* J. A. D. A., 22: 1164–1171 (July) 1935.

CHAPTER XXXIV

DENTAL AMALGAMS: DIMENSIONAL CHANGES

THE manner in which dental amalgams are manipulated by the dentist has considerable effect upon their physical properties. In practice the filings are triturated or mixed with mercury in a mortar and then mulled in the hand, thus completely coating the particles with mercury. This plastic mass is then condensed into the prepared cavity with an instrument which is similar to a gold foil condenser.

Mechanical mixers are available for the purpose of the trituration of the mercury and alloy by mechanical means, but most of them

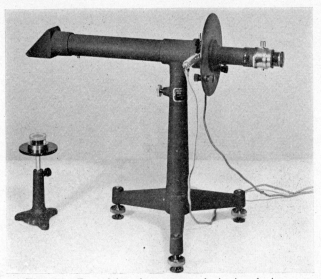

Fig. 109.—Dental interferometer and viewing device.

are unsatisfactory because they are likely to over-triturate the material.

The physical properties, which will be discussed in connection with the effects of manipulation, are dimensional changes, flow, and crushing strength.

The Dental Interferometer.—Dimensional changes which occur during the hardening of an amalgam are most conveniently observed by means of an interferometer and viewing device as shown in Fig. 109. Such an instrument is very accurate, its chief disadvantage being that it is subject to surface disturbances of the specimen.

It consists of two optically flat glass plates which are placed one above the other and held apart slightly by suitable supports. If they are placed at a small angle with each other, a collimated monochromatic light beam which strikes the top plate perpendicularly is partially reflected from the lower surface of the upper plate and from the top surface of the bottom plate. The two reflected waves meet at the bottom surface of the top plate. If the beams meet in phase, a fringe of light is seen. If they meet out of phase, they annul each other, as shown by a dark band or fringe. The number of alternate light and dark fringes in a unit length depends upon the angle between the plates. In the dental instrument, the top plate is supported at three points, which are spaced at the apices of an equilateral triangle. Two of the supports are steel pins or screws, whose height remains constant whereas the third is the amalgam specimen. When the amalgam changes in dimension in any manner, the angle between the plates is changed, which alters the number of fringes as observed

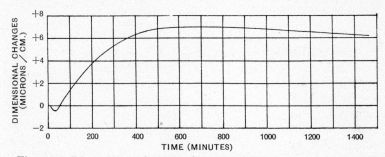

Fig. 110.—Dimensional changes of an amalgam over a twenty-four-hour period. Alloy: mercury ratio 5/9. Mortar trituration one minute, twenty-five seconds, 200 revolutions per minute. Hand kneading, twenty seconds, 15 strokes. Packing thrust: 8–10 pounds with 2.5 mm. condenser.

in the viewing device. The viewing apparatus is essentially a telescope focused for parallel light rays.

The number of fringes may be counted at various intervals between reference lines of known distance, and the change in length may be computed (usually in microns per centimeter) by means of a mathematical formula which depends upon the constants of the instrument.

The accuracy of the instrument is in the neighborhood of 0.00001 inch. It is not subject to lever disturbances which are likely to be quite prevalent in certain other forms of measuring equipment. A typical curve for a good amalgam showing the variation of dimensional changes over a period of twenty-four hours is given in Fig. 110. There is a short contraction followed by an expansion to a maximum, which is then followed by a slight contraction.

According to Gray,[1] this contraction slowly reaches a minimum, and then a second expansion begins, all of which usually occurs beyond the twenty-four-hour period shown in the figure. A contracting

21

amalgam shows a similar curve, except that the initial contraction is longer and of greater magnitude, the subsequent recovery not being great enough to bring the dimensions back to the original size (see curve 4, Fig. 111).

Desirability of Amalgam Expansion.—As noted in Chapter IV, page 36, the linear thermal expansion of dental amalgams is much greater than that of the tooth structure. In order to compensate for the different thermal expansions of the two substances during a temperature change, a slight expansion of the amalgam during the hardening period is desirable. Such an expansion will distend the dentin of the cavity walls so that when the differential thermal expansion takes place during a decrease in temperature for example, the dentin will follow the thermal contraction of the amalgam elastically. Souder[2] places the figure for optimum expansion on this basis at 8 microns per centimeter.

Too great an expansion will cause the restoration to extend out of the cavity preparation, and occasionally it may even fracture the tooth.

Theories of Dimensional Change.—There are various factors which determine whether an amalgam will contract or expand during hardening, but to give a theory which will adequately explain these phenomena is not easy. The effect of annealing of the alloy has already been discussed, but any alloy, regardless of its composition, will react differently to different methods of manipulation. It is true that a few amalgam alloys are available which will yield expanding amalgams under almost any reasonable technic normally practiced by the dentist, but they can be made to contract by going outside this range. Hence, any theory which attempts to explain these phenomena must include all methods of manipulation and compositions, in order to be completely comprehensive.

As previously mentioned, the metals in the amalgam alloy contribute to the dimensional changes in a certain degree, *provided* that standard manipulations are employed. There have been various attempts to correlate these tendencies in a universal theory, based upon the metallographical properties of the alloy. Such a theory would be very desirable, and will, perhaps, be formulated eventually. The most recent attempt along this line is that of Gayler,[3] which is briefly as follows:

If it is assumed that the alloy contains silver, copper, and tin, the tin content is the critical composition factor which determines whether the amalgam will expand or contract with a suitable method of manipulation. The copper may be substituted for the silver content within limits, but not for the tin. According to Gayler[3] the desirable range of tin in the alloy lies approximately between 25 and 26.8 per cent. Referring to the silver-tin diagram, Fig. 107, page 314, it may be noted that this composition occurs in the region of formation of the Ag_3Sn compound. If less than 25 per cent tin is used, the β substance appears and the amalgam prepared from the alloy exhibits expansion; in fact the greater the amount of β substance, the greater is the expansion. On the other hand, if more than 27 per cent of tin is used, a mixture of Ag_3Sn and tin results, and a contraction occurs after amalgamation. Hence, so far as composition is concerned, the dimensional changes may be controlled by the incorporation of the correct amount of the β substance in the alloy.

In arriving at the above conclusions, Gayler employed a very exact technic of manipulation. She was entirely cognizant of the effects of manipulation upon the dimensional changes, and she undoubtedly realized the limitations of such a theory. However, there can be no doubt but that the *tendencies* of the components under any condition are exactly as she described.

Gray[1, 4] has advanced a hypothesis by means of which many of the hardening phenomena may be explained and even predicted. Although the theory is by no means independent of the metallographic properties of the amalgam alloy, it is not primarily based upon them. A few of the assumptions in the hypothesis may be questionable, but its excellence lies in the fact that it takes into account the manipulation of the amalgam.

Considering Fig. 110, he accounts for the first contraction to a minimum by the solution of the alloy in mercury and the formation of compounds with silver and copper. Crystallization of the compound Ag_3Hg_4 then becomes predominant and the amalgam expands to a maximum. Because of the formation of the sheath around each alloy particle as previously described, further solution takes place with difficulty, and a gradual contraction occurs over a considerable period of time, which finally results in a second gradual expansion, not shown in the figure, due to a second slow crystallization.

According to the work of McBain and Joyner[5] the mercury reacts with the compound Ag_3Sn* in the alloy to form Ag_3Hg_4 and tin (see page 318). It has also been shown[6] that the formation of the compound Ag_3Hg_4 is accompanied by considerable contraction, but the tin amalgam formed by the free tin and excess mercury exhibits an expansion which is much less than the previously mentioned contraction; hence, on this basis, all amalgams should contract.

Gray rationalizes this inconsistency by the assumption that after the amalgam restoration has been condensed, each alloy grain touches its neighbor in a few places. Reaction with the mercury occurs mainly on the surfaces which are not in contact; this results in a skeleton formation which tends to resist contraction to some degree. During the combination period between the mercury and the filings, the contraction of the framework will be according to the amount of solution which increases with the amount of tin in the alloy. During the crystallization stage, the framework is nonresistant to the ensuing expansion which takes place in all directions because of the crystal growth between the grains.

* Very likely no silver-tin amalgam alloy employed in dental practice has ever contained less than 20 per cent tin, or more than 70 per cent tin. As may be noted from Fig. 107, page 314, all alloys within this range contain Ag_3Sn, hence the theory is not limited to a definite composition in a practical sense.

According to the theory, any procedure which prolongs the solution and combination stages should tend to increase the shrinkage, and, conversely, any manipulation which accelerates these stages should tend to increase the expansion.

Some experimental data showing the effect of different manipulation variables upon the dimensional changes of the amalgam will now be discussed, and applications of the theories will be made.

Effect of Trituration Time.—The general effect of increasing the mixing time is to decrease the expansion or to increase the contraction. Fig. 111[7] shows this effect. The composition of the alloy used for obtaining these data is given in Table LI, page 313, sample No. 20.

The form of the curves is interesting from the standpoint of Gray's theory. Curve 1 shows no initial contraction; presumably there was but little solution of the alloy during the short trituration period, and the contraction occurred before the measurement began. The curve reaches a maximum, and then begins to contract, as the theory predicts. Since all observations were stopped at the end of twenty-four hours, the second maximum does not appear in any of the curves. Curve 2 exhibits a slight contraction, which becomes progressively larger in the remaining curves as the trituration time increases.* Furthermore, the maxima gradually become less prominent, and occur earlier. Gray accounts for these changes on the basis that the reaction rates are increased, and the amount of observed crystallization decreases.

As is true with any similar manipulation, both time and rate of mixing should be considered. However, extremely rapid speeds of trituration are not indicated because of the frictional heat generated and its possible effect upon the amalgam; hence, the rate of trituration as a controlling factor is somewhat limited, and the time of trituration is of more importance.

The nature of the reaction is probably the same as that of any other similar reaction; the solution occurs until a certain concentration of mercury is reached, when the reaction takes place, followed by crystallization. The probability that a certain amount of crystallization takes place before the trituration is finished is very great; it must not be thought that the crystallization begins at the time the initial contraction terminates, for such is not the case. The two may occur simultaneously, but for a time the solution phase predominates, and is observed as a contraction; as the crystallization phase increases with its tendency to produce expansion, the two forces balance at the first minimum, after which the crystallization predominates and an expansion results.

* In interpreting any curves of this nature, the time should be recorded from the beginning of trituration, as the reactions start very early. Obviously the observations cannot possibly begin at zero time, since a period for manipulation must intervene. Regardless of how short this period is, it is conceivable that very significant data may have been missed.

On this basis, Gray assumes that any crystallization which occurs during trituration will not be observed on the interferometer, and this accounts for the decrease in the prominence of the first maximum as the trituration is prolonged. He further assumes that the reactions are accelerated as the trituration increases, and that, as a result, the maximum occurs earlier; both of these effects may be noted in Fig. 111. Had the manipulation time been prolonged still more, the maximum would probably have completely disappeared, as shown in curve R182, in Fig. 112.[8]

As may be noted from Fig. 111, prolonged trituration results in an increase in magnitude of the initial contraction. Prolongation of

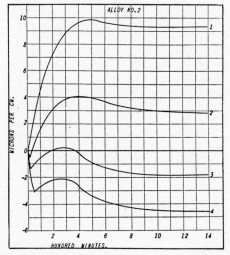

Fig. 111.—Effect of variation in mixing time: curve 1, thirty-five seconds in mortar, fifteen seconds in hand; curve 2, forty seconds in mortar, sixty seconds in hand; curve 3, sixty seconds in mortar, one hundred-twenty seconds in hand; curve 4, ninety seconds in mortar, one hundred-fifty seconds in hand. Packed under 8–10 pounds thrust with 2 mm. smooth circular condenser. (Ward and Scott: Jour. Amer. Dent. Assoc., October, 1932.)

the mixing causes an increase in the solution of the alloy. As the sheath forms around the filings, it is constantly rubbed off, which exposes fresh surfaces to the unsaturated mercury. Hence, the net result is an increased solution as noted; the initial contraction of the amalgam is increased and the contraction extends over a longer period of time.

Other factors being equal, the composition of the alloy affects the magnitudes of the above changes considerably. In this connection Gayler's theory is of considerable importance, as explaining, for example, why all amalgams do not shrink when triturated as was the amalgam used to obtain curve 4, Fig. 111.

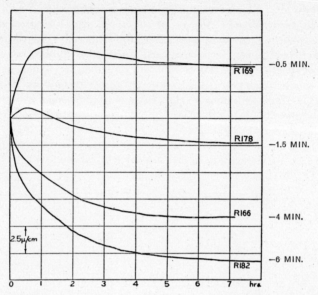

Fig. 112.—Effects produced by variation in mixing time. All specimens triturated in mortar only, as follows: R169, one-half minute; R178, one and one-half minutes; R166, four minutes; R182, six minutes. Machine packed under pressure of 7200 pounds per square inch. High-silver alloy, composition unknown. (Gray: Jour. of the Nat. Dent. Assoc., October, 1919.)

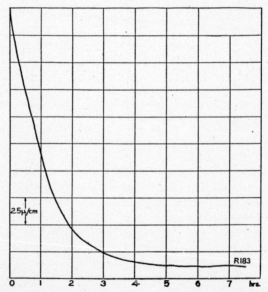

Fig. 113.—Amalgam from a low-silver alloy, manipulated as normally practiced by a dentist. (Gray: Jour. of the Nat. Dent. Assoc., October, 1919.)

Low-silver Amalgams.—Low-silver content amalgams always shrink under ordinary methods of manipulation; a typical dimensional change curve for a low-silver amalgam is shown in Fig. 113.[8] This fact might have been predicted from either theory.

According to Gray, the tin prolongs the solution and combination stages by acting as a diluent, thus preventing the crystallization of Ag_3Hg_4. The amalgam contracts and any expansion is masked. However, when he manipulated an amalgam of this type* so as to

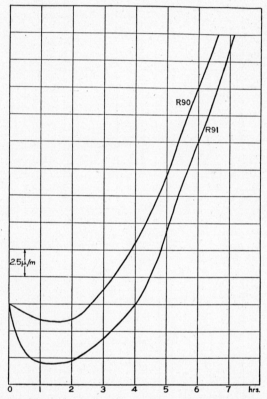

Fig. 114.—Amalgams from a low-silver alloy; prolonged manipulation. (Gray: Jour. of the Nat. Dent. Assoc., October, 1919.)

radically increase its rate of reaction, the curves in Fig. 114[8] resulted; presumably the expansions are due to second maxima.

However, it must not be concluded that these alloys are satisfactory for use in the mouth. Even though they can be made to expand, their expansion is evidently excessively great; moreover, their flow is so great and their crushing strengths so low under any circumstances that their use in the mouth is precluded.

* Private communication to the author.

Effect of Condensation Pressure.—If the trituration time is held constant, and if the pressure with which a high-silver content amalgam is packed into a prepared cavity is varied within the limits of normal dental practice, the effect of increased packing pressure is a

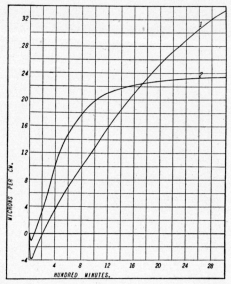

Fig. 115.—Effect of variation in packing pressure on dimensional changes: curve 1, amalgam jarred into the mold, with no mechanical condensation; curve 2, amalgam condensed under 500 pounds per square inch. (Ward and Scott: Jour. Amer. Dent. Assoc., October, 1932.)

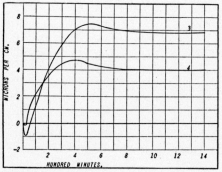

Fig. 116.—Effect of variation in packing pressure on dimensional changes: curve 3, amalgam condensed under 1000 pounds per square inch; curve 4, under 2000 pounds per square inch. (Ward and Scott: Jour. Amer. Dent. Assoc., October, 1932.)

decrease in expansion, as may be noted from Figs. 115 and 116.[7] Although none of the curves in the figures exhibit an ultimate contraction with increased packing pressure, yet such an observation is not at all uncommon with certain alloys.

Gray[1] is of the opinion that condensation must be classed with trituration as a further manipulation of the amalgam, and that the same theoretical principles apply in both cases. The resemblance between the progressive changes in the form of the curves in Figs. 115 and 116 as compared with similar changes in the curves shown in Fig. 111 is quite striking. As the condensing pressure is increased, the maxima decrease in magnitude, and occur at an earlier time. Gray

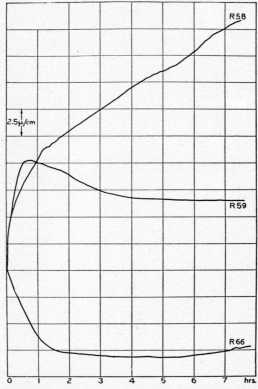

Fig. 117.—Effect on dimensional changes of a high-silver amalgam by varying the size of the alloy particles. R58, amalgam from alloy filings which failed to pass a 48-mesh sieve; R59, amalgam whose alloy filings passed a 200-mesh sieve; R66, amalgam from very fine particles. All amalgams manipulated under identical conditions. (Gray: Jour. of the Nat. Dent. Assoc., October, 1919.)

explains this upon the basis that the increase in packing pressure squeezes out more of the mechanically retained mercury, which carries with it a little dissolved tin and other metals, together with a certain amount of amalgam crystals, and this reduces the amount of subsequent reaction; the reaction is also accelerated by the more intimate contact between the mercury and alloy brought about by the increased pressure.

Effect of Alloy Particle Size.—Fig. 117[8] shows the effect of varying the size of the alloy particles. Like any other reactions of a similar nature, the smaller the particle size, the faster is the rate of reaction. This is evidenced by the decrease in the maxima and their movement to earlier periods, as may be noted in the figure. In the case of the large particles (curve R58), the first maximum was not reached in seven hours, but it is very prominent in the case of the medium size particles (curve R59) and appears within an hour. However, the rate of reaction is so rapid in the case of the small size particles (curve R66), that the first maximum was completely eradicated, and a contracting amalgam resulted. It is of interest to note that curve R66 was evidently approaching the second maximum when the test was abandoned.

This phenomenon is of particular practical interest in connection with the pressure exerted on the pestle during trituration. A heavy grinding pressure results in further comminution of the filings, which may produce a contracting amalgam.

Variations in temperature affect the dimensional changes during setting. It is known[3, 8] that expansion is less and contraction is greater at mouth temperatures than at ordinary room temperatures.

LITERATURE

1. Gray, A. W., *Volume Changes in Amalgams.* J. Inst. Metals, 29: 139–189 (1923).

2. Souder, Wilmer, Paper read at the Seventy-first Annual Midwinter Clinic of the Chicago Dental Society, 1935.

3. Gayler, Marie L. V., *The Setting of Dental Amalgams.* Brit. Dent. Jour., 58: 145–160 (Feb.) 1935.

4. Gray, A. W., *The Causes of Reaction Expansions in Amalgams.* Phys. Rev. (2nd Series), 19: 405, 406 (April) 1922.

5. McBain, J. W., and Joyner, R. A., *Amalgams Containing Tin, Silver, and Mercury.* Dent. Cos., 54: 641–650 (June) 1912.

6. McBain, J. W., and Knight, W. A., *The Chemical Constitution and the Physico-Chemical Properties of Dental Amalgams.* Dent. Cos., 57: 630–639 (June) 1915.

7. Ward, M. L., and Scott, E. O., *Effects of Variations in Manipulation on Dimensional Changes, Crushing Strength, and Flow of Amalgams.* J. A. D. A., 19: 1683–1705 (Oct.) 1932.

8. Gray, A. W., *Metallographic Phenomena Observed in Amalgams.* J. N. D. A., 6: 513–531 (June) 1919; 6: 909–925 (Oct.) 1919.

CHAPTER XXXV

DENTAL AMALGAMS (Continued): CRUSHING STRENGTH. FLOW. ADAPTATION. MANIPULATION

Crushing Strength.—Crushing strength is obviously a very important property from a dental standpoint. This property is no longer tested routinely since the revision of American Dental Association Specification No. 1 a few years ago. Formerly the amalgams were required to exhibit a minimum crushing strength of 2500 kg. per square centimeter (approximately 35,500 pounds per square inch).

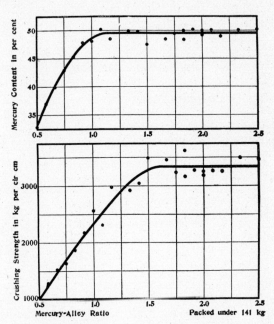

Fig. 118.—Effect of mercury: alloy ratio on crushing strength. (Gray: Jour. of the Nat. Dent. Assoc., June, 1919.)

However, under the present requirements for flow as outlined in the next section, a dental amalgam which meets the specification undoubtedly has sufficient strength.

As noted in a previous chapter, copper, silver and possibly zinc, when present in the alloy in proper amounts, contribute to the strength of the amalgam, whereas tin is definitely a weakening element. The effect of the mercury:alloy ratio upon crushing strength has been studied by Gray[1] and his results are shown in Fig. 118.

331

The units of pressure used in Fig. 118, and some of the subsequent figures, are kilograms per circular centimeter. Circular centimeters are the units obtained by squaring the diameter of a circular surface; they are proportional to the area of the surface. Hence, a unit load or stress in kilograms per circular centimeter, instead of kilograms per square centimeter, may be determined as follows:

$$\text{Unit load (kilograms per circular centimeter)} = \frac{\text{Load}}{(\text{Diameter})^2}$$

where the load is expressed in kilograms, and the diameter in centimeters. It follows that:

1 kg. per cir. cm. = 1.273 kg. per sq. cm. = 18.11 pounds per sq. in.

As may be noted from the curve, the crushing strength reaches a constant value above an approximate mercury:alloy ratio of 9:6 or 1.5,* below which value the crushing strength decreases markedly. Gray also found that the minimum mercury:alloy ratio needed for maximum crushing strength decreased with increase in packing pressure. Since amalgam alloys vary considerably as to composition, annealing time, etc., no general conclusions can be drawn as to the correct mercury:alloy ratio for all cases. Obviously, there must be sufficient mercury present to coat the filings thoroughly, and produce a plastic mass for subsequent manipulation.

TABLE LII

EFFECT OF TRITURATION TIME ON CRUSHING STRENGTH (LB./SQ. IN.)

Alloy No.	Undermix.	Normal mix.	Overmix.
1	41,570	46,580	51,680
2	35,100	44,470	51,567
3	34,880	46,300	52,800
4	34,200	47,500	48,200
5	37,066	44,300	49,800

The effect of mixing time on crushing strength, as determined by Ward and Scott,[2] is shown in Table LII. The compositions of the alloys used in the table are identical with those of numbers 25, 20, 24, 19, and 15 respectively, as given in Table LI, page 313. Although overmixing produces an increase in strength, its effect on other properties may be very deleterious.

The effect of packing pressure upon crushing strength and mercury retained by the hardened amalgam is shown in Fig. 119.[1] The upper curve represents the mercury content of the hardened amalgam in per cent as affected by packing pressure, whereas the lower curve represents the change in crushing strength with increasing packing

* Ordinarily, the ratio is given as alloy:mercury, but as a matter of convenience it is expressed in the figures reciprocally, as a quotient.

pressure. As previously noted, the greater the pressure during condensation, the larger is the amount of mercury expressed; furthermore, the greater the packing pressure, the greater is the crushing strength.*

Flow.—The flow of an amalgam is tested by placing a cylinder of arbitrary size, usually 4 mm. in diameter and 8 mm. long, under an empirically selected static load of 250 kg. per square centimeter (approximately 3550 pounds per square inch) for twenty-four hours or more; the test is started three hours after trituration. In order for the amalgam to be satisfactory, the flow must not be greater than 4 per cent during the initial twenty-four hours of the test.

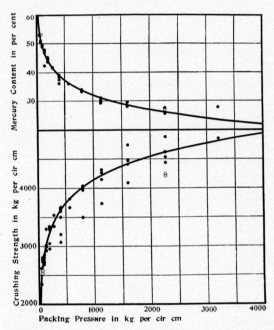

Fig. 119.—Crushing strength and mercury content as affected by packing pressure. (Gray: Jour. of the Nat. Dent. Assoc., June, 1919.)

Fig. 120 shows the flow of an amalgam tested under standard conditions; the percentage of flow is plotted as the ordinate, and the time as the abscissa. As may be noted, the flow is greatest during the first six to ten hours of the test, and gradually decreases as the test is continued, and the rate finally becomes constant for as long as the test is prolonged. This is very important, as it apparently indicates

---

* For the benefit of the reader who may be mathematically inclined, the relationship between packing pressure and crushing strength is evidently logarithmic. Gray[1] expresses the equation of the curve as: $S = A + B \log P$, where S is the crushing strength, P the packing pressure, and A and B are parameters depending upon such factors as the nature of the amalgam, temperature of crushing, etc.

that the flow continues slowly for an indefinite period; this fact is borne out by long time tests. Ward and Scott[3] account for this by assuming that the amalgam does not strain harden under the pressure, which is a reasonable assumption in view of the fact that certain of the products of the reaction are probably tin and a solid solution of tin and mercury. The recrystallization temperature of tin is only slightly above room temperature, and, as previously mentioned, the tin-mercury amalgam is very soft. The large flow at the start is probably due to the fact that the amalgam was not entirely hardened when the test began; hence, the test is very likely an indication of the hardening rate as well as the flow of the amalgam.

However, the fully hardened amalgams are not plastic under sudden blows. Like pitch, they are very brittle when struck suddenly,

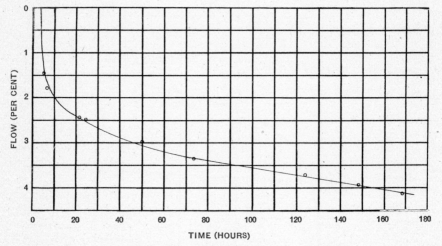

Fig. 120.—Typical flow curve for an amalgam.

yet when subjected to a continuous load of comparatively small magnitude, they flow continuously. To counteract this effect, Ward[3] advocates a special type of cavity preparation for amalgam restorations. Flow is exhibited clinically usually by gingival overhangs on two surface restorations after considerable use. On occlusal surfaces, the amalgam is likely to flow over the edge of the prepared cavity and break off, thus leaving a faulty margin which invites recurrence of caries.

Table LIII[2] shows the effect of mixing time on the flow of the same five alloys noted in Table LII. As may be noted, the flow is somewhat critically dependent upon the trituration in some of the alloys, particularly so in the case of alloy No. 1. The general effect of increase in packing pressure within normal limits is to decrease the flow.

TABLE LIII

EFFECT OF TRITURATION TIME ON FLOW (PER CENT)

Alloy No.	Undermix.	Normal mix.	Overmix.
1	5.25	3.53	7.06
2	2.82	2.87	3.22
3	3.57	3.04	4.07
4	4.32	3.64	3.26
5	3.38	2.77	3.28

Adaptation.—By adaptation is meant the degree of proximity of the filling material to the wall of the prepared cavity; the ideal condition is, of course, complete proximity.

It is very difficult to test quantitatively for adaptation. The dye test of Fletcher (see page 312) is employed at the present time in a modified form, as is the air pressure test. The latter test consists of the subjection of an amalgam specimen condensed in a steel die to air pressure, and noting the pressure at which it begins to leak air. Although both of these tests exhibit certain points of value, more thought must be given to their standardization before final conclusions can be drawn as to the results.

There can be little doubt of the fact that heavy condensing pressures tend to produce better adaptation. Another factor which enters into the adaptation of the amalgam is the alloy:mercury ratio; there should be sufficient mercury present to lubricate the particles, so that they may slide into position under pressure and pack tightly.

Particle size is very likely also a factor. Large irregular particles probably do not pack as densely as smaller smooth particles. Presumably irregular particles might cause a roughness of the amalgam surface adjacent to the cavity wall, which might result in leakage regardless of the amount of expansion of the filling. However, direct evidence is lacking in this regard, and such statements are highly conjectural.

The problem of adaptation is probably the most urgent of the research projects needed in amalgams at the present time, and it is very encouraging that so many research men are considering it. Control of dimensional changes has occupied too much thought and effort at the expense of the problem of adaptation.

MANIPULATION OF DENTAL AMALGAMS

Proportioning the Mercury and Alloy.—The proportions by weight of mercury and alloy to be used are usually expressed as the alloy: mercury ratio. The ratio is always less than 1, *i. e.*, the weight of the mercury used is always greater than that of the alloy. The ratio is not critical provided that enough mercury is used, and that the excess is removed in subsequent manipulations. Probably the average desirable alloy:mercury ratio is 5:8 by weight.

The manufacturer should state the alloy:mercury ratio to be used, as well as detailed instructions for the remaining manipulations. *In the light of the discussion given in the preceding pages, it should be unnecessary to emphasize the fact that such directions should be followed unreservedly* in dental practice, as they have presumably been balanced to give the best possible properties to the amalgam.

Trituration.—After the mercury and alloy have been proportioned, they are transferred to a ground glass mortar and triturated with a pestle at a given rate and for a given length of time usually specified by the manufacturer. The pestle should be held with a pen grasp rather than a palm grip, as with the latter grip too much pressure is likely to be exerted; too much pressure will overtriturate the amalgam, and this may result in considerable flow and contraction. After the filings have been thoroughly coated with mercury, the mass is transferred from the mortar to the hand, spread out and rolled up with the thumb of the other hand, a process which is called *mulling* or *kneading*. The kneading should be continued until a smooth bright mix results, which may be squeezed between the fingers with a characteristic "cry."

At no stage of the manipulation should additional mercury be added after the trituration has been started, as this results in a marked decrease in crushing strength.[4]

After trituration, the mass should be rolled into a cylinder approximately ⅛ inch in diameter, laid on a clean napkin or gauze, and cut crosswise into small pieces in preparation for condensation into the prepared cavity.

Condensation.—The next important step in the manipulation is the packing or condensing of the plastic mass into the prepared cavity. There are several satisfactory methods of accomplishing this. The following typical condensation method has been outlined with the general idea of eliminating contraindicated manipulations, rather than arbitrarily giving one technic to the exclusion of all others.

Although a discussion of the preparation of the cavity is not within the scope of this book, it is certainly in order to remark that the prepared cavity must be cleaned and dried thoroughly, and maintained in this condition throughout the condensation of the amalgam. The salts of the saliva weaken the hardened amalgam considerably.[4]

The first bit of amalgam should be placed in the prepared cavity without having previously expressed any of the mercury, unless the mass is definitely plashy. It should be packed by starting at the center and stepping toward the cavity walls; this brings the excess mercury to the surface, and assists in the obtaining of a good adaptation.

The next bit should be squeezed between the thumb and forefinger for the purpose of removing some of the excess mercury. The bit of amalgam then is packed against the portion already condensed. The restoration is thus built up gradually, expressing the mercury between the fingers each time, in order not to leave an excess in the finished restoration. However, it is important that each successive piece is packed against a surface of mercury to insure union; if an excess of mercury appears at any time during the condensation, it should be immediately removed.

The prepared cavity should be packed overfull. At this stage the amalgam may be wrung through a clean napkin or chamois, and then packed down on the already overfilled cavity preparation to blot up the last bit of mercury possible. A slight vibration of the surface with the condenser point is helpful in this regard, as it brings out additional mercury.

The expressing of considerable mercury from the mass immediately after mortar trituration or during the hand mulling process, is not good practice unless the mass is very plashy; a lack of mercury is likely to cause the amalgam to harden somewhat before packing. Once the amalgam crystals have started to form, they should be disturbed as little as possible. The surplus mercury aids in the delaying of the effective crystallization somewhat; hence, the removal of mercury from each piece just before packing is preferable. Furthermore, the mix should be soft and plastic, with the particles well lubricated with mercury while the amalgam is condensed. This allows the filings to slip over one another and pack into a dense mass, thus getting better adaptation and greater strength.

Condensing Pressure.—The condensers used for the packing of the amalgam into the prepared cavity are somewhat similar to the gold foil condensers, except that they may have a larger face area. The condensing or packing pressure employed has a considerable influence upon the physical properties of the amalgam, since the greater the packing pressure, the greater will be the amount of mercury expressed from the amalgam.

The size of the condenser point very largely governs the packing pressure for a given packing thrust. The dentist should distinguish between packing thrust and packing pressure. The former represents the number of pounds exerted by the condenser point on the amalgam, whereas the latter represents the pressure exerted in pounds per square inch of the surface of the condenser point. The manner in which the thrust for four different circular condenser points varies with the packing pressure is shown in Fig. 121. For example, a 10-pound thrust with a condenser point 1 mm. in diameter gives a packing pressure of approximately 8250 pounds per square inch, whereas the same thrust with a condenser 3.5 mm. in diameter gives only 670 pounds per square inch. This is due to the larger surface area in the second case, since the packing pressure for a given thrust will vary inversely with the square of the diameter of the condenser point. For example, a packing pressure of 80 pounds per square inch on a

22

1-mm. condenser would be only 20 pounds per square inch on a 2-mm. condenser with the thrust the same on both. In other words, the thrust on the 2-mm. condenser will have to be four times as great as that for the 1-mm. condenser in order to give the same packing pressure. 'This does not mean that the smaller condenser is necessarily proportionately more effective in the expressing of the mercury. Obviously, the mercury is, partially at least, merely changed in position from one point to another by the 1-mm. condenser. Nevertheless, experiments by the author have shown a considerable difference in dimensional changes when two condensers of different size are used with the same packing thrust. Black[5] advocates the use of a broad

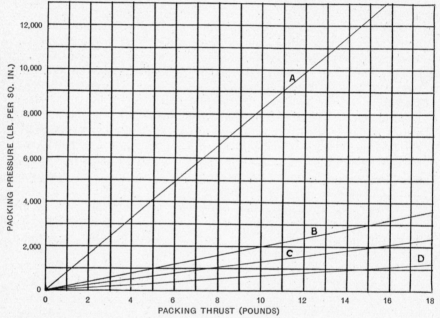

Fig. 121.—Variation of packing pressure with packing thrust. A, 1-mm. condenser; B, 2-mm. condenser; C, 2.5-mm. condenser; D, 3.5-mm. condenser.

condenser for gross condensation and the smaller condensers for adaptation purposes.

Theoretically, the absolute effective packing pressure is more or less of an average value, to be computed from a definite physical property which may be varied with the packing pressure according to a definite law. Such a law has been derived[1] from studies of crushing strength, and effective packing pressures have been computed.* Among 4 individuals it was found that the effective packing pressures on 20 different trials varied from 310 to 4300 pounds per square inch.[6]

* See footnote on page 333.

The condenser points are usually serrated. The reason for this is somewhat vague. It is true that a serrated surface enables the operator to pick up the amalgam more readily. However, this might be a detriment under some conditions, since there may be a certain adhesion of amalgam to the serrations when the condenser is withdrawn from the filling, a condition which leads one to speculate as to whether a certain amount of adaptation is not thus lost, especially at the start. Certainly the serrations soon become clogged, and this in effect renders the surface smooth.

Expressed Mercury.—As noted previously, during the condensation certain amounts of mercury and amalgam are removed, and the question as to whether the composition of the amalgam is greatly changed by the removal of these ingredients has been studied by Ray and Easton.[10]

After they had mixed the amalgam, they expressed the excess mercury much in the same manner as described above. This mercury was analyzed chemically, and another analysis was made of the semi-fluid portion which was removed during condensation. Finally the packed amalgam was analyzed, and all the analyses were calculated mercury-free for purposes of comparison. Typical results are shown in Table LIV. As may be noted from the table, the investigators were justified in concluding that the use of excess mercury and its subsequent removal from the amalgam does not greatly disturb the composition of the packed amalgam.

TABLE LIV

EFFECT ON THE COMPOSITION OF THE PACKED AMALGAM OF EXPRESSING
MERCURY DURING AMALGAMATION AND CONDENSATION*

Metal.	Alloy (per cent).	Packed amalgam (per cent).	Expressed excess mercury (per cent).	Semi-fluid portion removed during condensation (per cent).
Silver..........	68.67	68.90	36.77	68.50
Tin.............	26.24	26.14	50.43	26.48
Copper.........	4.98	5.01	2.19	3.86
Zinc...........	0.24	0.12	5.28	0.48
Total..........	100.13	100.17	94.67	99.32
Mercury in portion (per cent).........	48.50		96.00	63.00

*Results calculated mercury-free; alloy:mercury ratio, 5:9.

Finishing.—The mass should be carved as soon as it has hardened sufficiently, usually within three to five minutes after packing. No overhang on any margins should be allowed. The amalgam is extremely brittle, and the slightest portion extending over the enamel will break off in use, leaving a rough margin. Because of its brittleness, amalgam should not be burnished from the time it has reached a stiffness beyond a workable plasticity. As a general rule, the burnishing of an amalgam as a finishing procedure at any time is to be avoided—it endangers marginal adaptation.[9] The restoration should not be polished for at least twenty-four hours after its insertion.

Corrosion of Amalgams.—The fact that amalgam restorations are likely to tarnish in the mouth is well known, and for this reason their use in portions of the mouth exposed to view is precluded. The zinc and tin will obviously be the first metals to be affected, but the copper, silver and mercury will react also with acids in the presence of oxygen.

The discoloration or tarnish which occurs on amalgam restorations is very likely due to the formation of sulphides by reaction with hydrogen sulphide and oxygen. The copper sulphide may be oxidized to the sulphate which is soluble; hence, the copper amalgams usually corrode badly in the mouth. However, the silver and mercury sulphides are not readily oxidized, and, since they are quite insoluble, they may prevent actual corrosion of the restoration. It is very fortunate that the mercury sulphide does not change to a soluble form, as the salt would be poisonous. The mercury in the amalgam apparently exerts no poisonous action whatever during any stage of its manipulation by the dentist or subsequent use by the patient. This statement applies to both copper[7] and silver[8] amalgams.

Occasionally, a tooth containing an amalgam restoration becomes darkened, because of the metallic sulphides penetrating the dentinal tubuli. Such a condition usually results from a faulty margin, which allows leakage of saliva and acids between the restoration and the cavity wall.

Copper Amalgams.—Copper amalgam, as the name implies, is an amalgam of mercury and copper. Because of their lack of corrosion resistance, the use of these amalgams in dentistry is usually limited to the restoring of deciduous teeth and to the construction of models.

The copper and mercury are amalgamated by placing freshly precipitated copper in mercury. When the solution is complete, the excess mercury is removed, and the mass allowed to harden.* This is the product supplied to the dentist in the form of pellets.

In manipulation, the pellets are heated in an iron spoon or glass test tube over a flame. When droplets of mercury have definitely formed on the pellets, the mass is ground with a mortar and pestle, after which the manipulation is very similar to that outlined for the silver amalgams.

The copper amalgams harden slowly, requiring from eight to

* The amalgamation may also be carried out by electrolysis. See Ward: *American Textbook of Operative Dentistry* (6th Ed.), page 512, Lea and Febiger.

twelve hours. While hardening, they invariably contract from 8 to 30 microns per centimeter or more. Once hardened, their crushing strength is satisfactory, and they exhibit but little flow when tested by the standard method. They are bactericidal with respect to the mouth fluids.[7]

Specifications: American Dental Association Specification No. 1. See Appendix, page 381.

LITERATURE

1. Gray, A. W., *Metallographic Phenomena Observed in Amalgams.* J. N. D. A., 6: 513–531 (June) 1919; 6: 909–925 (Oct.) 1919.

2. Ward, M. L., and Scott, E. O., *Effects of Variations in Manipulation on Dimensional Changes, Crushing Strength, and Flow of Amalgams.* J. A. D. A., 19: 1683–1705 (Oct.) 1932.

3. Ward, M. L., and Scott, E. O., *Further Studies of the Effects of Variations in Manipulation on Dimensional Changes and Flow of Amalgams.* J. A. D. A., 22: 1164–1171 (July) 1935.

4. Taylor, N. O., *Amalgam Technic: Dependable and Dangerous Practices.* J. A. D. A., 17: 1880–1889 (Oct.) 1930.

5. *G. V. Black's Work on Operative Dentistry,* Revised by A. D. Black (7th Ed.) 2: 207. Medico-Dental Publishing Co.

6. Gray, A. W., *Transition Phenomena in Amalgams—A Discussion.* J. N. D. A., 8: 495 (June) 1921.

7. Harris, F. E., *Copper Amalgam.* Jour. Dent. Res., 14: 165, 166 (June) 1934.

8. Souder, Wilmer, and Sweeney, W. T., *Is Mercury Poisonous in Dental Amalgam Restorations?* Dent. Cos., 73: 1145–1152 (Dec.) 1931.

9. Reference (5), page 208.

10. Ray, K. W., and Easton, G. S., *Changes in Composition of Amalgam Alloys During Amalgamation and Condensation.* J. A. D. A., 18: 1076–1082 (June) 1931.

CHAPTER XXXVI

STEEL

By P. B. Taylor, A.M.

Steel finds its principal use in dentistry in the form of instruments and other accessories. Although the dentist seldom fabricates with ordinary steel, yet an understanding of its metallographical properties is essential in order that he may intelligently care for his instruments in their sharpening, tempering, etc.

Steel as an Alloy.—Iron and carbon form essentially a eutectiferous series of alloys, which are insoluble in each other in the solid state, except for a limited range of solubility of carbon in iron, probably in the form of iron carbide. The maximum solubility of carbon in iron in the solid state is 1.7 per cent; this is the composition which forms the basis for the classification of the iron-carbon alloys as either steel or cast iron. Steel is any such alloy having a carbon content of less than 1.7 per cent, whereas an iron-carbon alloy which contains a greater amount of carbon may be classified as *cast iron*.

Metallography of Iron.—Pure iron, when heated, undergoes a number of allotropic changes which are of particular import in the study of steel. Iron, at atmospheric temperatures, exists in what is known as the *alpha* form, which is magnetic and crystallizes in a body-centered cubic lattice. The metallographic term for this type of iron is *ferrite*. As the iron is heated, it loses its magnetic property, but shows no change in space lattice. This body-centered non-magnetic form is known as *beta* iron. At a slightly higher temperature, the iron transforms into a face-centered lattice, which is known as *gamma* iron, and it is in this form that the carbon is most soluble. At extremely high temperatures gamma iron again changes to a body-centered lattice, which is very similar to the alpha iron, the greatest difference probably being an increased capacity for the solution of carbon. This latter form is known as delta iron, and is of no importance in the present discussion. The beta iron is also of little practical importance from a dental standpoint; hence, only the alpha and gamma forms are of primary interest.

Constitution Diagram of Steel.—The section of the constitution diagram giving the composition of steels, in accordance with the above classification, appears in Fig. 122. Consider the cooling of an iron-carbon alloy containing 0.84 per cent carbon. As the alloy is cooled from above the liquidus line, KLM, the alloy will begin to solidify at a temperature of approximately 1490° C. (2712° F.), point 1, and between the temperatures indicated by points 1 and 2 (approximately

1260° C. or 2300° F.) it will be partially liquid and partially solid; the solid is a solid solution of iron carbide in gamma iron. After passing point 2, an alloy of this composition will be completely solidified, forming *austenite,* which is the metallographic term for a solid solution of an intermetallic compound, iron carbide, in gamma iron. Iron carbide has the chemical formula Fe_3C and is known as *cementite.* No further changes occur until the point E is reached, at which temperature a precipitation of *pearlite* occurs, which is the metallographic

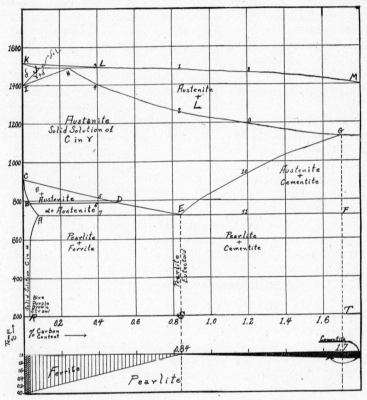

Fig. 122.—Constitution diagram for carbon steel.

term for a slowly cooled intimate mixture of cementite and ferrite. An intimate mixture of this sort, which is precipitated from a solid solution rather than a liquid solution, is termed a *eutectoid* rather than a eutectic. A steel of this composition which is composed entirely of the eutectoid is known as a *eutectoid steel.*

A second type of steel may be considered by the examination of an alloy which contains, for example, 0.4 per cent carbon. This steel would commence to solidify at a temperature of approximately 1500° C. (2732° F.), point 3, and it is completely solidified at a temperature of 1400° C. (2552° F.), point 4, when austenite is formed as in the previous case. At approximately 810° C. (1490° F.), point 5, the iron would begin to precipitate from the solid solution in the form of a body-centered cubic lattice, and at a temperature of approximately 790° C. (1454° F.), point 5, it would become magnetic in nature in addition to this change in lattice. All of the iron, however, would not undergo this precipitation, since in a range of temperature between points 6 and 7 the alloy would be a mixture of alpha iron plus austenite. However, at point 7 pearlite would be formed from the remaining austenite and the alloy would then be a mixture of pearlite and ferrite. If the chart immediately under the constitution diagram is noted, it is evident that the ratio of free ferrite to pearlite in an alloy of this composition would be approximately one to one. Alloys of this type, which are composed of a mixture of pearlite and free ferrite, are known as *hypoeutectoid* steels.

The third type of steel will be illustrated by the observation of the changes which occur in a steel containing more than 0.84 per cent carbon, for example, 1.2 per cent carbon. If this alloy is allowed to cool from the molten state, it will begin to solidify at the approximate temperature of 1460° C. (2657° F.), point 8, and complete the solidification, forming austenite after passing a temperature of 1200° C. (2192° F.), indicated by 9. At 10 (approximate temperature 940° C. or 1724° F.) cementite commences to precipitate out of the solid solution and continues until a temperature of 725° C. (1337° F.), point 11, is reached, when pearlite precipitates, and gives a mixture of pearlite and cementite. The mixture in this case, as shown by the chart at the bottom of Fig. 122, will be a mixture of about 94 per cent pearlite and 6 per cent cementite. Steels of this type, which are a mixture of free cementite and pearlite, are known as *hypereutectoid* steels.

The hardness of these three types of steels increases from a relatively low value for low carbon hypoeutectoid steels through the high carbon hypereutectoid steels where the hardness more than trebles itself. One might anticipate this from consideration of the B.H.N. of the constituents which, according to Sisco,[1] are approximately 80 to 100 for ferrite, 150 to 200 for pearlite, and probably well over 700 for cementite.

Heat Treatment.—The difference between a eutectic and a eutectoid is as follows:

If a eutectic is heated above the eutectic temperature and cooled, the components are very easily segregated because of the mobility of the atoms when in the molten state. However, when a eutectoid is heated above the precipitation temperature, it passes into a solid solution, and the time necessary for the alloy to completely homogenize would be relatively long since the rate of atomic diffusion in the solid state is very low. Similarly, when it is cooled through the eutectoid point, if sufficient time is not allowed, no appreciable separation of the constituents will occur. By varying the time of cooling, after a eutectoid has been heated above the critical temperature at which it is formed, the resulting metallographic structure may be controlled to a great extent. This principle forms the basis for the heat treatment of steel.

The most important types of heat treatments, and the only ones which will be discussed, are *annealing, normalizing, hardening,* and *tempering.* The most important purpose of annealing is to soften the steel for machining purposes. The principal function of a normalizing heat treatment is to refine the grain structure.* The hardening heat treatment is given to the material in order to increase its hardness and strength. The tempering process, which follows the hardening heat treatment, gives the material the precise hardness and

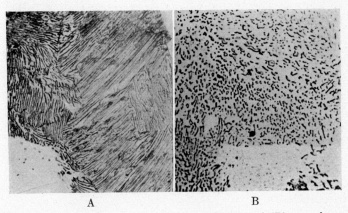

A   B

Fig. 123.—Microstructure of (A) lamellar pearlite, and (B) granular pearlite. × 100. (Greaves and Wrighton: *Practical Microscopical Metallography,* Chapman and Hall, Ltd., Publishers.)

strength desired, coupled with satisfactory reduction of brittleness, which is usually exhibited by a severely hardened steel.

Annealing.—The annealing operation consists of a heating of the steel slightly above the critical temperature, where it is held for sufficient time to allow for complete equilibrium, and then it is cooled slowly. This slow cooling treatment will produce *lamellar pearlite,* which is illustrated in Fig. 123A, or if the material is cooled more rapidly, the pearlite appears in a form as shown in Fig. 123B, which is known as *granular pearlite.* In this form, sufficient time has not been allowed for the ferrite and cementite to develop a grosser crystalline structure, such as is present in the lamellar pearlite. The smaller grains in the granular pearlite offer greater resistance to the formation of slip planes because of a keying action[2] as described on page 207; consequently this is a harder material. It may be stated, then, that in

* Normalizing is particularly applicable to hypereutectoid steels.

general the annealing process is a treatment whereby a steel is heated slightly above the critical temperature and allowed to cool slowly, thereby forming the lamellar type of pearlite. In practice this temperature will rarely exceed the critical temperature by more than 50° C. (90° F.), the critical temperature being given by CDEG in Fig. 122.

Normalizing.—The second treatment mentioned has been termed the normalizing treatment. This treatment is usually necessary in cases where the steel has been hot forged, in which event the sustained high temperature gives rise to considerable grain growth which is undesirable. In the treatment, advantage is taken of the fact that the grain size of the steel at ordinary room temperatures is not much dependent upon the grain size of the parent austenite, but rather it is principally a function of the cooling rate from above the critical temperature. It has been found that a rapid cooling of the steel from above the critical range gives rise to a fine grain structure. The normalizing treatment consists in the heating of the steel to a temperature about 50° C. (90° F.) above the annealing temperature, after which it is cooled very rapidly. This treatment will give a steel with a fine grain structure, but such a treatment leaves the steel in a very hard condition, and it is therefore followed by the usual annealing heat treatment. In the normalizing process, any *free cementite*, which might be present around the grain boundaries, would be completely dissolved when heated to this relatively high temperature. Therefore, in addition to the fine grain structure, the normalized steel has been homogenized so that subsequent hardening and tempering treatments will give a steel which will be uniform in texture and hardness.

Hardening and Tempering.—After the steel has been completely shaped, it must be given the proper hardness and strength in order to serve its function. In order to achieve this, the steel must first be given what is known as the *hardening heat treatment*. In this treatment it is heated to the critical temperature, where it is held long enough to heat it completely throughout, and then it is cooled rapidly. The rapidity with which the work is cooled will determine the hardness of the final product. The steel may be quenched, in which case the hardest form obtainable will result. This has a definite metallographic structure which is shown in Fig. 124a, and is known as *martensite*. Steel in this form will usually show a B.H.N. ranging from 400 to 700. When the steel is quenched from above the critical range, the precipitation has been effected so rapidly that the cementite particles have practically no time to grow, and are very small; consequently very little opportunity for slip planes will exist. This gives rise to the extreme hardness of martensite. If the steel is given a less rigorous quenching, the metallographic appearance will be similar to that illustrated by Fig. 124b. This is known as *troostite*, and it will probably have a B.H.N. between 300 and 400. In this case, sufficient time has elapsed so that the precipitated cementite is able to form particles of a slightly larger size than in the case of martensite, and this accounts for the decreased hardness, in accordance with the theory of keying action. In like manner, if the material is cooled still more slowly, a steel would result with a B.H.N. from 200 to 300 and a metallographic structure such as is shown in Fig. 124c; this form is known as *sorbite*. In this case the cementite particles are finally large enough so that they can be distinguished by the microscope. Generally it is relatively difficult to control the cooling rate satisfactorily in order to form martensite, troostite, or sorbite at will. The usual procedure, therefore, is to produce a martensitic structure, and to follow this treatment with the tempering process in order to produce the desired properties.

The *tempering heat treatment*, therefore, is a softening heat treatment given to the steel usually in martensitic structure, in order to

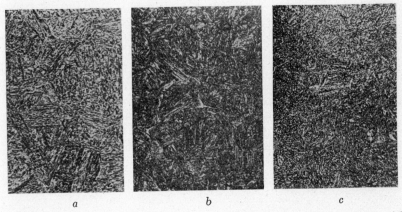

a   b   c

Fig. 124.—(a) Martensitic structure. (b) Microstructure of troostite. (c) Sorbitic structure. × 500. (Sisco: *The Constitution of Steel and Cast Iron*, Amer. Soc. Steel Treating.)

produce the metallographic form with the desired hardness and strength. In the tempering process, the steel is not heated to the critical range, but rather to some temperature which is considerably below the temperature at which the first allotropic transformation would occur. The temperatures are usually determined by the color of the oxide coating on a well-polished piece of work; the thickness of the oxide coating gives the characteristic colors and indicates the temperature to which the steel has been heated. Table LV gives the temperatures at which the various temper colors appear and also the type of instrument for which each temper color would be desirable. These temperatures for the various colors are applicable only to alloys which are essentially carbon steels. If, for example, a 12 to 14 per cent chromium steel was used, a blue color would appear at a

TABLE LV[4]

TEMPER COLORS FOR CARBON STEEL

Temperature.		Color.	Temper.
(° C.)	(° F.)		
220–238	428–461	Straw.	Lancets, razors, surgical instruments, enamel chisels.
243	470	Full yellow.	Excavators, very small cold chisels.
25	488	Brown.	Pluggers, scissors, penknives.
265	509	Brown with purple spots.	Axes, plane irons, saws, cold chisels.
276	529	Purple.	Table knives, large shears.
287	549	Bright blue.	Swords, watch springs.
292	558	Full blue.	Fine saws, augers.
315	600	Dark blue.	Hand and pit saws.

temperature of about 530° C. (986° F.), so that the nature of the steel must be known when this procedure is attempted. A graphic conception of the relationship of these temperatures to the critical temperature can be obtained by referring to Fig. 122, upon which is indicated the location of four of these colors.

As soon as the temper color is obtained, the usual practice is to quench immediately. However, as stated by Sauveur,[3] "the same amount of temper would result from heating hardened steel to 550° F.* when its color is bright blue, followed by immediate cooling, and heating it to 490° F.† when its color is brown, and maintaining it at that temperature until it is colored bright blue." In the tempering process, the metallographic appearance of the steel gradually changes from martensite through troostite, sorbite, and finally to sorbitic pearlite, with an accompanying reduction in B.H.N. The tempering treatment, then, consists in slightly elevating the temperature, and thus the cementite particles are permitted to grow sufficiently so as to decrease the hardness to the desired value; hence, a given steel appliance can be made to perform the rôle to which it is to be assigned with maximum efficiency.

Effect of Modifiers.—The discussion thus far has dealt entirely with steels whose composition is iron and carbon, with no impurities or modifiers. Practical steels of today are generally not simply this binary alloy, but rather they have one or more modifying elements added. The effect of modifying agents will be considered briefly, such as are likely to be found present in steels which may be used in various phases of dental operations and manipulations.

* 288° C.
† 254° C.

In general, the alloying elements may be divided into one of two classifications: (1) those elements which form carbides with some of the carbon present when added to a carbon steel, and (2) those which do not form these supplementary carbides. The principal elements added to steels of dental interest are chromium, nickel, manganese, molybdenum, and silicon. Chromium, manganese, and molybdenum may form carbides, whereas the nickel is soluble in both the gamma and alpha iron in all proportions so that no carbides of nickel will be formed. Silicon is present in such small quantities that this factor does not merit consideration at the present time.

The effect of the addition of chromium to steel will be discussed more completely in Chapter XXXVII. At the present time it is sufficient to make the following notations concerning its effect. Chromium dissolves in pure iron forming a solid solution. However, if carbon is present, complex carbides may be formed, the formulae of which are not known at the present time. The addition of chromium also lowers the critical temperature of the steel, but not as severely as in the case of nickel, and as the chromium content is progressively increased the structure of the steel at room temperature will change from the original pearlitic structure to a martensitic one, and finally, after sufficient addition of chromium, a cementitic structure will be produced. A further effect is the reduction in the amount of carbon necessary to form the eutectoid as the amount of chromium present is increased. Chromium also considerably enhances the hardness, strength, and elastic limit of the steel.

Nickel also lowers the critical temperature markedly. The metallographic structure is affected somewhat differently by this modifier, however; the structure, at room temperature, progresses successively from pearlitic to martensitic and finally to austenitic steel. The amount of carbon required to produce the pure eutectoid is also reduced by the addition of nickel. Furthermore, the ability to harden by heat treatment is considerably intensified by the addition of this element to the alloy.

Manganese dissolves in pure iron forming a solid solution, but if carbon is present, it reacts to form the compound MnC_3 which is very similar to cementite. The addition of manganese causes both a reduction of the critical temperature, which is nearly double the effect evidenced by nickel, and also a reduction in the amount of carbon necessary to produce the eutectoid. It has an added advantage in that it is an excellent deoxidizer with the result that it is used as a general scavenger; hence, there is usually some manganese present in all steels. However the amount is generally small, since it is present in the final product in quantity less than 1 per cent.

Molybdenum is generally present in the dental steels only to the extent of about 0.5 per cent or less, and in these amounts the only practical effect which results is perhaps a slight increase in strength, elastic limit, and hardness, with but little reduction in ductility. This element also inhibits grain growth during heat treatment.

Often small quantities of silicon may be found in many dental steels, but in the quantities in which it is present it probably has little effect, other than it may produce a slight increase in elasticity. Some sulphur and phosphorus may occasionally be noted, but these elements are undesirable and should be minimized, as they tend to produce brittleness. With this brief notation concerning the effects of these elements, the composition of a few dental steels will be given.

Dental Steels: Composition and Properties.—First, the composition of a dental steel such as is used by most manufacturers for standard dental instruments may be considered.* The composition of this type of steel appears in Table LVI. From the considerations

TABLE LVI

COMPOSITION OF STEELS USED FOR DENTAL INSTRUMENTS (PER CENT BY WEIGHT)

Dental instruments.		Forceps.	
C	1.1–1.2	C	0.4–0.5
Cr	0.2–0.3	Cr	0.4–0.5
Mn	0.2–0.3	Mn	2.0–2.3
Si	0.4	Si	0.1–0.2
Ni	Trace	Mo	0.5
		S and P	Low

noted above it can be seen that this is a hypereutectoid steel. There are also small amounts of nickel, manganese and chromium present, which tend to increase the strength, elasticity, and hardness to a value above that which occurs in the case of a regular carbon steel. In addition to this, these elements contribute to a good hardening heat treatment when the steel is cooled more slowly than would be necessary if a plain carbon steel was used. The fact that the hardening treatment may be effected by a decreased cooling rate would give a more uniformly treated steel. This is fairly obvious, if one considers that when a body is quenched from an elevated temperature, the outer portion will necessarily cool more rapidly than the interior, with the result that an exterior shell is formed with a greater hardness than the inside portion. The dental instrument, especially a cutting instrument, should be of relatively uniform hardness throughout, otherwise repeated sharpening will grind away this hardened shell, with a soft core remaining as a potential cutting edge, which would be absolutely worthless from the standpoint of utility. It should also be noted, that these small quantities of modifiers would have little effect upon the critical temperature, hence, the heat treating temperatures are essentially unaltered.

The steel used in the manufacture of forceps would have approximately the composition indicated in Table LVI. This steel differs

* Cleveland Dental Manufacturing Company.

from the preceding steel in that there are larger amounts of chromium, manganese, and also some molybdenum present. The carbon content is fairly low, but the additional amounts of chromium and manganese are sufficient to produce a steel which will closely approach a composition of a eutectoid nature. As mentioned above, these elements, along with molybdenum, will enhance the strength and elasticity as well as the elastic limit of this steel, and these are the properties which are of the greatest importance. Sulphur and phosphorus must be kept very low in amount, since brittleness, or any tendency toward brittleness in forceps, would be even more undesirable than in other types of instruments.

LITERATURE

1. Sisco, F. T., *The Constitution of Steel and Cast Iron.* Amer. Soc. Steel Treating.

2. Jeffries, Zay, and Archer, R. S., *The Slip Interference Theory of the Hardening of Metals.* Chem. and Met. Eng., June 5, 1921, p. 1061.

3. Sauveur, A., *Metallography and Heat Treatment of Iron and Steel,* p. 247.

4. Hodgen, J. D., *Practical Dental Metallurgy* (7th Ed.) p. 242. C. V. Mosby Co.

CHAPTER XXXVII

STAINLESS STEEL

By P. B. Taylor, A. M.

Stainless steels, although more than a century old, have only recently been produced commercially on a large scale for industrial use. Such steels were probably first used for dental purposes in Germany during the latter part of the World War, but they were introduced into this country as a substitute for precious metal alloys a comparatively few years ago. At the present time these materials are being used to some extent in prosthetic and orthodontic services, as well as in the form of instruments. The stainless steels used in dental instruments will first be considered before the more controversial question of the use of such steels in the mouth is discussed.

Chromium Steels.—The most important effect of adding chromium to steel in sizable amounts is the increase in resistance to tarnish and corrosion. The effect upon the iron-carbon diagram by the addition of chromium in increasing amounts is the gradual reduction of the range in which the solid solution of the carbides in the gamma iron is in the stable form. For a 20 per cent chromium content alloy, a steel which will respond favorably to heat treatment would have a carbon content in the range of approximately 0.4 to 0.8 per cent.

According to Krivobok,[1] in order to be classified as truly stainless, the steels must contain at least 10 per cent chromium. Steels which approximate this percentage of chromium content are used extensively in the making of cutlery and some stainless dental instruments. These latter stainless steels generally contain approximately 12 to 14 per cent chromium, and their carbon content is usually from 0.3 to 0.5 per cent. The carbon content should be kept low in order that the chromium carbides will not be precipitated in appreciable amount.

A high chromium content steel is also used to some extent in the manufacture of stainless steel instruments. The analyses* of two steels of this class used in the making of dental instruments appear as follows:

	Per Cent	
Carbon	0.62	0.60
Chromium	17.74	17.93
Sulphur	0.01	0.28
Silicon	0.11	0.23
Nickel	0.25	0.12

*Cleveland Dental Manufacturing Company.

These higher chromium content steels have greater amounts of carbon available for the formation of carbides, which, as shown in the preceding chapter, are the agent by which steel is given the desired hardness. As might be anticipated, such steels would show a greater enhancement of hardness upon heat treatment than the 12 to 14 per cent chromium steel.

In both the 12 to 14 and the 17 to 20 per cent chromium steels, the carbides precipitated are not only those of iron but also chromium carbides. If these latter carbides are agglomerated in any sizable amounts, a pronounced reduction in the corrosion resistance is observed. Because of this fact, the material must be given a hardening heat treatment so that martensite will be formed, rather than the

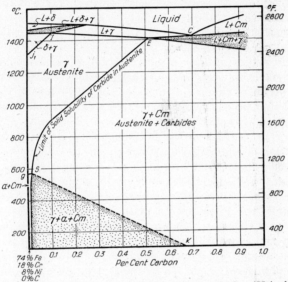

Fig. 125.—Constitution diagram for "18-8" stainless steel. (Krivobok in *The Book of Stainless Steels,* Amer. Soc. for Metals.)

large free cementite particles such as are present in the softened condition, since this latter condition would obviously impair its stainless nature. These steels have the advantage mentioned in the preceding chapter in that they may be cooled slowly when they are heat treated.

"18-8" Stainless Steels.—Stainless steels which are used in the mouth for dental appliances are usually of the "18-8" variety, the "18" referring to the percentage of chromium present, and the "8" to the percentage of nickel. The effect upon the iron-carbon diagram by this modification is illustrated in Fig. 125. The equilibrium condition is reached only with great difficulty in steels of this type, since the rate of diffusion of solid in solid is decreased to such an extent by the large amounts of nickel and chromium. In general, a steel of this composition is austenitic in structure.

23

Attention should be called to the line ES of the diagram, since it is of prime importance in the manipulation of this type of alloy. It has been found in the manipulation of these steels that any fabrication process which calls for the heating of the steel so that the temperature indicated by ES is involved tends to precipitate chromium carbides, and such a precipitation causes a very marked reduction in the resistance to corrosion. If such carbides are analyzed, they will be found to be composed mainly of chromium with very small amounts of carbon.

As a result of the precipitation of these carbides, the region immediately in the vicinity of the carbide particles is "robbed" of considerable of its chromium content. Since chromium is passive under normal conditions, it is the constituent which gives rise to the corrosion resistance of the steel; hence, a marked reduction of this property necessarily follows in such regions where the metal is present in too small an amount.

These carbides are precipitated at the grain boundaries, hence, the corrosion is intergranular in nature, which causes a partial disintegration and weakening of the structure. Obviously, if the carbon content should be sufficiently decreased so that these carbides could not be formed, this effect would not occur. This method, however, is not a very practical solution to the problem from the commercial standpoint, since the cost of producing a steel of this very low carbon content would make the material more expensive than necessary.

Krivobok[2] has suggested a number of methods of attack for this particular problem: (a) to increase the solubility of carbides at all temperatures, (b) to produce a matrix which would resist migration of carbides to the grain boundaries and their agglomeration, (c) to produce a matrix which in itself (even if carbides have separated) would resist corrosion, (d) the formation of carbides of elements other than chromium, and (e) to render the matrix less susceptible to phase change.

Up to the present time the methods which have been adopted to combat this effect have been largely by the formation of carbides of other elements. At the present time, this is effected by the addition of tungsten,[3] 0.3 per cent; titanium,[4] 0.1 to 2 per cent; vanadium,[4] 0.3 to 2 per cent; columbium,[5] up to 10 per cent; or molybdenum,[6] 2 to 4 per cent.

Another method for solving this problem is to add 0.5 to 6 per cent silicon, and heat treat the steel, intentionally precipitating the carbides as evenly distributed spherical particles, in which case it is claimed that no intergranular weakness occurs.

The question of carbide precipitation, from a dental standpoint, is capable of being solved by any of the methods enumerated above. Actually, most of these carbide inhibitors mentioned do not prevent the formation of the chromium carbides, but they are merely effective in the retarding of the rate at which the carbides are produced. As a result, many steels which contain these modifying agents will evidence intergranular corrosion if subjected to elevated temperatures for sufficient time to permit the precipitation of the carbides. However, in the dental manipulations of stainless steels, such as soldering or welding, the elevated temperatures are maintained for a sufficiently short time that the chromium carbides will not be formed in any significant amounts, if such inhibiting agents are present. Stainless steels, which are thus modified, are generally known to the profession as *stabilized stainless steels,* and it is this type of steel which should be selected if the manipulation is to require heating of the appliance in the neighborhood of 600° to 700° C. (1112°–1292° F.) or more.

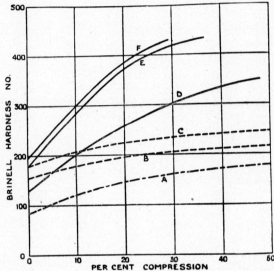

Fig. 126.—Effect of cold work on stainless steels. Curve A, nickel silver; curve B, mild steel; curve C, Ni 0.27 per cent, Cr 13.5 per cent, C 0.1 per cent; curve D, Ni 10.9 per cent, Cr 16 per cent, C 0.09 per cent; curve E, Ni 8.2 per cent, Cr 18 per cent, C 0.12 per cent; curve F, Ni 6.64 per cent, Cr 20.5 per cent; C 0.23 per cent. (Monypenny: *Stainless Iron and Steel,* John Wiley and Sons.)

These steels are not capable of being hardened by heat treatment, since they remain austenitic at room temperatures. However, they do respond remarkably to strain hardening by cold work as is shown graphically by Fig. 126. These curves give a comparison of the rates of strain hardening of these steels with nickel silver and mild steel. The writer has found that a steel which has been softened by annealing at 800° C. (1472° F.) for one minute may have its tensile strength increased as much as 40 per cent, when it is polished on a leather wheel at 5000 r.p.m. for four minutes. The diameter of the wire used in this particular case was 0.03 inch. Hence, if a steel has been slightly annealed during the process of fabrication, a certain amount of recovery may be effected by cold working.

It should be noted, however, that one cannot abuse this material and, by cold work, expect to effect an enhancement of the physical properties to anywhere near their original value, as is possible by heat treating gold alloys. The annealing gives rise to a much greater reduction in the physical properties of the material in this case than is observed in the softening heat treatment of dental gold alloys.

Comparison of 18-8 Stainless Steel with Dental Gold Alloys.—The density of stainless steel is about 7.9 grams per cubic centimeter, whereas that of a typical gold alloy such as might be used for a denture base, would be 17.5 grams per cubic centimeter; hence, a denture fabricated with a gold alloy will be approximately twice as heavy as one of the same volume made from stainless steel.

The thermal conductivity of denture base materials is an important consideration in their selection. If it is assumed that a given steel denture base is one-half as thick as an identically similar structure made from gold, calculations based upon thermal conductivity data show that the gold base will respond to thermal changes seven times as rapidly as would the steel base.

When gold is compared with steels with respect to the ability of both to resist impact forces elastically, one must be careful to select them on the basis of their moduli of resilience rather than by their proportional limits. For example, consider a stainless steel wire 0.03 inch in diameter. This wire was found to have a proportional limit of 130,000 pounds per square inch and a modulus of resilience of 310 inch-pounds per cubic inch. Let this be compared with two typical gold wires. For example, wire C, as given in the reference,* has a proportional limit in the hardened condition of 133,000 pounds per square inch. If the above steel is compared with this gold upon the basis of proportional limit, the gold would show a slight superiority over the steel. However, when their moduli of resilience are compared, that of the gold is 473 inch-pounds per cubic inch, which obviously makes the gold much superior to the steel. Again, this steel may be compared with a second gold wire A (see reference), in the hardened condition, with a proportional limit of 110,000 pounds per square inch, which might lead a casual observer to consider such a gold as actually being inferior to the steel. However, a consideration of their moduli of resilience shows the gold to have a modulus of resilience of 332 inch-pounds per cubic inch, which compares quite favorably with the steel, as noted above.

In general, stainless steels will compare favorably with wrought golds whose proportional limit does not exceed 100,000 pounds per square inch. The above comparison should modify a prevalent notion that for clasps and orthodontic appliances, a smaller wire may be used if gold is replaced by steel. This is only true where strength rather than resilience is the primary factor.

* Coleman, Table 7, p. 889, B. of S. Research Paper No. 32.

From the standpoint of esthetics, cost, bulk, and weight, stainless steel has an advantage over the gold alloys, but with respect to the other factors, gold is probably superior to steel.

Effect of Heat.—There are very few dental manipulations in which heat is not employed; hence, the effect of heat upon the physical properties of a material is an important factor and must always be considered. The effect of heat upon stainless steel may be studied by means of the results shown in Fig. 127. This graph was constructed from tensile strength values obtained by the heating of specimens of stabilized 18-8 wire, 0.04 inch in diameter, for fifteen seconds and quenching from the temperatures indicated. The actual strengths of the wire, in each case, were probably less than those shown on the curve, since a certain amount of strain hardening would necessarily take place during the tensile test. However, the curve obviously demonstrates that if the steel is heated above 725° C. (1337° F.) the physical properties will be rapidly affected in a deleterious manner.

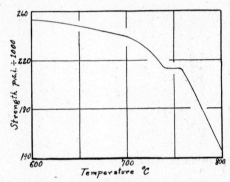

Fig. 127.—Effect of quenching temperature upon the tensile strength of 18–8 stainless steel wire.

Joining of Stainless Steel.—In the fabrication of appliances, it is very rare when some situation does not present itself which requires the joining of two or more pieces. The classical procedure for carrying out this union, so far as dentistry is concerned, is by soldering. In the soldering of gold structures, an annealing of the material will not irretrievably damage the mechanical properties; if the soldering procedure is followed by a suitable heat treatment, the physical properties may be restored to satisfactory values. However, as has been mentioned, such a procedure is impossible in the case of the 18-8 stainless steel.

In the soldering of this material, various silver solders are utilized as well as low-carat gold solders. In Fig. 128 is plotted a series of curves to show the distribution of the strength of the soldered joints by using three different solders.

Curve 1 was obtained by using a 10-carat solder; curve 2 shows the results realized by the use of a special commercial solder, which was developed especially for stainless steel by a firm in Germany. The third curve is that which was obtained by an experimental solder.* Data have also been taken using a 14-carat solder, but the temperatures required to flow this solder and the low strength exhibited by the soldered joint have precluded its consideration in this discussion. As may be noted, the frequency of occurrence has been plotted in per cent as a function of the unions which fall in the various strength ranges. For example, it was found that when a 10-carat gold solder was used, slightly over 39 per cent of the joints had strengths ranging from 70,000 to less than 80,000 pounds per square inch. It is therefore apparent that the 10-carat solder is inferior to the other two materials from the standpoint of tensile strength, since the bulk of

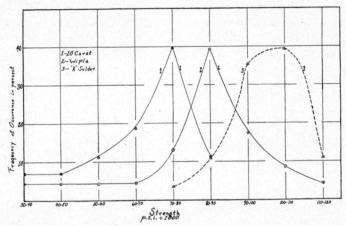

Fig. 128.—Tensile strength of stainless steel soldered joints. Curve 1, joints soldered with 10-carat gold solder; curve 2, with a commercial solder; and curve 3, with an experimental solder.

soldered unions produced in the latter two cases had strengths in excess of the most probable strength found when the gold solder was used.

The experimental solder, as well as other less satisfactory experimental solders, was modified by the addition of various amounts of gold. The data obtained from these experimental solders, together with results obtained by the comparison of standard gold solders of varying carat, seem to indicate that the lower the gold content of a solder, the greater will be the strength of the soldered union. It was found that, regardless of the flux employed, the presence of gold seemed to give rise to a tendency of the solder to melt and to spheroid before it flowed over the surface of the steel, and considerably higher

* The experimental solder has the following composition: silver, 42 per cent; copper, 31 per cent; zinc, 20 per cent, and cadmium, 7 per cent.

temperatures were required to overcome this spheroiding tendency. However, it is not entirely improbable that a suitable flux may be found, which will permit the flowing of some 10- or 12-carat solder on steel at a very much lower temperature.

These base metal solders, as might be expected, do not unreservedly withstand tarnish and corrosion in service. However, in the majority of mouths the solders mentioned will prove relatively satisfactory; they tarnish slowly enough in most cases, so that the polishing action to which they are subjected by normal habits of mouth hygiene will be sufficient to keep the restorations and appliances reasonably well polished.

A unique effect of these soldered unions is sometimes observed. In approximately 2 per cent of the cases placed in the mouth, the solder, for some reason, will separate from the steel after it has been in the mouth from six to eight weeks, but, strangely enough, very rarely does the effect reappear after the union has been resoldered. It might, then, reasonably be assumed that the effect is due, not to the oral environment, but rather to a personal factor which is always present in a manipulation such as a soldering procedure, and as yet not under control.

Flux.—Borax is not a satisfactory flux for this type of material because it does not wet the surface of the steel readily, and because it requires a higher soldering temperature than other agents. Several manufacturers have satisfactory fluxes on the market, and certain writers have suggested various compositions which vary little from that given by Brusse and Carman:[9]

Hydrochloric acid	2 minims
Potassium fluoride	300 grains
Boric acid	200 grains
Borax	50 grains
Silica (150 mesh)	50 grains
Sodium carbonate	50 grains

The basic ingredients seem to be the potassium fluoride, boric acid, and hydrochloric acid. The other ingredients seem to have little effect upon the efficiency of the flux, if these three components are present in sufficient amounts. For example, a mixture which consists of three parts of potassium fluoride and one part boric acid moistened with dilute hydrochloric acid is very satisfactory. The ingredients are mixed to a pasty consistency and water is added from time to time as necessary to maintain this consistency.

Welding.—With the advent of stainless steel, there has been introduced into dentistry the idea of the fabrication of appliances by spot welding rather than by soldering. A number of claims for the advantages of this method of joining materials have been set forth and they may be well founded, provided that the welding procedure is carried out in the proper manner.

A diagram of a circuit for a spot welder is sketched in Fig. 129, where P is the primary of a transformer and S is the secondary. At E the electrodes are shown between which the work to be welded is held. The blocked square labeled T. S. is a timing switch. The welding operation is carried out by holding the two pieces of the work in contact by means of the electrodes E and permitting a very large current to flow for a definite time. The resistance of the junction of the two pieces to be welded is very much greater than the resistance of the remainder of the secondary circuit, so that practically all the heat created by the flow of the current is liberated at the junction to be welded. The current should be of sufficient magnitude, 300 to 1000 amperes, so that the work will be brought near the melting point of the material. The welding is then accomplished by the pressure of the electrodes on the two pieces, while in this nearly molten state. The current must not be high enough to melt the metal, and the pressure must be sufficient to effect the weld; both of these factors lend themselves readily to fairly accurate control. Of course, if this operation is accomplished in a very short time, and since a very small portion of the metal will be heated, the region of the joint will heat and cool

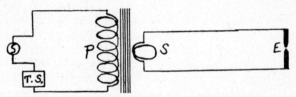

Fig. 129.—Circuit diagram for a spot welder.

so rapidly that there should be no appreciable metallographic disturbance.

In regard to the time factor, Whiteley[10] states: "A duration of weld of one or two cycles* gives the best result, particularly for thin gauge material." The cycle referred to by Whiteley corresponds to a time of one-fiftieth of a second; hence, it can readily be seen that a very delicate and precise timing mechanism is imperative for the satisfactory welding of stainless steel, especially with thin gauges such as are used in dentistry. In the above quotation the allusion is to sheet material, between 0.030 and 0.040 inches in thickness, which is comparable to materials such as are used in dentistry. The total energy dissipated at the junction of the two materials to be welded is dependent both upon this time factor and the current. In other words, if one-fiftieth of a second will produce a satisfactory weld with a given current, and

* An alternating current is thus named because its direction of flow is alternately positive and negative. The completion of one such alternation is known as a *cycle,* and the time required is termed the *period.* For example: a 50-cycle alternating current means that in one second (unit time) the current makes 50 such complete alternations from positive to negative and again to the original positive value.

the time should happen to be increased by another fiftieth of a second, the weld would obviously be carried to too high a temperature to produce satisfactory results, since the energy dissipated at the joint would be doubled.

The timing devices used in industry for the satisfactory control of welding periods of such short intervals are usually electronic valve arrangements. Timing devices of this nature are so expensive, that the possibility of their extensive adoption by the dental profession is quite doubtful. At the present time, the majority of the welding machines used by dental technicians, who have adopted this procedure, are manually controlled with respect to the welding time. It is quite obvious that reproductions of time intervals for the execution of a given operation, when such small increments of time are involved, is beyond the realm of practicability; hence, the efficiency of such units is very poor even under the best of conditions.

A mechanical timer might be invented so that the operator could merely set a mechanical device in motion which would maintain the time of actual contact constant for each successive operation. Such arrangements have been discussed[10] by various authors, and about the maximum constancy one can expect is plus or minus 1 or 2 cycles.

A suggestion for producing uniform timing is the insertion of a lamp in the primary circuit of the transformer. When the primary circuit is closed, there will be an initial surge while the filament of the lamp is still cold; as the lamp filament heats up, the current is reduced to a value much less than would effect the welding process. The last mentioned method for the timing of the welding process has been found by the writer to give relatively satisfactory results when using the heavier gauge stainless steels.

When the lighter gauge materials are welded, such as when finger springs are joined to arch wires in orthodontics, the only method by which a joint of satisfactory mechanical properties may be obtained is to anneal the finger spring in the region to be welded before the operation is performed, and then the annealed portion is coiled about the arch wire in order to obtain the resilience required for its function.

However, it may be concluded, all factors considered, that stainless steel may be soldered with relative satisfaction, but the possibility of successful welding with the present equipment is very doubtful.

LITERATURE

1. Krivobok, V. N., *The Book of Stainless Steels* (Edited by E. E. Thum, 2nd Ed.) p. 29. Amer. Soc. for Metals.

2. *Ibid.*, p. 52.

3. Brit. Pat. 316, 964.

4. Brit. Pat. Application 22875.

5. Becket and Franks, *Effects of Columbium in Cr-Ni Steels,* Am. Inst. Mining Met. Eng. Tech. Pub. 519, Jan., 1934.

6. Reference (1) p. 436.

7. Brit. Pat. 348, 586.

8. Brit. Pat. 305, 654.

9. Brusse, A., and Carman, J. L., *Chrome Alloy,* Int. Jour. of Orth. and Dent. for Child., 20: 339 (April) 1934.

10. Symposium on the Welding of Iron and Steel (Group 2) May 2 and 3, 1935, Iron and Steel Institute, London.

A. L. Whiteley—Thyraton Control of Resistance Welding.

M. Mathieu—Some Theoretical Problems Relating to Res. Welding.

J. E. Languepin—The Development of Res. Welding in France.

P. W. Townsend—The Control of Electric Resistance Welding.

J. W. Dawson—Ignitron Timing of Resistance Welding.

CHAPTER XXXVIII

MISCELLANEOUS MANIPULATIONS OF STEEL IN
DENTISTRY

By P. B. TAYLOR, A. M.

Dental Instruments.—Steel instruments to be used in dentistry should be classified into two groups, and the instruments of each group should never be employed interchangeably. These two groups are: those instruments, such as wax spatulas, the use of which requires that they be heated to a high temperature, and those instruments which are not heated, other than that heat incidental to their sterilization, such as operative instruments, forceps, etc. The instruments of the first group are not in a critically tempered condition; hence, temperature considerations are relatively unimportant. On the other hand, the second group consists of those dental instruments which have been carefully hardened and tempered by the manufacturer, and they cannot be heated without deleteriously affecting their efficiency in use. Such heat treatment by the manufacturer would be destroyed even though the temperatures employed are relatively low, since the transformation toward the sorbitic structure takes place slowly even at low temperatures. Although the softening of stainless steel instruments progresses much more slowly, the effect would eventually become quite significant, since the phenomenon is cumulative; furthermore, the initial hardness of stainless steel is somewhat less than that of the heat-treated carbon steel.

However, it may happen that a tempered instrument might be softened accidentally, or perhaps the dentist might wish to modify the design of the instrument. Hence, a few notations of a satisfactory heat treatment will be considered. The heat treatment to be suggested will give a cutting edge which will have a B.H.N. of 450 or above, depending upon the skill of the operator.

Heat Treatment Processes for the Dentist.—The ordinary carbon steel instrument may be softened by heating it to a dull red in a Bunsen flame and allowing it to cool slowly.* The instrument may be cooled by holding it above the flame during the initial part of the cooling process, or by plunging it into a vessel filled with hot sand or asbestos. This treatment will render the steel soft for machining purposes such as shaping with a file, polishing, etc. If any appreciable

---

* All of the temperature colors which follow are to be observed in a shadow against a dark background, but the temper colors require skylight for their proper recognition. The temperatures indicated by the first mentioned colors appear on page 165.

forging or bending is to be done, it should be carried out with the steel heated to a fairly bright red color after which the instrument should be given a normalizing heat treatment. The normalizing treatment may be accomplished by heating the instrument to a cherry-red color for about thirty seconds and then quenching it in water. This should be followed by the softening treatment described above. It is not necessary to heat treat the shaft of the instrument.

After the instrument has been completely shaped and polished, it may be given a hardening heat treatment by again heating it to a dull red and quenching it in water. The hardening heat treatment is then followed by a tempering process, after the surface has been carefully polished.

It is essential that the surface be well polished and be cleaned free of the polishing agent, so that the temper colors may be clearly distinguished. The tempering process may be carried out quite satisfactorily in an open flame, if a small portion of the end of the blade or nib is covered with a pair of pliers. The pliers will conduct the heat away so that it will be possible to carry the shank or angle of the instrument to a slightly higher temper color than the working end. The angle or shank is treated by holding it approximately ½ inch above the flame and by heating it until a blue temper color begins to appear. The instrument is then quickly withdrawn from the flame and the pliers are removed; this permits the working end of the instrument to heat up by thermal conduction from the bulkier portion which is at the more elevated temperature. In the case of a cutting instrument, it should be quenched in water as soon as a perceptible straw color appears at the cutting edge. Amalgam and gold foil condensers generally have their nibs tempered to a brown color, which requires that a longer time elapse before they are quenched. After removal from the quenching bath, if the colors have progressed beyond those desired, the process must be repeated in its entirety. If an instrument has been softened inadvertently, it should be given a softening heat treatment after which it is subjected to the hardening and tempering process as outlined above.

In the case of stainless steel instruments, the heat treatment carried out in this manner is probably not as satisfactory as in the case of carbon steel. Briefly, this is due to the decrease in the rate at which the precipitation transformation takes place upon the addition of chromium in sizable amounts. A treatment which is fairly satisfactory may be given in essentially the same manner as outlined for the carbon steels with the following modifications, which are necessary due to the alteration of the constitution diagram and to the altered rate of solid diffusion.

If such steel is to be worked while hot, the fabrication should be carried out with the steel heated to a deep orange color, instead of a dull red as before. The steel should be maintained at approximately this temperature for a short time after the forging process and then quenched. A satisfactory annealing process may be effected by heating the steel to a cherry-red and allowing it to cool in air. After the shaping and polishing have been finished, the instrument should be heated to a color approximately between a deep orange of the forging temperature and a cherry-red which was used in the annealing process and quenched in water. As before, if the instrument is to be tempered, it must be given a high polish before the tempering heat treatment.

Although the tempering process is not imperative in the case of a stainless steel, some benefit may be derived by grasping the blade or nib with pliers as before and quenching the angle from a brown temper color without removing the pliers from the cutting edge or nib. The cutting edge in this case is not given a temper color since the hardness would be reduced to too low a value. The brown rather than the blue color is placed on the angle or the shank, since the temper colors for stainless steels are indicative of higher temperatures than the same color on the carbon steel. This is due to the retardation of oxide formation by the stainless material. Both the 13 per cent and 18 per cent chromium steels, which were described in Chapter XXXVII have been used for dental instruments, and may be subjected to the above heat treatment. However, the higher chromium content steel should be heated to a slightly more intense color, the temperature of which is approximately 100° F. (55° C.) above that for the 12 to 13 per cent chromium steel.

Sharpening Dental Instruments.—The most important factor in the sharpening of dental instruments is the selection of a satisfactory stone. The stone should be very hard and of fairly fine grit. It is important that the stone be soaked frequently with oil and wiped off in order to keep the surface free from filings of the steel which might imbed themselves between the granules of the abrasive. If at any time the surface of the stone becomes grooved or uneven, it may be rendered flat by grinding it on a piece of plate glass with coarse carborundum powder in oil, and finishing with a very fine grit of carborundum.

When the instruments are sharpened they should be held so that the hand is in a comfortable position; in general, a pen grip may be used. The instrument must be held so that the desired bevel will be maintained, and in order to accomplish this, the second finger may rest on the surface of the stone and act as a guide.

During the operation, most of the sharpening is carried out during the stroke when the instrument is traveling so that the bevel leads the cutting edge. More pressure should be exerted during this stroke than in the return, since, if too much pressure is applied when the cutting edge is leading the bevel, the instrument is apt to "chatter," which dulls the edge put on by the preceding stroke and thus renders the maintaining of the proper bevel extremely difficult.

Stainless Steel in Dental Prosthesis.—Probably the type of prosthetic appliance in which stainless steel has found its most extensive acceptance is complete denture base construction. For some reason, the majority of the dental profession, in the United States at least, are of the opinion that a swaged stainless steel denture base cannot be constructed without a great deal of special and expensive equipment. Such an idea is not entirely true. Even though the swaging of the stainless steel denture base plate may be conceded to be somewhat more difficult than the similar process when a gold alloy is employed, it is not by any means a procedure which is necessarily excluded from the dentist's own laboratory. The stainless steel for the base may be obtained in a softened condition and, for the majority of cases, a swaging process may be completed without further annealing being necessary. However, if the case is characterized by a number of pronounced irregularities, such as would require considerable swaging, an annealing may be carried out by placing the plate in a common salt (NaCl) bath and heating it to approximately 1150° C. (2100° F.), which would be a deep orange color.[1] The material should be held at this temperature for a short time (one to two minutes) and allowed to cool to a dull red before quenching.

The swaging may be carried out by the use of a series of zinc dies with lead or Babbitt metal counterdies.* Usually two or three sets will be necessary for this preliminary swaging, because of the extreme rapidity with which this material work hardens. The base is then finished on a Babbitt die with a zinc counterdie. The actual mechanics of the swaging process are identical with those used in the case of gold. After the base has been swaged, the steel should be pickled; for this purpose, a satisfactory solution is a mixture of equal parts of commercial hydrochloric acid and water, to which is added about 5 per cent of nitric acid by volume.

The action of the pickling solution in this type of work differs somewhat from that in the case of gold alloys. In the case of gold alloys, the oxide coating is completely dissolved by the pickling solution, whereas in this case, the oxide coating consists of a series of oxides with varying oxygen content, which exhibit a variation in solubility in the pickling solution. The oxides adjacent to the steel contain very little oxygen and those on the outside layer are composed of high oxides. Since these high oxides are fairly insoluble, the pickling merely loosens the surface impurities by dissolving the lower oxides adjacent to the surface of the steel. Hence the material often will appear not to be pickled, whereas if the surface is scrubbed thoroughly, the impurities will be completely removed. The pickling solution may have its action upon the steel proper reduced to a negligible amount by the addition of about 0.1 per cent of a commercial inhibitor. For this purpose, glue sizing is relatively satisfactory. When pickling, the solution should be heated to between 50° and 60° C. (90° and 108° F.).

* The metals used for dies and counterdies will be discussed in Chapter XXXIX.

As is always true of any stainless steel, the iron oxide rouges should be avoided for polishing purposes, since the surface would be contaminated by iron which might reduce the corrosion resistance. The polishing should be carried out with pumice followed by chromium oxide. It is best that the base be given a high polish before mounting the teeth, since after the denture is finished, it is possible to polish only the exposed portions. The unpolished portions under a resin or vulcanite veneer might then be susceptible to corrosion due to a seepage of saliva between the steel and the veneer.

If it is necessary to trim or to grind the finished case, the use of steel burs should be avoided since the surface would be contaminated by the carbon steel of the bur and the tarnish and corrosion resistance would be very markedly lowered. A stainless steel denture base might easily be ruined by this means, hence carborundum stones are definitely indicated for this purpose.

The austenitic stainless steels also lend themselves quite well to the construction of partial denture appliances. However, such construction is of necessity quite complicated, and its discussion is not within the scope of this book.

Orthodontics.—This material adapts itself fairly well to the fabrication of orthodontic appliances, since such structures are continually readjusted and revised; hence, even though the solder might tend to discolor in some cases, the orthodontist is able to maintain the desirable esthetic properties. Most of the joining of the various parts is done by free-hand soldering or welding, and final adjustments are made at the time of the insertion of the appliance into the mouth.

If a soldering technic is employed, little modification of the usual procedure is necessary, aside from a few precautions which must be observed. When soldering stainless steel, it is desirable that the soldering be accomplished as rapidly as possible, and for this reason a hot flame should be employed. A satisfactory flame may be described as one which has its inner cone about 1 inch in height and the air adjusted to just below the "hissing point." The work should be held about ⅛ inch above the tip of this blue cone, and the soldering should always be done against a black background, so that the temperature may be gauged accurately by the color of the work, which should never exceed a dull red. If difficulty is encountered in the fluxing procedure, it may be alleviated by filing the wire, and heating it slightly before applying the flux.

In applying the solder, the operator should not wait until the soldering temperature is attained since the likelihood of overheating would be enhanced. A better practice for this type of material is to place a piece of solder of the required size on the work at about the time the flux dehydrates and starts to flow. The solder should always be placed on the heavier gauge materials, which are then heated to the soldering temperature, when the lighter gauge material is brought to position and the work withdrawn from the flame. The low fusing solders solidify over a considerable range of temperature; hence, it is imperative that the parts be held in rigid apposition for a longer time than is the general practice when using gold. It is suggested that this rigid apposition be maintained for approximately one second before quenching. Although the solder will probably not require this long to solidify, the procedure will alleviate a weakening of the union through interference with its crystallization.

LITERATURE

1. Hutchinson, A. C. W., *Stainless Steel as a Base for Artificial Dentures.* Brit. Dent. Jour., 51: 724–738 (July 1) 1930.

CHAPTER XXXIX

TECHNIC METALS AND ALLOYS

THERE are various base metal alloys which are not used in the mouth, but rather are employed as accessory materials and for teaching purposes. They may be classed as (1) those alloys or metals used for the construction of models, dies, and counterdies, and (2) the alloys used as gold substitutes for practice work in casting, swaging, etc., in the dental laboratory.

MODEL, DIE, AND COUNTERDIE METALS AND ALLOYS

Fusible Alloys.—By the term "fusible metal" is usually meant those alloys which have a melting point or solidification range below the melting point of pure tin, which is 231.9° C. (449° F.).[1] Table LVII[1] lists a large number of these alloys, and gives their compositions and fusion temperatures.*

As may be noted, the alloys melt below the fusion point of their constituents; this fact indicates that they are eutectiferous systems. Most of them are ternary alloys of bismuth, lead, and tin, mixed in certain proportions in order to give the desired melting range. The addition of bismuth to the alloy is of importance from a dental standpoint, inasmuch as this metal expands upon solidifying, and in general it may contribute this attribute to its alloys. However, there is a limit to which the fusing temperatures may be lowered by the use of these three metals alone; this temperature is obviously that of the ternary eutectic. The composition of this eutectic, as given in the table, is bismuth 52.5 per cent, lead 32 per cent, and tin 15.5 per cent, with a melting point of 96° C. (204.8° F.).

By the addition of cadmium to the ternary alloy Bi-Pb-Sn, still lower fusion temperatures may be obtained from the formation of the quaternary alloys, whose eutectic composition is bismuth 49.5 per cent, lead 27.27 per cent, tin 13.13 per cent, and cadmium 10.1 per cent. It melts at 65.5° C. (149.9° F.)[4]; hence, 65.5° C. (149.9° F.) is the lowest possible fusion temperature obtainable with this system. Fusion temperatures as low as may be desired, even below room temperature, may be obtained by the addition of mercury in suitable quantities to these alloys, but very likely the strength and hardness are reduced.

Antimony also exhibits the phenomenon of expanding when freezing, and is occasionally used in this type of alloy. One very popular

* The table has been abridged, and somewhat modified from the original (see reference).

24   369

TABLE LVII

Low Melting Alloys

Melting point, degrees.		Composition, per cent.					Name.
Fahr.	Cent.	Bi.	Cd.	Pb.	Sn.	Hg.	
154.4	68	50	12.5	25	12.5		Wood's alloy.
154.4	68	50.1	10	26.6	13.3		Lipowitz' alloy.
158	70	45.3	12.3	17.9	24.5		Very fusible alloy.
158	70	44.5		30	16.5	5–10	Fusible teaspoons.
159.8	71	38.4	15.4	30.8	15.4		Fusible alloy.
196.7	91.5	51.6	8.1	40.2			Ternary eutectic alloy.
197.6	92	50		30	20		Onion's or Lichtenberg's alloy for fine castings.
199.4	93	50		25	25		Darcet's alloy for fine castings (Rose No. 1).
201.2	94	50		31.2	18.8		Newton's alloy.
203	95	50.1	16.6		33.3		Fusible alloy.
203	95	55.6	11.1		33.3		Fusible alloy.
203	95	50	25		25		Fusible alloy.
204.8	96	52.5		32	15.5		Ternary eutectic alloy.
212	100	50		32.2	17.8		Alloy for fine castings.
212	100	53.8		15.4	30.8		Darcet's No. 1.
212	100	50		12.5	37.5		Darcet's No. 3.
212	100	59.4		14.8	25.8		Darcet's No. 2.
212	100	57.2		17.8	25		
212	100	53.5		20	26.5		
226.4	108	50		28	22		Rose's alloy.
235.4	113	42.1		42.1	15.8		Rose No. 2.
253.4	123	40		40	20		Bismuth solder.
275	135	33.3		33.3	33.3		
281.4	138	58			42		Binary eutectic alloy.
300.2	149	22.2		44.5	33.3		
320	160	10.5		42	47.5		
323.6	162	10		40	50		
341.6	172	12.8		49	38.2		

antimony alloy used in dentistry is Babbitt metal.* Haskell's formula[5] for this material is tin 72.7 per cent, antimony 18.2 per cent, and copper 9.1 per cent, a composition which melts at 260° C. (500° F.). Taylor[2] gives an approximate formula of this alloy as 80 per cent tin, 10 per cent copper, and 10 per cent antimony; he further states that the composition may vary in dental alloys of this nature as follows: tin 66 to 90 per cent, antimony 4 to 25 per cent, and copper 4 to 15 per cent.

Many of these alloys are quite hard and successfully resist the deformation which occurs during swaging and similar operations. In general, the eutectic composition is not indicated for such uses, as it

Fig. 130.—Microstructure of Babbitt metal, composition Sn 82 per cent, Sb 10 per cent, Cu 8 per cent. The cubical crystals are SbSn, and the dendrites are Cu_3Sn. The matrix is excess tin. × 100. (Courtesy of S. D. Tylman.)

is likely to be weaker than the alloys containing primary crystals and eutectic. According to Taylor,[2] such alloys contain hard crystalline particles (usually primary crystals, see Fig. 130) imbedded in a matrix of a softer metal or alloy, which "allows slight readjustments of the hard particles, but acts as a cementing material, and prevents the deformation of the material under stress or its rupture from the sudden shocks of swaging."[2]

Uses in Dentistry.—These alloys are sold to the dentist under various trade names. Most of the fusible alloys are easily com-

* Strictly speaking, Babbitt metal should not be classed as a fusible alloy because of its high melting point.

pounded by heating the ingredients, covered with charcoal, over a gas burner, and if they are used in sizable amounts, considerable economy may be effected by compounding them as needed in the dental office.

They are often used for model purposes, but they are particularly valuable for use as dies and counterdies, such as are used in swaging denture bases. For this purpose the die may be constructed by pouring the fused metal into a negative formed in molding sand* from an artificial stone model. Some of the lower fusing alloys may be successfully poured into impressions made with the colloidal impression materials, described on page 73. Requirements of the alloys, other than a reasonably low fusion temperature, are that they do not change dimension while solidifying, and that they exhibit a sufficiently high fluidity and low surface tension while molten, so that they may fill the impression completely, thus reproducing all fine details with accuracy.

One of the popular materials employed for the construction of dies is zinc, but there are several objections to its use. Its fusion temperature is 419.5° C. (787° F.) which is higher than is advantageous. Furthermore, the zinc contracts abnormally upon freezing. According to Prothero,[6] this contraction amounts to $5/16$ inch per linear foot, which is approximately 2.6 per cent. No model material yet invented will even approximately compensate for such a shrinkage while setting.

Many of the alloys listed in Table LVII may be used successfully as die alloys for swaging, although some are rather soft for complete denture service. Babbitt metal is often used successfully for this purpose in place of zinc. Other fusible alloys which are popularly used are Newton's† and Darcet's alloys, although many others may be used quite as successfully.

In swaging, the plate metal is driven onto the surface of the die, thus fabricating it to the desired form for use in the mouth. This fabrication may be accomplished in several ways, but the most popular method is the employment of a *counterdie*. A counterdie is essentially a negative of the die. The plate metal is first hammered or pressed into the approximate form of the die surface, and then the counterdie is placed over the plate on the die, and hammered or pressed until the plate metal is accurately adapted.

The counterdie is usually cast directly against the die, which requires that the metal or alloy used for the former have a fusion temperature less than that of the die alloy. Furthermore, the counterdie material must be softer than the die alloy, in order that the latter will not be distorted while swaging.

* A product said to be composed of glycerin and powdered marble is being used extensively at the present time in preference to molding sand.

† Often improperly called "Melotte's Metal." See Hodgen: Practical Dental Metallurgy (7th Ed.), p. 176.

Pure lead, melting point 327.4° C. (621° F.), is largely employed as a counterdie material for dies constructed of zinc. Lead offers the disadvantage of danger of contamination to the gold plate while swaging.

During such fabrication lead atoms are apt to diffuse or be driven into the gold alloy, which makes the latter so brittle in such regions as to be almost worthless. When a lead counterdie is employed, it may be separated from the gold plate by means of parchment or thin leather, the use of which offers certain advantages in the obtaining of a more perfect adaptation.

When Babbitt metal is used as a die material, an alloy recommended for use as a counterdie is tin 12.5 per cent, and lead 87.5 per cent.[7] This alloy melts at approximately 210° C. (410° F.).

When any of the fusible alloys given in Table LVII are employed, another fusible alloy of lower melting temperature may be selected for the counterdie. Usually the fusible alloys are used in conjunction with some swaging device or press.

In practice, it is often necessary to construct several dies, particularly when swaging stainless steel plate as described in the previous chapter. As one die becomes distorted, a new one is substituted.

GOLD SUBSTITUTE TECHNIC METALS

In practice work, whether carried on by the dental student in the preclinical courses, or the dentist in his laboratory, no small amount of metal is required for casting technic cases. The use of dental golds for this purpose is very expensive, hence, the need for a base metal alloy for use as a substitute.

Naturally, the first requisite of such a material is that it resemble gold in all its properties, and yet be economical in cost. It should melt and cast cleanly in the temperature ranges of and similar to the casting gold alloys; it should be capable of a heat treatment similar to that of the gold alloys; it should be capable of being soldered with the gold and silver solders ordinarily used in dentistry; its casting shrinkage should be similar to that of gold; and it should be capable of maintaining a high polish, color, and luster, similar to that of gold, with a reasonable resistance to tarnish in air. Needless to state, these alloys are intended for technic purposes only, and are not to be used in the mouth for any purpose whatever.

Casting Alloys.—Most of the materials of this nature, sold under various trade names, are essentially alloys of silver and copper. The composition of four of these alloys, as given by Taylor,[2] are given in Table LVIII.

Alloy B is gold colored due to the large amount of copper present. High copper content alloys are difficult to solder because of oxidation. However, they may be cast fairly readily, and are capable of being burnished. The other three alloys are high in silver content; they

TABLE LVIII

COMPOSITION (BY WEIGHT) OF INLAY TECHNIC METALS

Alloy.	Copper (per cent).	Silver (per cent).	Gold (per cent).	Nickel (per cent).	Tin (per cent).
A.........	13.7	82.2	4.1		
B.........	65.5	34.4	0.1		
C.........	12.6	86.8	...	0.6	
D.........	4.9	68.7	...	...	26.4

cast well, but they are white in color. It may be noted that alloy D is essentially an amalgam alloy. None of these alloys are capable of heat treatment, and very likely their physical properties are unsatisfactory when compared with dental gold alloys used in practice.

Easton and Ray[8] list a number of experimental alloys containing copper, zinc, silver, silicon, and other metals. Some of these combinations are capable of heat treatment, but such alloys fail to cast well, and do not exhibit the proper physical properties. After an exhaustive study, an alloy was discovered of composition, copper 67 per cent, silver 12 per cent, zinc 20 per cent, and silicon 1 per cent, which is known as *"K" metal*. The metal is essentially a solid solution alloy, with a color which so closely resembles that of certain types of dental gold alloys as to make a choice between the two very difficult, if selected by sight only. Table LIX shows the physical proper-

TABLE LIX

PROPERTIES OF TYPE B GOLD AND "K" METAL COMPARED

	Elongation (per cent in 2 inches).	B.H.N.	Yield point (lbs./sq. in.).	Tensile strength (lbs./sq. in.).	Fusion temp. (wire method).	Melting range.
Type B gold...	12 (minimum)	70–100	22,000 (minimum)	Not included in specification	Above 1650° F.	Not included in specification.
"K" metal.....	14	84	22,000	42,000	1710° F.	1705–1725° F.

ties of "K" metal as given by the above mentioned authors, in comparison to similar properties of a Type B inlay gold, specified in American Dental Association Specification No. 5.*

As may be noted, with the possible exception of its yield point which barely meets the specification requirements, the alloy has all the desirable physical characteristics of a medium hard inlay gold. It casts in a manner very similar to that of dental gold alloys, with the possible exception of requiring slightly more flux. It may be readily burnished and polished and it is fairly resistant to tarnish in the air. It solders readily, but it is not susceptible to heat treatment.

* See Appendix, page 388.

The alloy may be used successfully for technic purposes for the smallest inlay or for large partial denture castings. It is probably the best gold substitute casting technic metal yet devised.

Wrought Metal Substitutes.—The possibilities of wrought gold metal substitutes have not as yet been sufficiently investigated, and there is no metal available in this field which compares as favorably with the wrought gold alloys, as does "K" metal with the casting golds. Probably the most popular wrought materials used for this purpose are *nickel silver* and *brass*. Nickel silver is a ternary alloy of copper, zinc, and nickel, a representative composition of which is copper 55 per cent, zinc 25 per cent, and nickel 20 per cent. However, it leaves much to be desired as a technic metal, since its physical properties are not sufficiently close to those of the wrought golds. It is white in color when polished, and corrodes in air. It is not amenable to heat treatment.

LITERATURE

1. Van Horn, K. R., *Fusible Alloys*. National Metals Handbook (1933 Ed.) pp. 1001–1005. Amer. Soc. for Steel Treating.

2. Taylor, N. O., *Dental Technic Metals*. J. A. D. A., 14: 798–803 (May) 1927.

3. Parravano, N., and Sirovitch, G., *Quaternary Alloys of Lead, Cadmium, Bismuth and Tin*. Compt. Rend., 42: 630, 1912.

4. Budgen, N. F., *Properties of Fusible Alloys*. J. Soc. Chem. Ind., 43: 200, 1924.

5. Prothero, J. H., *Prosthetic Dentistry* (4th Ed.) p. 588. Medico-Dental Pub. Co.

6. *Ibid.*, p. 586.

7. *Ibid.*, p. 591.

8. Easton, G. S., and Ray, K. W., *Technic Alloys for Inlay Casting*. Dent. Cos., 74: 972–976 (Oct.) 1932.

CHAPTER XL

GUTTA-PERCHA

Sources and Production.—The chief source of gutta-percha is the Malay Archipelago, where it is extracted from trees of the family *Sapotaceae;* other varieties of the same family are sources of the rubber hydrocarbon.

It is extracted from the tree in much the same manner as is rubber latex. Slits are made in the cambium layer, and the latex or juice is collected in vessels. It is also extracted from the leaves and buds of the tree. The latex is a colloidal suspension, which is coagulated by boiling or other means.

Chemical Composition and Properties.—Chemically, the essential constituent of gutta-percha is *gutta,* a hydrocarbon with the empirical formula C_5H_8 which is isomeric with rubber. At least two resinous materials are found in the crude product—albanes and fluavils. Table LX exhibits the composition of a number of different brands of gutta-percha.

As supplied to the consumer, compounding ingredients are often added, such as Burgundy pitch, zinc oxide, chalk, carbon, Kieselguhr, barytes, magnesium oxide, etc.

Gutta-percha is not affected by alkaline solutions or dilute acids, but concentrated sulphuric or nitric acids attack it by oxidation. It is readily soluble in chloroform and carbon disulphide, and to a lesser degree, in certain oils, such as eucalyptol and oil of cajuput.

When exposed to air, gutta-percha deteriorates to a hard brittle resinous material which is very likely a result of the absorption of oxygen with a resulting oxidation. Such an effect is often observed in tooth fillings made with this material.

Physical Properties.—In its purest form, gutta-percha is almost colorless, with a tendency toward a pinkish or grayish hue, depending upon the variety. It is cellular in structure but becomes fibrous when stretched. It exhibits two modifications, the α and β forms; the α form is stable below 60° C. (140° F.), whereas the β form appears when the material is heated above this temperature.[2]

At room temperature, it is comparatively hard, but when heated to a higher temperature, it softens, and exhibits a plasticity which permits it to be molded readily to a shape which is maintained upon hardening. As may be noted from Table LX,[1] the composition has a considerable effect upon the softening temperature as well as upon the hardening time. It is very evident that the resin content is the determining factor in this respect, since the tendency is for the soft-

TABLE LX·

CHEMICAL COMPOSITION AND PHYSICAL PROPERTIES OF GUTTA-PERCHA

Sample.	Chemical composition (per cent).				Softening.		Hardening time (min.).	Ultimate strength (kg./ sq. cm.).
	Gutta.	Resin.	Dirt.	Water.	Begins (° C.).	Pliable* (° C.).		
Genuine { Pahang	78.1	19.2	1.5	1.2	47.7	66.5	3.33	322
Banjer red	67.0	30.2	1.5	1.3	43.8	66.1	6.75	252
Bulongan red	68.6	29.0	1.4	1.0	45.5	63.3	8	250
Soondie { Bagan	57.5	40.9	1.0	0.6	40.0	61.6	9.5	172
Kotaringin Goolie red	52.2	42.9	1.2	0.7	39.4	60.5	20	148
Serapong	56.2	42.4	0.9	0.5	40.5	60.5	15.75	167
White { Bulongan	52.2	45.4	1.5	0.9	41.1	67.7	23.5	172
Mixed	49.8	47.4	1.1	1.7	42.7	76.1	21.5	179
Banjer	51.8	44.1	1.8	2.3	42.2	73.3	28.5	204
Medium quality cleaned	54.7	39.4	2.7	3.2	37.7	58.8	17	112
Medium quality hardened by extracting resin	93.0	2.8	2.5	1.7	57.2	91.1	0.75	399

* Temperature at which a strip 70 mm. × 25 mm. × 2 mm. tears under a load of 14.2 grams.

ening temperature to be lower and the hardening time longer with increase in resinous content. As may be noted, the sample from which most of the resin was extracted softens at a much higher temperature than the other specimens, and its hardening time is distinctly less.

According to Ward,[3] gutta-percha is supplied for dental use in three forms: "low heat," which softens below 200° F. (93.4° C.); "medium heat," which becomes plastic within the range of 200° to 212° F. (93.4°–100° C.); and "high heat," which softens from 210° to 220° F. (99°–104.5° C.). Very likely such softening temperatures are governed partially by the compounding ingredients, which markedly affect the softening temperatures, both according to the type and amount of the ingredient used; the softening temperature generally is higher, the more ingredient incorporated.

Although gutta-percha differs from rubber in many respects, the most marked difference is that the material under discussion exhibits little elasticity at any temperature.

The ultimate strength of gutta-percha is given in Table LX. Here again, the resin content appears to be a factor; a tendency toward lessened strength values with greater resin content is apparent.

In comparison with rubber, the water absorption of gutta-percha is quite low. For this reason it is extensively used as an insulator for cables and telephone conduits in preference to rubber.

The thermal conductivity of gutta-percha is very low, but unfortunately its thermal expansion is quite high. There are various thermal coefficients of linear expansion given in the literature for this material, but the generally accepted value[6] is 0.001983 per degree C.*

According to the investigations of Miller,[5] gutta-percha exhibits distortions comparable to those described for waxes. His results for the linear thermal expansion coefficients of a dental gutta-percha are given in Table LXI.

TABLE LXI

Coefficients of Linear Expansion for a Dental Gutta-percha

Temperature.		Linear expansion
° C.	° F.	(per ° C.).
23–38	73–100	0.0000549
38–55	100–131	0.0000870
55–75	131–167	0.0000070

As may be noted, the thermal expansion is distinctly irregular, as the temperature increases. Furthermore, the material was probably not pure gutta-percha, judging from the difference between Miller's results and the generally accepted value.

Miller further demonstrated that serious warpage may occur in the material while it is expanding or contracting thermally.

If all of these factors are taken into consideration, it appears that

* Compare with the same constant for other dental materials given in Table II, page 36.

aside from its low thermal conductivity gutta-percha is ill-adapted for use as a permanent tooth restorative material.

Although no studies have been published so far as can be discovered, undoubtedly the material exhibits a plastic flow. Its specific gravity varies from 0.96 to 1.

Uses in Dentistry.—It is used extensively in dentistry as a filling material for root canals, as a thermal insulator beneath metallic or other restorations, and as a temporary restorative material during treatment.

In the past, it has been advocated for use as a permanent restorative material, but it has not been successful in this regard, because of its lack of resistance to abrasion, and its permeability to mouth fluids, the latter resulting in a tendency to become foul.

Temporary Stopping.—These materials might be termed as gutta-percha substitutes, since they generally contain gutta-percha in minor amounts. The remainder of the constituents are probably waxes, zinc oxide, and fatty acids, with the possible addition of powdered silex or feldspar. A superficial examination of some of them indicates that they resemble a poor grade of modeling compound.

Judging from clinical use, practically all of these materials are distinctly inferior to a base plate gutta-percha of good quality, even for temporary restorative purposes. They appear to flow badly, and even dissolve in the mouth fluids in most cases. Their only advantage is their ease of manipulation in comparison to gutta-percha, but the advisability of their use is questionable.

Chloropercha.—Chloropercha is the name given to the material formed by dissolving gutta-percha in chloroform. A distinct increase in volume of the gutta-percha occurs during such solution, which obviously must be decreased in like amount when the chloroform evaporates, if porosity is to be avoided. Hence, when such a material is placed in a tooth, a contraction must be expected. According to Miller,[4] the contraction may be very large. For example, he reports a volume shrinkage of 24 per cent upon the spontaneous drying of chloropercha for eight weeks, after which time it was found necessary to dry it at 70° C. (160° F.) for sixty hours in order to expel all of the chloroform, the final contraction being approximately 67 per cent. During the drying process, a hard surface layer was formed, which effectively prevented the volatilization of the chloroform beneath. Furthermore, the dried material exhibited no adhesion whatever to the walls of the drying vessel.

Although the above data may appear to be somewhat extreme in magnitude, yet they clearly contraindicate the successful use of such material in the mouth.

Eucapercha.—Eucapercha is presumably gutta-percha dissolved in eucalyptol. Experiments by Miller,[5] similar to those outlined for chloropercha, gave equally discouraging results. Upon drying, the material showed evidence of surface cracks; little or no adherence to the container was observed. After eight weeks of spontaneous drying, the material had shrunk 13 per cent by volume. After drying sixty hours at 70° C. (169° F.), the material shrank 20 per cent of its original volume, but it was not yet hard. It became "hard" only after drying it for twenty hours at 96° C. (205° F.), when it had decreased 76 per cent in volume, but it solidified in a lumpy or curdled form, and exhibited no adhesion. On this basis it may be concluded that neither chloropercha nor eucapercha will harden completely in the mouth.

Manipulation.—In the light of the above data, it is very evident that the solvents for gutta-percha should be used sparingly, the use of chloroform being entirely contraindicated because of the formation of the thick skin as described.

In placing a restoration of gutta-percha, the material should be carefully softened by heat. It should never be placed directly in the flame, as this invariably causes it to burn with a resulting oxidation which injures it seriously. It is then molded into the preparation piece by piece, and allowed to harden. Because of the large thermal contraction involved, the restoration cannot possibly be entirely leak proof, and, hence, it cannot be called permanent in any sense.

Although the use of eucalyptol or other oils in small amounts aid in softening the material and adapting it to the prepared cavity, they do not render the material adhesive when hardened, and undoubtedly they prolong or even prevent complete hardening. If such solvents would evaporate completely, they would very likely be of some help, but, instead, they probably diffuse throughout the mass, and thus weaken the entire restoration to some extent.

LITERATURE

1. Nat'l Crit. Tables, 2: 294 (Table 149).
2. Clark, G. L., *Applied X-rays,* p. 451. McGraw-Hill Book Co.
3. Ward, M. L., *The American Textbook of Operative Dentistry* (6th ed.) p. 539, Lea and Febiger.
4. Nat'l Crit. Tables, 2: 294 (Table 154).
5. Miller, Dayton C., report in a paper by Price, W. C., *Properties of Root Filling Materials.* J. N. D. A., 5: 1260–1280 (Nov.), 1918.
6. Smithsonian Tables (8th ed.), p. 281.

APPENDIX

AMERICAN DENTAL ASSOCIATION SPECIFICATION NO. 1 FOR DENTAL AMALGAM ALLOYS

(First Revision, January 1, 1934)

I. Types:
   1. This specification is for the so-called "silver" amalgams which are to be used for restorations in the mouth.
   2. The alloy may be furnished as:
      Type A. Filings.
      Type B. Shavings.

II. Material:
   The comminuted alloy shall be free of foreign materials and shall be uniform and the amalgamated alloy shall not produce excessive blackening of the hands or white paper when rubbed against the hand or paper.

III. General Requirements:
   Amalgam alloys shall possess the following features, known as satisfactory working qualities:
   1. Thorough amalgamation in three minutes.
   2. Absence of granular or sandy consistency when amalgamated.
   3. Susceptibility to carving for at least fifteen minutes after amalgamation.
   4. Susceptibility to receiving and retaining a polish twenty-four hours after amalgamation.

IV. Detail Requirements:
   1. Chemical composition shall be within the following limits:
      Silver, 65 per cent minimum.
      Copper, 6 per cent maximum.
      Zinc, 2 per cent maximum.
      Tin, 25 per cent minimum.
      Gold and platinum will not be regarded as foreign materials.
   2. Flow. Specimens subjected to a constant pressure of 250 kg. per square centimeter (approximately 3550 pounds per square inch) shall not show more than 4 per cent flow (i. e., more than 4 per cent shortening in length of specimen) in a period of twenty-four hours.
   3. Setting changes. Twenty-four hours after amalgamation the length shall have increased between 3 and 13 microns per centimeter.

V. Methods of Sampling and Tests:
   The test specimens shall be made according to the published directions which shall accompany each package. These directions shall not require complicated equipment and shall be in harmony with recognized dental practice. The following details shall be included in these directions: ratio of alloy to mercury, type of mortar and pestle, whether the alloy and mercury shall be stirred or ground, mixing time, mixing speed (revolutions of pestle or number of times amalgam is spread out and rolled up in the hand), when and how the excess mercury shall be expressed and the method of packing. The following details relative to test methods shall be observed:

381

1. Flow. Specimens shall be cylinders 4 mm. in diameter and 8 mm. long. These shall be prepared by condensing the amalgam into a cavity of these dimensions in a rigid block using the technic given in the sheet of instructions accompanying the alloy.

The ends of the cylinders shall be surfaced plane at right angles to the axis. Tests shall be made at temperatures between 20° and 25° C. Three hours after condensing, the specimen shall be subjected to a constant pressure of 250 kg. per square centimeter (approximately 3550 pounds per square inch).

2. Setting changes. Specimens shall be prepared by condensing into a cavity or matrix. These shall be removed as soon as condensation is completed and shall not be subject to restraint during the test. Measurements shall begin fifteen minutes after amalgamation (time spent in mulling and condensing to be included as a part of the fifteen minutes).

VI. Packing:

1. The alloy shall be packed in moisture-resisting containers and in quantities of 1, 2 or 5 troy ounces.
2. Accurate and adequate instructions for proportioning and manipulation shall accompany each package.
3. Each package of alloy shall be marked with a serial number or a combination of letters and numbers which shall refer to the manufacturer's records for the particular lot or batch of alloy.
4. The date of manufacture (year and month) shall be indicated on the package as a separate item or as a part of the serial number.
5. Containers shall not be made, in whole or in part, of materials which will amalgamate readily with mercury.

VII. Notes:

1. Manufacturers of amalgam alloys may indicate that their materials comply with this specification by (a) a statement on the package guaranteeing the material contained therein to meet the requirements of this specification, or (b) a statement as to the chemical and physical properties of the alloy.
2. The American Dental Association will not assume responsibility for, or guarantee compliance of, material so labeled by manufacturers, but will, in event of a dispute between a member of the Association and a manufacturer, act in an advisory capacity and will designate testing laboratories having equipment for testing dental amalgam alloys when necessary tests may be made.

Reference, J. A. D. A.: April, 1934, page 658.

AMERICAN DENTAL ASSOCIATION SPECIFICATION NO. 2

Tentative Specification for Dental Inlay Casting Investment
(Approved July 24, 1930)

I. General Specification:

This material shall be a powder composed essentially of plaster of Paris and silica or material of these types which when mixed with water in proper ratio, applied to the dental wax pattern, and heated in the usual manner will be found satisfactory for use in casting dental restorations.

II. Types:

Only one type of material is required. Time of setting may be modified to suit the needs of the operator.

III. Material:

The material shall be uniform and free of foreign material, partly set or caked lumps.

Coloring material as such will not be regarded as foreign material.

IV. General Requirements:

1. The material shall not crack in heating.

2. The material shall not contaminate the alloy cast into it and shall not cause pitting, roughness of surfaces or voids in the alloy.

3. When heated the material shall not give off poisonous or offensive odors.

V. Detail Requirements:

1. The setting expansion shall be 0.05 per cent or over at the end of twenty-four hours.

2. The thermal expansion shall be 0.7 per cent or over when heated from room temperature to 700° C. A thermal expansion curve or sufficient data shall be supplied to enable the purchaser to make proper use of the material.

3. During the preceding test (V-2) the specimen shall not, at any temperature above 200° C., show a length less than the original length at room temperature, and shall not at any higher temperature show a shrinkage or decrease in length of more than 0.15 per cent of the maximum length at any lower temperature.

4. The compressive strength shall be not less than 350 pounds per square inch.

5. The time of set shall be not less than five nor more than thirty minutes and shall be indicated on the package. The time of set shall not vary over ±20 per cent from the manufacturer's stated value.

6. Eighty-five per cent shall pass a number 200 sieve, 95 per cent shall pass a number 100 sieve, and 100 per cent shall pass a number 30 sieve.

VI. Methods of Inspection and Tests:

1. Sampling:

Ten pounds of material taken at random shall be submitted for test. The material, if taken from original packages, shall be submitted in moisture-proof containers bearing the name of the manufacturer.

2. Testing Consistency:

The investment used in making all test samples shall be mixed with sufficient water to produce a mix of "testing consistency" in accordance with the following directions to give a "slump" within the following limits:

Mixes shall be spatulated mechanically by 100 turns of a stiff blade in approximately fifteen seconds.

A cylindrical mold 2 inches long with an internal diameter of 1⅜ inches shall be placed on a dry glass plate and filled.

Two minutes from the time of starting the mix, the mold shall be lifted and the mixture allowed to slump or spread over the plate.

The average of the maximum and minimum diameters of spread of the slumped mixture shall come between the limits of 2¼ and 3 inches.

These measurements shall be made one minute after the cylinder is lifted.

3. Setting Expansion:

The change in dimension on setting shall be determined on a 30-cm. specimen by observing the change with a micrometer microscope comparator or equipment of equal accuracy.

Reference: Dental Cosmos, p. 746, August, 1926; Bureau of Standards Journal of Research, December, 1928. (Research Paper No. 32.)

4. Thermal Expansion:

The thermal expansion will be measured on a specimen (1.2 cm. in diameter by 20 cm. long, approximately) by the "Fused Quartz Expansion Apparatus" method, or by the use of equipment of equal accuracy.

Reference: Bureau of Standards Research Paper No. 29, November, 1928, Supt. of Documents, U. S. Government Printing Office. Price, 10 cents.

5. Time of Setting:

Two hundred grams of the sample shall be mixed with enough water to make a paste of "testing consistency" (see VI-2) and tested with a Vicat needle. Setting is considered complete when the needle no longer penetrates to the bottom of the specimen.

Reference: A. S. T. M. Standards, Part II, page 32, 1927, or U. S. Government Master Specification No. 248.

6. Fineness:

Fineness shall be determined by screening 100 grams of the dried sample through the sieves specified, and determining the amount of material remaining on each sieve. The material shall be shaken through the sieve with as little abrasion as possible.

7. Compressive Strength:

The compressive strength shall be based on five specimens each prepared as follows: 100 grams of the sample shall be mixed with enough water to make a paste of "testing consistency" and poured into a cylindrical mold, 1.3 inches in diameter by 2 inches high, the containing vessel being moved back and forth over the mold while pouring. The sample shall be worked slightly to remove air bubbles and struck off level. The cylinders shall be removed from the molds as soon as they are hard enough to handle, and stored in air at a temperature between 60° and 100° F. Tests shall be made after seven days.

In computing the average strength, any cylinder whose strength varies more than 15 per cent from the average shall be discarded. In case three or more cylinders vary more than 15 per cent from the average, the lot shall be discarded and the test repeated.

VII. Packing:

1. Material shall be packed in moisture-resisting containers.

2. Accurate and adequate instructions for proportioning and manipulation shall accompany each package.

3. Each package shall be marked with a serial number or a combination of letters and numbers which shall refer to manufacturers' records for the particular lot or batch of material.

4. The date of manufacture (year and month) shall be indicated on the package as a separate item or as a part of the serial number.

5. The minimum net weight of the contents shall be marked on each package.

VIII. Notes:

1. Manufacturers of inlay casting investments may indicate that their materials comply with this specification by (a) a statement on the

package guaranteeing the material contained therein to meet the requirements of this specification, or (b) a statement as to physical properties of the material. Thermal expansion data shall be supplied in either case.

2. The American Dental Association will not assume responsibility for, or guarantee compliance of, materials so labeled by manufacturers, but will, in event of a dispute between a member of the Association and a manufacturer, act in an advisory capacity and will designate testing laboratories having equipment for testing dental inlay casting investment where necessary tests may be made.

Reference: J. A. D. A., December, 1930, page 2266.

AMERICAN DENTAL ASSOCIATION SPECIFICATION NO. 3

TENTATIVE SPECIFICATION FOR DENTAL IMPRESSION COMPOUND

(Approved July 24, 1930)

I. Material:

The compound shall be free from foreign materials and uniformly fine grained.

II. General Requirements:

Impression compounds shall have the following features known as satisfactory working properties:

1. A smooth glossy surface after flaming.
2. Ability to trim, at room temperature, without appreciable flaking.
3. Firm, smooth margins after trimming.

III. Detail Requirements:

1. A sample 10 mm. in diameter and 6 mm. long shall not decrease in length more than 2 per cent when subjected to a constant load of 2000 grams for ten minutes at 35° C.
2. The softening point as evidenced by a flow of 10 per cent or over when tested as in III-1 shall not fall below 35° C.
3. The working range as evidenced by a flow of 85 per cent when tested as in III-1 shall be between 45° and 55° C.
4. The shrinkage of the material from 40° to 25° C. (104° to 77° F.) shall not exceed 0.5 per cent.

IV. Methods of Test:

1. Flow tests shall be made on samples 10 mm. in diameter and 6 mm. long under loads of 2000 grams. The sample shall have been maintained at the testing temperature for at least twenty minutes prior to testing and the test shall be calculated as per cent of the original length.
2. The shrinkage of the material shall be determined by first heating a sample in a water bath to slightly above 40° C. and then observing the dimensional changes occurring as the temperature falls. The equipment used shall be sufficiently exact to insure an accuracy of ± 0.05 per cent in the data obtained.

V. Packing:

1. The minimum net weight of the contents shall be indicated on all packages.
2. Each package shall be marked with a serial number or a combination of letters and numbers which shall refer to the manufacturer's records for the particular lot or batch of compound.
3. The date of manufacture (year and month) shall be indicated on the package as a separate item or as a part of the serial number.

25

VI. Notes:

1. Manufacturers may indicate that their materials comply with this specification by (A) a statement on the package guaranteeing the material contained therein to meet the requirements of this specification, or (B) a statement as to the physical properties of the compound.

2. The American Dental Association will not assume responsibility for, or guarantee compliance of, materials so labeled by manufacturers, but will, in event of a dispute between a member of the Association and a manufacturer, act in an advisory capacity and will designate testing laboratories having equipment for testing dental impression compounds where tests may be made.

Reference: J. A. D. A., January, 1931, page 53.

AMERICAN DENTAL ASSOCIATION SPECIFICATION NO. 4

TENTATIVE SPECIFICATION FOR DENTAL INLAY CASTING WAX
(Approved July 24, 1930)

I. 1. This specification is for the waxes used as patterns in the production of cast inlays. They are essentially waxes and hydrocarbons of the paraffin series.

2. The wax may be furnished as sticks or cones.

II. Material:

The wax shall be uniform in quality and free of foreign material.

III. General Requirements:

Waxes shall possess the following features:

1. The color shall be such as to facilitate the carving of patterns through contrast with the hard and soft tissues of the mouth.

2. The materials shall soften without becoming flaky.

3. The materials shall trim to a fine margin without appreciable chipping or flaking.

4. The materials shall be capable of being melted and vaporized without leaving solid residues other than carbon.

IV. Detail Requirements:

1. Flow at mouth temperature. Samples 1 cm. in diameter shall not shorten more than 1 per cent in length when subjected to a load of 2000 grams for ten minutes at 37.5° C.

2. Softening point. The softening point of the material shall be between 38° and 42° C.

3. Working range. The material shall soften sharply and a working plasticity shall be obtained at or below 43° C.

4. Thermal expansion. A curve or numerical data shall be supplied with the material which will enable the purchaser to make the proper use of the material in technics requiring wax expansion.

V. Methods of Test:

1. Flow at mouth temperature. Specimens shall be cylinders 10 mm. in diameter and 6 mm. in length. The ends shall be surfaced plane at right angles to the axis. Sample shall be maintained at the testing temperature for at least twenty minutes prior to testing. A load of 2000 grams shall be applied for ten minutes, the temperature being maintained at 37.5° C. The change in length shall be calculated in percentage of original length.

2. Softening point. The softening point shall be determined from a curve obtained by plotting values for percentage of flow as obtained by the method outlined in V-1, against variations in temperature. The materials shall be considered to have softened when the flow exceeds 5 per cent.

3. Working range. The working range shall be considered the temperature range within which the materials will exhibit a percentage of flow of from 50 to 60 per cent when subjected to pressure as outlined in V-1.

4. Thermal expansion. The thermal expansion characteristics of the materials shall be determined by methods which will insure an accuracy of ± 0.05 per cent, up to the temperature at which warpage occurs.

VI. Packing:

1. The minimum net weight of the contents shall be indicated on all packages.

2. Each package shall be marked with a serial number or combination of letters and numbers which shall refer to the manufacturer's records for the particular lot of wax.

3. The date of manufacture (year and month) shall be indicated on the package as a separate item or as a part of the serial number.

VII. Notes:

1. Manufacturers of waxes may indicate that their products comply with this specification by (a) a statement on the package guaranteeing the material contained there to meet the requirements of this specification, or (b) a statement of the physical properties of the wax. In either case, thermal expansion data shall be supplied.

2. The American Dental Association will not assume responsibility for, or guarantee compliance of, materials so labeled by manufacturers, but will, in event of a dispute between a member of the Association and a manufacturer, act in an advisory capacity and will designate laboratories having equipment for testing waxes, where necessary tests may be made.

Reference: J. A. D. A., January, 1931, page 40.

AMERICAN DENTAL ASSOCIATION SPECIFICATION NO. 5

TENTATIVE SPECIFICATION FOR DENTAL INLAY CASTING GOLDS
(Approved October 19–23, 1931)

I. Alloys for cast inlays shall be divided into three groups as follows:
  A. Soft.
  B. Medium.
  C. Hard.

II. General Requirements:

1. Color. The color of the gold shall be the color specified by the purchaser.

2. Casting. The molten gold shall fill the mold completely when cast into dental casting investment.

3. Physical properties. Physical properties of the gold with the exception of fusion temperature shall be determined on castings quenched from 1290° F.

III. Detail Requirements:
  The detail requirements are given in the accompanying table.

DETAIL REQUIREMENTS FOR DENTAL INLAY CASTING GOLDS

Type.	Gold and platinum group metals, per cent, minimum.	Silver, per cent.		Brinell number.		Elongation, 2-in. gauge length, per cent, minimum.	Yield point, lbs. per sq. in., minimum.	Fusion temperature, degrees F., minimum.
		Min.	Max.	Min.	Max.			
A.............	83	3	12	40	75	18	.....	1725
B.............	78	0	15	70	100	12*	22,000	1650
C.............	78	0	15	90	140	12*	27,000	1650

*This value shall be reduced 0.5 per cent for each 1 per cent of platinum group metals in the alloy, and 8 per cent shall be the minimum elongation allowed for any alloy.

IV. Methods of Inspection and Test:
   1. Composition. The determined values for metallic constituents shall be recorded as the nearest 0.5 per cent. When a determined value falls midway between a half and a whole number, the whole number shall be recorded.
   2. Physical properties. Physical properties other than fusion temperatures shall be determined on cast samples placed in a furnace at 1290° F. for ten minutes and quenched in water at room temperature. Cast samples shall be prepared by casting into a dental casting investment which complies with American Dental Association Specification No. 2 by any dental casting method. The use of a wax pattern is not required.
   An alloy complies with this specification when all of the recorded values for the properties of three or more of a series of six castings meet the requirements. The recorded value for each property shall be obtained by averaging the determined values for all samples meeting the requirements of the specification.
   3. Brinell number. The Brinell number shall be determined by applying a load of 27.8 pounds (12.6 kg.) on the sample through a $^1/_{16}$-inch hardened steel ball for thirty seconds. The diameter of the depression shall be determined by measuring two diameters perpendicular to each other and the average diameter used in the calculation of the hardness number. The determined value shall be recorded as the nearest whole number. When the determined number falls midway between two numbers, the even number shall be recorded.
   4. Yield point:
      A. The yield point shall be determined on cast samples whose diameters are between 0.07 inch and 0.09 inch. The gauge length used shall not be less than 2 inches. An averaging strain gauge shall be used.
      B. An initial load calculated to produce a stress of 5000 pounds per square inch shall be applied to the sample and the strain gauge read. The load shall then be increased to the minimum values for the yield point (Type B, 22,000 pounds per square inch; Type C, 27,000 pounds per square inch), and a second reading taken. The maximum strain permitted between the limits specified is: Type B, 0.0017 inch per inch; Type C, 0.002 inch per inch. The determined value for strain shall be recorded to the nearest 0.0001 inch per inch. When the determined strain falls midway between two numbers, the nearest even number shall be recorded.
      C. As an alternate method, loads above and below the two limits specified may be applied provided they do not vary the stress

over 500 pounds per square inch from the specified loads. The recorded strain may be determined graphically.

5. Elongation:

    A. Elongation shall be determined on the samples used in the test for yield point. The load shall be applied slowly and continuously after the strain gauge is removed until rupture occurs. Castings which break outside the gauge marks may be repulled. Elongation shall be measured on a 2-inch gauge length. The determined value shall be recorded as the nearest 0.5 per cent. When the determined value falls midway between a half and a whole number, the whole number shall be recorded.

    B. If deductions are to be made for the presence of platinum group metals, the manufacturer shall either (1) state a minimum guaranteed platinum metals content on the package or (2) guarantee on the package that the alloy contains 1 per cent or more of the platinum group metals for each 0.5 per cent that the elongation falls below 12 per cent.

6. Fusion temperature, wire method. The fusion temperature is the temperature at which a wire 0.028 to 0.032 inch in diameter and approximately $1/16$ inch long, supported at both ends, will break when subjected to a cross-bending load of 3 ounces avoirdupois. The heating rate within 100° F. of the breaking point shall be between 10° and 50° F. per minute.

V. Packing:

1. The minimum net weight of the contents shall be marked on each package.

2. Each package shall be marked with a serial number or combination of letters and numbers which shall refer to the manufacturer's records for the particular lot or batch of alloy.

VI. Notes:

1. Types:

    The requirements given cover only those types of golds primarily used for inlays. Requirements for harder casting golds and for wrought alloys are in process of development.

2. Uses:

    The usual uses for the three types of alloy specified are: Type A soft inlays, easily burnished and subject to very slight stress; Type B, inlays subject to moderate stress, three-quarter crowns, abutments, pontics, full crowns and sometimes soft saddles; Type C, inlays subject to high stress, thin three-quarter crowns, thin cast backings, abutments, pontics, full crowns and saddles.

3. Hardness number:

    The use of a 13.9-pound (6.3 kg.) load for the determination of hardness numbers below 50 is permissible.

4. Guarantee:

    Manufacturers may indicate that their products comply with these requirements by (a) a statement on the package guaranteeing the material contained therein to meet the requirements of this specification or (b) a statement of the chemical and physical properties of the material in such detail as to cover all the requirements specified.

5. Responsibility for any guarantee:

    All statements or guarantees that products meet this specification are made by manufacturers on their own responsibility. In the event of disagreement between purchaser and manufacturer, the

American Dental Association will act in an advisory capacity and will designate testing laboratories having equipment for making tests of dental golds.

Reference: J. A. D. A., January, 1932, page 36.

AMERICAN DENTAL ASSOCIATION SPECIFICATION NO. 6

TENTATIVE SPECIFICATION FOR DENTAL MERCURY
(Approved October 18, 1931)

I. This specification is to cover the properties of mercury for use in the production of dental amalgams.

II. General Requirements:

1. The mercury shall have a bright mirror-like surface free from film or scum. Under certain conditions of storage, mercury may develop a slight film. Such mercury should readily be separated from this film by filtration through chamois skin or some similar filtration medium, and when filtered, the mercury should remain bright after agitation with air.

2. The mercury shall pour freely and in entirety from a thoroughly clean glass container.

III. Detail Requirement:

The mercury shall have a nonvolatile residue of not more than 0.02 per cent when the mercury is evaporated from a porcelain crucible at a temperature below its boiling point and the crucible then ignited at a dull red heat.

IV. Methods of Inspection and Test:

The determination of nonvolatile residues shall be made on samples having a weight of from 10 to 15 grams.

V. Packing:

1. The minimum net weight of the contents shall be marked on each package.

2. Mercury shall be packed in clean, clear, glass containers.

VI. Notes:

1. Guarantee:

Manufacturers may indicate that their products comply with these requirements by placing a statement on the package guaranteeing the material contained therein to meet the requirements of this specification.

2. Responsibility for any guarantee:

All statements or guarantees that products meet this specification are made by the manufacturers on their own responsibility. In the event of disagreement between purchaser and manufacturer, the American Dental Association will act in an advisory capacity and will designate testing laboratories having equipment for making necessary tests.

Reference: J. A. D. A., March, 1932, page 409.

AMERICAN DENTAL ASSOCIATION TENTATIVE SPECIFICATION NO. 7 FOR DENTAL WROUGHT GOLD WIRE ALLOYS

I. Wrought gold wire alloys which are used in prosthesis and orthodontia are considered in this specification.

II. General Requirements:

1. Color. The color of the gold alloys shall be the color specified by

the purchaser. This specification applies both to the white golds
and to the gold-color alloys.
2. Physical properties. These shall be determined on wrought round
wire in the quenched (softened) and in the "oven-cooled" (hardened) condition.
III. Detail Requirements:
The detailed requirements are given in the accompanying table.

DETAIL REQUIREMENTS FOR DENTAL WROUGHT GOLD ALLOYS

Gold and platinum group metals, per cent.	Fusion temperature wire method.	Ultimate tensile strength, pounds per square inch.	Yield point, pounds per square inch.	Elongation 2-inch gauge length, per cent.	
Minimum, 75	Degrees F. Minimum, 1750	"Oven-cooled." Minimum, 150,000	"Oven-cooled." Minimum, 125,000	Quenched. Minimum, 15	"Oven-cooled." Minimum, 4

IV. Methods of Inspection and Test:
1. Composition. The determined values for metallic constituents shall
be recorded as the nearest 0.5 per cent. When a determined value
falls midway between a half and a whole number, the whole number shall be recorded.
2. Physical properties. These shall be determined on round wrought
wire samples: (a) quenched: placed in a furnace at 1290° F. for
ten minutes and immediately quenched in water at room temperature; (b) "oven-cooled": placed in a furnace at 1290° F. for
ten minutes and immediately quenched in water at room temperature, then placed in the furnace at 840° F. for two minutes and uniformly slow cooled to 480° F. in thirty minutes.
An alloy complies with this specification when the values of the physical properties of the average of three or more out of a series of
five samples meet the requirements.
3. Yield point:
(a) The yield point shall be determined on round wrought samples
whose diameters are between 0.038 and 0.042 inch. The gauge
length used shall not be less than 2 inches. An averaging
strain gauge shall be used.
(b) An initial load calculated to produce a stress of 20,000 pounds
per square inch shall be applied to the "oven-cooled" sample
and the strain gauge read. The load shall then be increased
to the minimum value for yield point (125,000 pounds per
square inch) and a second reading taken. The maximum
strain permitted between the limits specified is 0.0085 inch
per inch. The determined value for strain shall be recorded
to the nearest 0.0001 inch per inch. When the determined
value falls midway between two numbers, the even number
shall be recorded.
(c) As an alternate method, loads above and below the two limits
specified may be applied provided they do not vary the
stress by more than 1000 pounds per square inch from the
specified loads. The recorded strain may be determined
graphically.
4. Elongation:
This shall be determined on the samples used for the test for yield
point. The load shall be applied slowly (not more than twenty
minutes between initial load and rupture) and continuously after

the strain gauge is removed until rupture occurs. Samples which break outside the gauge length may be repulled. Elongation shall be measured on a 2-inch gauge length. The determined value shall be recorded to the nearest 0.5 per cent. When the determined value falls midway between a half and a whole number the whole number shall be recorded.

5. Fusion temperature, wire method:

The fusion temperature is the lowest temperature at which a wire from 0.028 to 0.032 inch in diameter and approximately $1/_{16}$ inch long will break when subjected to a cross-bending load of 3 ounces avoirdupois. The heating rate within 100° F. of the breaking point shall be between 10 and 50 degrees per minute. The test is made by fusing or welding the sample under test, between two wires of a platinum, platinum-rhodium thermocouple so that the two welds or fused balls are separated by approximately $1/_{16}$ inch of wire. The 3-ounce weight is attached to the sample by means of a hook of high-fusing noble metal or noble metal alloy. The hook shall have approximately the same diameter as the test sample.

V. Packing:

1. The minimum net weight of the contents shall be marked on each package.

2. Each package shall be marked with a serial number or combination of letters and numbers which shall refer to the manufacturer's records for the particular lot or batch of alloy.

VI. Notes:

1. Guarantee:

Manufacturers may indicate that their products comply with these requirements by (a) a statement on the package guaranteeing the material contained therein to meet the requirements of this specification, or (b) a statement of the chemical and physical properties of the material in such detail as to cover all the requirements specified.

2. Responsibility for any guarantee:

All statements or guarantees that products meet this specification are made by manufacturers on their own responsibility. In the event of disagreement between purchaser and manufacturer, the American Dental Association will act in an advisory capacity and will designate testing laboratories having equipment for making tests of dental golds.

Reference: J. A. D. A., December, 1932, page 2079.

AMERICAN DENTAL ASSOCIATION TENTATIVE SPECIFICATION NO. 8 FOR DENTAL CEMENTING MEDIUM

A. *General Specification:*

This specification is for dental cements whose primary uses are:

A-1. To join or to seal dental appliances to oral structures or to other appliances.

A-2. To serve as a base or foundation for other filling material.

A-3. To serve as a temporary filling material.

B. *Types:*

Only one type of material is specified. The consistency of the mix which different uses require can be varied by the individual operator to suit his own needs.

C. *Material:*

C-1. These cements shall consist of a powder and a liquid which, when mixed in the proper manner, will harden or set.

C-2. The powder and liquid shall be uniform and free from poisonous foreign materials.

C-3. Colors for the set cement shall be specified by the purchaser.

D. *General Requirements:*

D-1. The liquid shall be free from cloudiness, precipitates, deposits or sediment.

D-2. Cements when spatulated in the proper manner shall not:

D-2a. Form lumps or granules.

D-2b. Evolve gas.

D-2c. Contain pulp devitalizing agents such as arsenic.

D-2d. Discolor tooth structures.

E. *Detail Requirements:*

E-1. Time of setting.—The time of setting shall not be less than four nor more than ten minutes.

E-2. Ultimate compressive strength.—The ultimate compressive strength shall not be less than:

E-2a. Three hundred and fifty kg. per square centimeter (approximately 5000 pounds per square inch) for specimens crushed one hour after mixing.

E-2b. Eight hundred and forty kg. per square centimeter (approximately 12,000 pounds per square inch) for specimens crushed seven days after mixing.

E-3. Film thickness (see paragraph I). The film thickness shall not exceed 0.05 mm. (0.002 inch).

E-4. Disintegration (see paragraph J). The disintegration of the cement shall not exceed 1 per cent by weight after immersion for seven days in distilled water.

F. *Methods of Inspection and Test:*

F-1. Preparation of test specimens. The preparation of the test specimens shall be conducted at a temperature between 65° and 75° F. at a relative humidity between 55 and 75 per cent. The powder:liquid ratio used shall be determined by the consistency test. The mixing technics employed in the preparation of all test specimens shall be those which accompany the packages of cement except that the temperature and humidity may vary within the foregoing limits.

All apparatus and instruments shall be clean, dry and free from particles of hardened cement.

F-2. Testing consistency.—One type of apparatus for measuring consistency is shown in Fig. 131. This apparatus consists of a glass tube (inside diameter approximately 6.5 mm.) which will deliver a definite volume (0.5 cc.) of mixed cement, two flat plates and a weight. (The combined weight of the top plate and the weight shall be 120 grams.)

F-2a. Trial amounts of powder are mixed with 0.5 cc. of liquid. Then 0.5 cc. of mixed but unset cement is placed in a measuring device and deposited on a flat glass plate. Three minutes after the mix is started, another glass plate (weighing approximately 20 grams) and the additional weight shall be carefully placed on the soft cement. Trials shall be made until the average of the major and minor diameters of the slumped mass of cement shall be 30 ±1 mm. ten minutes after starting the mix. The average of the amounts of powder used in three such determinations shall be the amount of powder (combined with 0.5 cc. of liquid) necessary to produce a mix of standard consistency.

F-3. The tests for arsenic and similar poisonous material shall conform to those designated by the United States Pharmacopoeia (current edition).

G. *Time of Setting:*

A ring 5 mm. high and 10 mm. in diameter is placed on a flat plate and filled with cement of standard consistency. Three minutes after starting the mix, the specimen is transferred to an atmosphere of 100 per cent relative humidity at 99° F. A standard Gillmore needle (weighing 1 pound and having an end $1/24$ inch in diameter) is lowered vertically until the surface of the cement is touched.

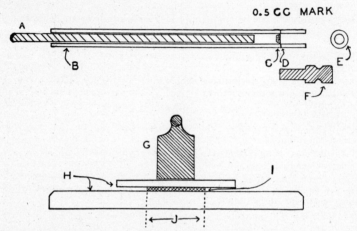

Fig. 131.—Apparatus for consistency tests. A, brass rod plunger; B, glass tube; C, rubber plug; D, cellophane disk; E, end view of tube; F, brass plug gauge; G, 100-gram weight; H, glass plates (top plate approximately 20 grams); I, specimen; J, diameter of specimen. (Paffenbarger, Sweeney and Isaacs: Jour. Amer. Dent. Assoc., Nov., 1934.)

This is repeated at frequent intervals. The time of setting shall be the number of minutes elapsed from the starting of the mix to the time when the needle fails to make a perceptible circle on the surface of the specimen. The setting time shall be reported to the nearest minute.

H. *Ultimate Compressive Strength:*

A cylindrical mold 12 mm. high and 6 mm. in diameter is placed on a flat plate and slightly overfilled with cement of standard consistency. A second flat plate is pressed on top of the mold to remove excess cement. The molds shall be made of hard rubber, glass, or other substance that will not be corroded by the cement. (Painting the molds with a thin solution of a hard wax in benzene will facilitate removal of the specimens.) Three minutes after starting the mix, the molds are transferred to an atmosphere of 100 per cent relative humidity at 99° F. Thirty minutes later the specimens are immersed in distilled water at room temperature.

The ends of the cylinder shall be surfaced plane at right angles to the axis. The ends of the specimens may be ground flat by the use of a small amount of carborundum powder (200 mesh) and water. The molds containing the specimens are drawn back and forth across a glass plate coated with the abrasive and water. They should be rotated about one quarter turn every few strokes. The test specimens shall be kept wet during the grinding and until after crushing. The machine used in crushing the test specimens shall be operated at a rate of speed which will move the crushing head 0.25 mm. per minute.

The value for compressive strength shall be reported as the average of three or more from a lot of five specimens and shall be rounded off to the nearest 10 kg. per cm.^{2} (150 pounds per inch^2). If the values for individual specimens vary more than 15 per cent from the average they shall be discarded and the average of the remaining specimens shall be reported. In case more than two of the specimens are eliminated, the test shall be repeated.

I. *Film Thickness:*

A portion of a mix of standard consistency is placed between two flat square or round plates of uniform thickness. The surfaces of the plates between which the cement is spread shall be approximately 2 square centimeters. Three minutes after the mix is started, a load of 15 kg. shall be applied vertically on the top plate.

Ten minutes after the mix is started, the thickness of the two plates with the cement film between them shall be determined. The difference in the thickness of the plates with and without the cement film shall be considered as the film thickness. An average of three tests shall be reported to the nearest 5 microns (0.0002 inch).

J. *Disintegration:*

The disintegration of a cement is a measure of the erosion plus the extraction of soluble material from the cement by the action of water.

One-half cubic centimeter (0.5 cc.) of cement of standard consistency is pressed between two flat plates until the cement is 20 mm. in diameter. (A piece of waxed thread placed in the soft cement before the specimens are formed provides a convenient method of holding the specimens.) Three minutes after the mix is started, the plates and cement are placed in an oven at 99° F. for one hour. Two such specimens shall be used for each determination.

After one hour the specimens are withdrawn from the oven and quickly weighed. The combined weight of the two, less the weight of the waxed threads, shall be taken as the weight of the specimens of cement. The specimens are immediately submerged in 100 cc. of distilled water in a weighed stoppered flask and stored for a period of seven days at 99° F. The specimens are then removed from the water. There shall be no evidence of crystal growth or extensions from the surface of the specimen. The water is evaporated at a temperature just below 212° F. The flask is then dried at 300° F. to constant weight. The flask and contents are weighed. The difference between the final weight of the flask and its initial weight is the amount of disintegration. The gain in weight divided by the weight of the specimens times 100 gives the percentage of disintegration. The average of duplicate tests (two flasks containing two specimens each) shall be reported to the nearest 0.1 per cent.

K. *Packaging:*

K-1. The cement powder and liquid shall be supplied in glass containers. The net weight of the powder shall be indicated on the container. The liquid shall be supplied in an amount 20 per cent in excess of that necessary to combine with the total amount of powder when mixed to a testing consistency.

K-2. Adequate and accurate instructions for proportioning and manipulation shall accompany each package. These instructions shall include the temperature of the slab, the powder:liquid ratio, the rate of powder incorporation and the time of mixing.

K-3. Each package of powder and liquid shall be marked with a serial number or a combination of letters and numbers which shall refer to the manufacturer's records for that particular lot or batch of cement powder and liquid.

K-4. The date of manufacture (year and month) shall be indicated on the package as a separate item or as a part of the serial number.

L. *Notes:*

L-1. Manufacturers of dental cements may indicate that their materials comply with this specification by: (A) a statement on the package guaranteeing the material contained therein to meet the requirements of this specification; or (B) a statement of the physical properties of the material in such detail as to cover all of the requirements specified.

L-2. The American Dental Association will not assume responsibility for, or guarantee compliance of, material so labeled by manufacturers, but will, in event of a dispute between a member of the Association and a manufacturer, act in an advisory capacity and will designate testing laboratories having equipment for testing dental cements where necessary tests may be made.

INDEX